Reading the World

Contemporary Literature from Around the Globe

Perfection Learning

EDITORIAL DIRECTOR	Julie A. Schumacher
SENIOR EDITOR	Rebecca Christian
EDITOR	Rebecca Burke
ASSISTANT EDITOR	Lucy Anello
EDITORIAL ASSISTANTS	Suzanne Foggia, Megan Snyder
PERMISSIONS	Meghan Schumacher
COVER DESIGN	William Seabright and Associates, Glencoe, IL
INSIDE DESIGN	Mark Hagenberg
PHOTO RESEARCH	Lisa Lorimor
RESEARCH HANDBOOK	Cecelia Munzenmaier
TEACHER REVIEW BOARD	Mark Storer, Teacher of English, Adolfo Camarillo High School, Camarillo, CA
	LoAn Campbell, Former Teacher of English, Ames High School, Ames, IA

6 7 8 9 10 11 RD 12 11 10 09 08
Paperback ISBN13: 978 0-7891-5941-0
Paperback ISBN10: 0-7891-5941-4
Hardback ISBN13: 978-0-7569-9951-3
Hardback ISBN10: 0-7569-9951-0

Reading the World

Contemporary Literature from Around the Globe

Perfection Learning

Table of Contents

UNIT ONE The Americas

 indicates Nobel laureate

indicates Nobel laureate

7

UNIT FOUR   The Middle East & South Asia

Ⓝ indicates Nobel laureate

ⓝ indicates Nobel laureate

Who Are These Strangers?

I n *Reading the World: Contemporary Literature from Around the Globe*, you will hear the familiar sound of English, but in tones and accents that have the flavor of elsewhere. The writers come from all over the world—China, Nigeria, Syria, Ireland, and Argentina—and include Nobel Prize winners along with other outstanding writers from the last one hundred years.

Many of the writers in this book have had lives as intriguing as their poetry or prose. Like South African Nobel laureate Wole Soyinka, they have been imprisoned for being of the wrong race, faith, or political belief. Many of them started out in one country and ended up in another, often in search of a safe and stable home in which to write freely.

No matter what a writer's origins, certain themes and events have been hard to run away from in the 20th and early 21st centuries. Injustice still permeates countries with histories of colonial rule and civil war, or with stark divisions between rich and poor. Devastation from war and environmental disasters has led to massive worldwide emigration. Millions of people are having to figure out where they fit in this newly "globalized" world.

Other themes are ever present, everywhere. Girls in many cultures struggle to find freedom and respect. Family and community life bring both solace and conflict. Love, beauty, and laughter are necessary components to the good life.

Reading literature from around the world is unlikely to teach you everything there is to know about a culture. But it may help you to consider which differences among cultures actually matter. The Pulitzer Prize-winning poet Gwendolyn Brooks, a champion of ordinary people, said, "I believe that we should all know each other, we human carriers of so many pleasurable differences. To not know is to doubt, to shrink from, sidestep or destroy."

For the curious and open-minded, literature is one of the best places to go for clues to the tantalizing question: Who are these strangers—my neighbors on this shrinking planet Earth?

The Art of Translation

Khaled Mattawa

Professor of English, The University of Texas, Austin

While there is a grain of truth in the phrase "lost in translation," its opposite is much truer. Without translation, the English language would be missing many great works, such as Homer's *Odyssey* (originally in Greek) and Tolstoy's *War and Peace* (originally in Russian). Clearly we gain a great deal from translation.

What are the necessary skills of a translator? The translator must have mastery in reading the original language (the language from which the text is being translated) as well as mastery in the host language (the language into which it is being translated). Translation experts have argued through the ages as to which is more important.

I think both skills are essential. A good poet in her own language with weak command of the original language may be able to translate a poem in very readable fashion, but it may have glaring errors. And a person with excellent command of the original language but poor skills in the host language may deliver a very accurate but literal poem—one that doesn't "sing."

In every act of creativity, bad execution will mar a brilliant idea. Most translations are collaborative projects between a scholar of the original language and a poet skilled in the poetic techniques of his or her own language.

And translations do not take place in a political and social vacuum. When we read a translated poem, we bring with us

assumptions—often unconscious—about the culture of the original poem. This happens to translators as well. As in any dialogue, if you're not listening to what a person is saying, you are likely to assume something based on what you already think of that person. You aim, as a translator, to understand *why* it is being said the way it is being said. And then you do your best to paraphrase what you hear, keeping all the nuances intact.

When I translate Arabic poetry, I create various renditions of a poem. In my lap will be an English dictionary, an Arabic dictionary, and a thesaurus. If I still don't understand a word or a line, I ask the poet (if he or she is available). I check with scholars of Arabic and have them go through my renditions. And finally, I show it to poets who don't know the original language to see if the poem is coherent in English and if it has a musical quality. I leave the poem alone for a few days or weeks, and go over it again and again until I feel I have satisfied both my concerns about accuracy and about the quality of the result.

Translated poems tend to sound slightly unfamiliar, but they have a logic all their own. In a sense, that is what other cultures are like. When translating, I avoid informal American English and allow the poem's own images and metaphors to present its ideas. Some poems refuse translations: they possess linguistic qualities and word play unique to the original language. They are like plants that will not grow outside their native soil or climate. An overly simplified or unskillful attempt at translating them might rob them of the originality and brilliance they possess in their original language.

Translation is a process that requires fidelity, devotion, open-mindedness, and creativity. And this too is how we should speak to each other—with empathy and attention. We have much to gain from reading translations that abide by these principles.

The Literature of the Americas

Kimberly Koza

Professor of English, Central College, Pella, Iowa

Canada, the Caribbean, and Latin America are our neighbors, yet many Americans are more familiar with the entertainment they offer us—from food and dance to music and vacation spots—than with their literature. Although geographically and culturally unique, they share a common history of European conquest and colonization.

Canada's literature began with its native people, the North American Indians, and was further influenced by two very different colonial cultures: French and British. Contemporary Canada is further energized by the more recent arrival of immigrants from former British colonies in Asia, Africa, and the Caribbean.

The Caribbean, a scattering of islands in the Caribbean Sea, is also called the West Indies. Because of how these islands were colonized, English, Spanish, French, and Dutch are spoken along with hundreds of dialects. The Caribbean is also a lively mix of different cultures. A majority of its people are heirs to the African slaves forced to work on the huge plantations of sugar, tobacco, and bananas. Many others descend from indentured servants brought over from India. If all that you knew about the Caribbean were its palm trees, steel drums, and reggae music, you would be missing a lot.

Latin America encompasses Mexico and the countries of Central and South America, as well as some islands on the Caribbean Sea. The primary languages spoken—Spanish, Portuguese, and French—all developed from Latin, giving the region its name. Needless to say, Latin America is multicultural, with European descendants living side by side with the native Indian peoples. In countries such as Mexico there is also a strong mestizo, or racially mixed, culture.

Naturally, literature from Canada, the Caribbean, and Latin America reflects the huge diversity of cultures in each region.

A prominent concern of Canadian literature is the search for a national identity. Canadian writers often explore what makes Canada distinct—especially from America. A former Canadian prime minister, Pierre Trudeau, is famously quoted as saying to an American audience, "Living next to you is in some ways like sleeping with an elephant. No matter how friendly and even-tempered the beast, one is affected by every twitch and grunt."

The same could probably be said by politicians and writers from the Caribbean and Latin America. Twentieth-century Caribbean authors strive for a distinct Caribbean identity. These writers highlight the hybrid culture of this region, sometimes using the colorful pidgin and Creole dialects to give voice to ordinary people. A related theme of cultural displacement—the sense of rootlessness—is also prominent in Caribbean literature.

Long influenced by European literary traditions, many 20th-century Latin American authors began to experiment with literary modes such as surrealism and magic realism. Surrealism stresses the importance of dreams and the unconscious mind and often juxtaposes bizarre or startling images. Magic realism, made famous by authors such as Gabriel García Márquez, blends reality with fantasy, portraying fantastic occurrences as a matter of fact. All of a sudden, animals can speak and human beings can levitate. After all, what could be stranger than life itself? Especially in a region with such extreme divides between its rich and poor, forms of government (totalitarian and democratic), cultures, and climates. In the 1960s—a period known as the "Latin American Boom"—this bold and innovative style brought worldwide attention to Latin American authors.

The vibrant literature of Canada, the Caribbean, and Latin America is valuable for introducing us to new cultures as well as illuminating the multicultural nature of American society. By discovering the literature of our neighbors, we may also learn about ourselves.

Literary Map of
the Americas

CANADA

UNITED STATES
OF AMERICA

CENTRAL
AMERICA

Octavio Paz   Mexico

Juan Rulfo   Mexico

Carlos Solórzano   Guatemala/Mexico

Rosario Ferré   Puerto Rico

Samuel Selvon   Trinidad and Tobago

Gabriela Mistral   Chile

Pablo Neruda   Chile

Isabel Allende   Chile

Thomas King   Canada

Alice Munro   Canada

Herberto Padilla   Cuba

Margaret Atwood   Canada

James Berry   Jamaica

Derek Walcott   St. Lucia

SOUTH AMERICA

Gabriel García Márquez   Colombia

João Guimarães Rosa   Brazil

Jorge Luis Borges   Argentina

Luisa Valenzuela   Argentina

Literary Map   19

Borders

Thomas King

In order to make way for the trans-Canadian railroad, the Canadian government signed an 1877 treaty confining certain Indians (especially those deemed unlikely to blend into "civilization") to small "reserves." After this, natives who shared ethnic roots with U.S. tribes, such as the Cree, Sioux, and Blackfoot, were divided from their tribespeople by two distinct borders: international and reserve.

The United States and Canada have similar percentages of Native Americans in their populations, hovering at around one percent. However, the First Nations of Canada have a highly visible cultural and political presence, with many groups in place to address Indian issues. Over 50 native languages and many dialects contribute to a sense of cultural vitality.

It is understandable why writer Thomas King—a Canadian with U.S. roots, who is part Blackfoot—may have given a lot of thought to borders.

When I was twelve, maybe thirteen, my mother announced that we were going to go to Salt Lake City to visit my sister who had left the reserve, moved across the line, and found a job. Laetitia had not left home with my mother's blessing, but over time my mother had come to be proud of the fact that Laetitia had done all of this on her own.

"She did real good," my mother would say.

Then there were the fine points to Laetitia's going. She had not, as my mother liked to tell Mrs. Manyfingers, gone floating after some man like a balloon on a string. She hadn't snuck out of the house, either, and gone to Vancouver or Edmonton or Toronto to chase rainbows down alleys. And she hadn't been pregnant.

"She did real good."

I was seven or eight when Laetitia left home. She was seventeen. Our father was from Rocky Boy on the American side.

"Dad's American," Laetitia told my mother, "so I can go and come as I please."

"Send us a postcard."

Laetitia packed her things, and we headed for the border. Just outside of Milk River, Laetitia told us to watch for the water tower.

"Over the next rise. It's the first thing you see."

"We got a water tower on the reserve," my mother said. "There's a big one in Lethbridge, too."

"You'll be able to see the tops of the flagpoles, too. That's where the border is."

When we got to Coutts, my mother stopped at the convenience store and bought her and Laetitia a cup of coffee. I got an Orange Crush.

"This is real lousy coffee."

"You're just angry because I want to see the world."

"It's the water. From here on down, they got lousy water."

"I can catch the bus from Sweetgrass. You don't have to lift a finger."

"You're going to have to buy your water in bottles if you want good coffee."

There was an old wooden building about a block away, with a tall sign in the yard that said "Museum." Most of the roof had been blown away. Mom told me to go and see when the place was open. There were boards over the windows and doors. You could tell that the place was closed, and I told Mom so, but she said to go and check anyway. Mom and Laetitia stayed by the car. Neither one of them moved. I sat down on the steps of the museum and watched them, and I don't know that they ever said anything to each other. Finally, Laetitia got her bag out of the trunk and gave Mom a hug.

I wandered back to the car. The wind had come up, and it blew Laetitia's hair across her face. Mom reached out and pulled the strands out of Laetitia's eyes, and Laetitia let her.

"You can still see the mountain from here," my mother told Laetitia in Blackfoot.

"Lots of mountains in Salt Lake," Laetitia told her in English.

"The place is closed," I said. "Just like I told you."

Laetitia tucked her hair into her jacket and dragged her bag down the road to the brick building with the American flag flapping on a pole. When she got to where the guards were waiting, she turned, put the bag down, and waved to us. We waved back. Then my mother turned the car around, and we came home.

We got postcards from Laetitia regular, and, if she wasn't spreading jelly on the truth, she was happy. She found a good job and rented an apartment with a pool.

"And she can't even swim," my mother told Mrs. Manyfingers.

Most of the postcards said we should come down and see the city, but whenever I mentioned this, my mother would stiffen up.

So I was surprised when she bought two new tires for the car and put on her blue dress with the green and yellow flowers. I had to dress up, too, for my mother did not want us crossing the border looking like Americans. We made sandwiches and put them in a big box with pop and potato chips and some apples and bananas and a big jar of water.

"But we can stop at one of those restaurants, too, right?"

"We maybe should take some blankets in case you get sleepy."

"But we can stop at one of those restaurants, too, right?"

The border was actually two towns, though neither one was big enough to amount to anything. Coutts was on the Canadian side and consisted of the convenience store and gas station, the museum that was closed and boarded up, and a motel. Sweetgrass was on the American side, but all you could see was an overpass that arched across the highway and disappeared into the prairies. Just hearing the names of these towns, you would expect that Sweetgrass, which is a nice name and sounds like it is related to other places such as Medicine Hat and Moose Jaw and Kicking Horse Pass, would be on the Canadian side, and that Coutts, which sounds abrupt and rude, would be on the American side. But this was not the case.

Between the two borders was a duty-free shop where you could buy cigarettes and liquor and flags. Stuff like that.

We left the reserve in the morning and drove until we got to Coutts.

"Last time we stopped here," my mother said, "you had an Orange Crush. You remember that?"

"Sure," I said. "That was when Laetitia took off."

"You want another Orange Crush?"

"That means we're not going to stop at a restaurant, right?"

My mother got a coffee at the convenience store, and we stood around and watched the prairies move in the sunlight. Then we climbed back in the car. My mother straightened the dress across her thighs, leaned against the wheel, and drove all the way to the border in first gear, slowly, as if she were trying to see through a bad storm or riding high on black ice.

The border guard was an old guy. As he walked to the car, he swayed from side to side, his feet set wide apart, the holster on his hip pitching up and down. He leaned into the window, looked into the back seat, and looked at my mother and me.

"Morning, ma'am."

"Good morning."

"Where you heading?"

"Salt Lake City."

"Purpose of your visit?"

"Visit my daughter."

"Citizenship?"

"Blackfoot," my mother told him.

"Ma'am?"

"Blackfoot," my mother repeated.

"Canadian?"

"Blackfoot."

It would have been easier if my mother had just said "Canadian" and been done with it, but I could see she wasn't going to do that. The guard wasn't angry or anything. He smiled and looked towards the building. Then he turned back and nodded.

"Morning, ma'am."

"Good morning."

"Any firearms or tobacco?"

"No."

"Citizenship?"

"Blackfoot."

He told us to sit in the car and wait, and we did. In about five minutes, another guard came out with the first man. They were talking as they came, both men swaying back and forth like two cowboys headed for a bar or a gunfight.

"Morning, ma'am."

"Good morning."

"Cecil tells me you and the boy are Blackfoot."

"That's right."

"Now, I know that we got Blackfeet on the American side and the Canadian got Blackfeet on their side. Just so we can keep our records straight, what side do you come from?"

I knew exactly what my mother was going to say, and I could have told them if they had asked me.

"Canadian side or American side?" asked the guard.

"Blackfoot side," she said.

It didn't take them long to lose their sense of humor. I can tell you that. The one guard stopped smiling altogether and told us to park our car at the side of the building and come in.

We sat on a wood bench for about an hour before anyone came over to talk to us. This time it was a woman. She had a gun, too.

"Hi," she said. "I'm Inspector Pratt. I understand there is a little misunderstanding."

"I'm going to visit my daughter in Salt Lake City," my mother told her. "We don't have any guns or beer."

"It's a legal technicality, that's all."

"My daughter's Blackfoot, too."

The woman opened a briefcase and took out a couple of forms and began to write on one of them. "Everyone who crosses our border has to declare their citizenship. Even Americans. It helps us keep track of the visitors we get from the various countries."

She went on like that for maybe fifteen minutes, and a lot of the stuff she told us was interesting.

"I can understand how you feel about having to tell us your citizenship, and here's what I'll do. You tell me, and I won't put it down on the form. No one will know but you and me."

Her gun was silver. There were several chips in the wood handle and the name "Stella" was scratched into the metal butt.

We were in the border office for about four hours, and we talked to almost everyone there. One of the men bought me a Coke. My mother brought a couple of sandwiches in from the car. I offered part of mine to Stella, but she said she wasn't hungry.

I told Stella that we were Blackfoot and Canadian, but she said that that didn't count because I was a minor. In the end, she told us that if my mother didn't declare her citizenship, we would have to go back to where we came from. My mother stood up and thanked Stella for her time. Then we got back in the car and drove to the Canadian border, which was only about a hundred yards away.

I was disappointed. I hadn't seen Laetitia for a long time, and I had never been to Salt Lake City. When she was still at home, Laetitia would go on and on about Salt Lake City. She had never been there, but her boyfriend Lester Tallbull had spent a year in Salt Lake at a technical school.

"It's a great place," Lester would say. "Nothing but blondes in the whole state."

Whenever he said that, Laetitia would slug him on his shoulder hard enough to make him flinch. He had some brochures on Salt Lake and some maps, and every so often the two of them would spread them out on the table.

"That's the temple. It's right downtown. You got to have a pass to get in."

"Charlotte says anyone can go in and look around."

"When was Charlotte in Salt Lake? Just when the hell was Charlotte in Salt Lake?"

"Last year."

"This is Liberty Park. It's got a zoo. There's good skiing in the mountains."

"Got all the skiing we can use," my mother would say. "People come from all over the world to ski at Banff. Cardston's got a temple, if you like those kinds of things."

"Oh, this one is real big," Lester would say. "They got armed guards and everything."

"Not what Charlotte says."

"What does she know?"

Lester and Laetitia broke up, but I guess the idea of Salt Lake stuck in her mind.

◆ ◆ ◆ ◆ ◆

The Canadian border guard was a young woman, and she seemed happy to see us. "Hi," she said. "You folks sure have a great day for a trip. Where are you coming from?"

"Standoff."

"Is that in Montana?"

"No."

"Where are you going?"

"Standoff."

The woman's name was Carol and I don't guess she was any older than Laetitia. "Wow, you both Canadians?"

"Blackfoot."

"Really? I have a friend I went to school with who is Blackfoot. Do you know Mike Harley?"

"No."

"He went to school in Lethbridge, but he's really from Browning."

It was a nice conversation and there were no cars behind us, so there was no rush.

"You're not bringing any liquor back, are you?"

"No."

"Any cigarettes or plants or stuff like that?"

"No."

"Citizenship?"

"Blackfoot."

"I know," said the woman, "and I'd be proud of being Blackfoot if I were Blackfoot. But you have to be American or Canadian."

". . . and I'd be proud of being Blackfoot if I were Blackfoot. But you have to be American or Canadian."

♦ ♦ ♦ ♦ ♦

When Laetitia and Lester broke up, Lester took his brochures and maps with him, so Laetitia wrote to someone in Salt Lake City, and, about a month later, she got a big envelope of stuff. We sat at the table and opened up all the brochures, and Laetitia read each one out loud.

"Salt Lake City is the gateway to some of the world's most magnificent skiing.

"Salt Lake City is the home of one of the newest professional basketball franchises, the Utah Jazz.

"The Great Salt Lake is one of the natural wonders of the world."

It was kind of exciting seeing all those color brochures on the table and listening to Laetitia read all about how Salt Lake City was one of the best places in the entire world.

"That Salt Lake City place sounds too good to be true," my mother told her.

"It has everything."

"We got everything right here."

"It's boring here."

"People in Salt Lake City are probably sending away for brochures of Calgary and Lethbridge and Pincher Creek right now."

In the end, my mother would say that maybe Laetitia should go to Salt Lake City, and Laetitia would say that maybe she would.

◆ ◆ ◆ ◆ ◆

We parked the car to the side of the building and Carol led us into a small room on the second floor. I found a comfortable spot on the couch and flipped through some back issues of *Saturday Night* and *Alberta Report*.

When I woke up, my mother was just coming out of another office. She didn't say a word to me. I followed her down the stairs and out to the car. I thought we were going home, but she turned the car around and drove back towards the American border, which made me think we were going to visit Laetitia in Salt Lake City after all. Instead she pulled into the parking lot of the duty-free store and stopped.

"We going to see Laetitia?"

"No."

"We going home?"

Pride is a good thing to have, you know. Laetitia had a lot of pride, and so did my mother. I figured that someday, I'd have it too.

"So where are we going?"

Most of that day, we wandered around the duty-free store, which wasn't very large. The manager had a name tag with a tiny American flag on one side and a tiny Canadian flag on the other. His name was Mel. Towards evening, he began suggesting that we should be on our way. I told him we had nowhere to go, that neither the Americans nor the Canadians would let us in. He laughed at that and told us that we should buy something or leave.

The car was not very comfortable, but we did have all that food and it was April, so even if it did snow as it sometimes does on the prairies, we wouldn't freeze. The next morning my mother drove to the American border.

It was a different guard this time, but the questions were the same. We didn't spend as much time in the office as we had the day before. By noon, we were back at the Canadian border. By two we were back in the duty-free shop parking lot.

The second night in the car was not as much fun as the first, but my mother seemed in good spirits, and, all in all, it was as much an adventure as an inconvenience. There wasn't much food left and that was a problem, but we had lots of water as there was a faucet at the side of the duty-free shop.

♦♦♦♦♦

One Sunday, Laetitia and I were watching television. Mom was over at Mrs. Manyfingers's. Right in the middle of the program, Laetitia turned off the set and said she was going to Salt Lake City, that life around here was too boring. I had wanted to see the rest of the program and really didn't care if Laetitia went to Salt Lake City or not. When Mom got home, I told her what Laetitia had said.

What surprised me was how angry Laetitia got when she found out that I had told Mom.

"You got a big mouth."

"That's what you said."

"What I said is none of your business."

"I didn't say anything."

"Well, I'm going for sure, now."

That weekend, Laetitia packed her bags, and we drove her to the border.

♦♦♦♦♦

Mel turned out to be friendly. When he closed up for the night and found us still parked in the lot, he came over and asked us if our car was broken down or something. My mother thanked him for his concern and told him that we were fine, that things would get straightened out in the morning.

"You're kidding," said Mel. "You'd think they could handle the simple things."

"We got some apples and a banana," I said, "but we're all out of ham sandwiches."

"You know, you read about these things, but you just don't believe, it. You just don't believe it."

"Hamburgers would be even better because they got more stuff for energy."

My mother slept in the backseat. I slept in the front because I was smaller and could lie under the steering wheel. Late that night, I heard my mother open the car door. I found her sitting on her blanket leaning against the bumper of the car.

"You see all those stars," she said. "When I was a little girl, my grandmother used to take me and my sisters out on the prairies and tell us stories about all the stars."

"Do you think Mel is going to bring us any hamburgers?"

"Every one of those stars has a story. You see that bunch of stars over there that look like a fish?"

"He didn't say no."

"Coyote went fishing, one day. That's how it all started." We sat out under the stars that night, and my mother told me all sorts of stories. She was serious about it, too. She'd tell them slow, repeating parts as she went, as if she expected me to remember each one.

Early the next morning, the television vans began to arrive, and guys in suits and women in dresses came trotting over to us, dragging microphones and cameras and lights behind them. One of the vans had a table set up with orange juice and sandwiches and fruit. It was for the crew, but when I told them we hadn't eaten for a while, a really skinny blonde woman told us we could eat as much as we wanted.

They mostly talked to my mother. Every so often one of the reporters would come over and ask me questions about how it felt to be an Indian without a country. I told them we had a nice house on the reserve and that my cousins had a couple of horses we rode when we went fishing. Some of the television people went over to the American border, and then they went to the Canadian border.

Around noon, a good-looking guy in a dark blue suit and an orange tie with little ducks on it drove up in a fancy car. He talked to my mother for a while, and, after they were done talking, my mother called me over, and we got into our car. Just as my mother started the engine, Mel came over and gave us a bag of peanut brittle and told us that justice was a damn hard thing to get, but that we shouldn't give up.

I would have preferred lemon drops, but it was nice of Mel anyway.

"Where are we going now?"

"Going to visit Laetitia."

The guard who came out to our car was all smiles. The television lights were so bright they hurt my eyes, and, if you tried to look through the windshield in certain directions, you couldn't see a thing.

"Morning, ma'am."

"Good morning."

"Where you heading?"

"Salt Lake City."

"Purpose of your visit?"

"Visit my daughter."

"Any tobacco, liquor, or firearms?"

"Don't smoke."

"Any plants or fruit?"

"Not any more."

"Citizenship?"

"Blackfoot."

The guard rocked back on his heels and jammed his thumbs into his gun belt. "Thank you," he said, his fingers patting the butt of the revolver. "Have a pleasant trip."

My mother rolled the car forward, and the television people had to scramble out of the way. They ran alongside the car as we pulled away from the border, and, when they couldn't run any farther, they stood in the middle of the highway and waved and waved and waved.

We got to Salt Lake City the next day. Laetitia was happy to see us, and, that first night, she took us out to a restaurant that made really good soups. The list of pies took up a whole page. I had cherry. Mom had chocolate. Laetitia said that she saw us on television the night before and, during the meal, she had us tell her the story over and over again.

Laetitia took us everywhere. We went to a fancy ski resort. We went to the temple. We got to go shopping in a couple of large malls, but they weren't as large as the one in Edmonton, and Mom said so.

After a week or so, I got bored and wasn't at all sad when my mother said we should be heading back home. Laetitia wanted us to stay longer, but Mom said no, that she had things to do back home and that, next time, Laetitia should come up and visit. Laetitia said she was thinking about moving back, and Mom told her to do as she pleased, and Laetitia said that she would.

On the way home, we stopped at the duty-free shop, and my mother gave Mel a green hat that said "Salt Lake" across the front. Mel was a funny guy. He took the hat and blew his nose and told my mother that she was an inspiration to us all. He gave us some more peanut brittle and came out into the parking lot and waved at us all the way to the Canadian border.

It was almost evening when we left Coutts. I watched the border through the rear window until all you could see were the tops of the flagpoles and the blue water tower, and then they rolled over a hill and disappeared.

Responding to the Selection

1. Why do you think the author chooses to tell this story from the eyes of a young boy?

2. Is your understanding of the story different when you learn that the author has Native American roots?

3. Why does the mother tell the son her stories at a time when the two of them are an "international incident"?

4. Why doesn't the mother just say "Canadian" in answer to the border guards' query about her citizenship?

At the Tourist Centre in Boston

Margaret Atwood

Many Americans mistake Canada for a quieter, colder version of the United States. Influential writers such as Margaret Atwood are not the only Canadians who resent Americans' lack of knowledge about their neighbor to the north. The second-largest country in the world, Canada has a wilderness terrain of stunning variety and is equally notable for its diverse population. Unlike the United States, with its "melting pot" credo, Canada has not made assimilation the goal of citizenship for new immigrants.

WORLD LENS

♦♦♦

CANADA

There is my country under glass,
a white relief-
map with red dots for the cities,
reduced to the size of a wall

and beside it 10 blownup snapshots
one for each province,
in purple-browns and odd reds,
the green of the trees dulled;
all blues however
of an assertive purity.

Mountains and lakes and more lakes
(though Quebec[1] is a restaurant and Ontario[2] the empty
interior of the parliament buildings),
with nobody climbing the trails and hauling out
the fish and splashing in the water

---

1 **Quebec:** a French-speaking province in eastern Canada
2 **Ontario:** a Canadian province bordering the Great Lakes

but arrangements of grinning tourists—
look here, Saskatchewan[3]
is a flat lake, some convenient rocks
where two children pose with a father
and the mother is cooking something
in immaculate slacks by a smokeless fire,
her teeth white as detergent.

Whose dream is this, I would like to know:
is this a manufactured
hallucination, a cynical fiction, a lure
for export only?

VENTE TROTTOIR FIN DE SOIRÉE, Raphael Montpetit

---

3 **Saskatchewan:** a western province of Canada

I seem to remember people,
at least in the cities, also slush,
machines and assorted garbage. Perhaps
that was my private mirage

which will just evaporate
when I go back. Or the citizens will be gone,
run off to the peculiarly-
green forests
to wait among the brownish mountains
for the platoons of tourists
and plan their odd red massacres.

Unsuspecting
window lady, I ask you:

Do you see nothing
watching you from under the water?

Was the sky ever that blue?

Who really lives there?

Responding to the Selection

1. What does the poet object to about the portrayal of her country in the tourist center?

2. What are some differences in perspectives between viewing a country as a place to visit and a place to live?

3. The tourism industry tends to construct a set of stereotypes about a country. Name some things that are left off of the "tourist map," such as poverty, trouble sites, and so forth.

4. What point do you think the author is making by ending the poem with these three questions?

Day of the Butterfly

Alice Munro

WORLD LENS

♦♦♦

CANADA

Alice Munro, who began publishing her stories as a teenager, is one of the most celebrated contemporary short story writers in the English world. "Day of the Butterfly" reveals some of her ongoing subject matter and themes: small-town life in provincial Canada, girls coming of age, and the mysteries of ordinary life. The central Canadian province of Ontario, where she has spent much of her life, is often the setting in which she explores frustration, loneliness, and moral breakdown.

Depicting rural communities allows Munro to demonstrate how close people can be without really knowing each other at all. She has said, "In small towns, you have no privacy at all. You have a role, a character, but one that other people have made up for you." In the following story, the truth of that remark can easily be seen.

I do not remember when Myra Sayla came to town, though she must have been in our class at school for two or three years. I start remembering her in the last year, when her little brother Jimmy Sayla was in Grade One. Jimmy Sayla was not used to going to the bathroom by himself and he would have to come to the Grade Six door and ask for Myra and she would take him downstairs. Quite often he would not get to Myra in time and there would be a big dark stain on his little button-on cotton pants. Then Myra had to come and ask the teacher: "Please may I take my brother home, he has wet himself?"

That was what she said the first time and everybody in the front seats heard her—though Myra's voice was the lightest singsong—and there was a muted giggling which alerted the rest of the class. Our teacher, a cold gentle girl who wore glasses with thin gold rims and in the stiff **solicitude** of certain poses resembled a giraffe, wrote something on a piece of paper and

solicitude
concern; care

showed it to Myra. And Myra recited uncertainly: "My brother has had an accident, please, teacher."

Everybody knew of Jimmy Sayla's shame and at recess (if he was not being kept in, as he often was, for doing something he shouldn't in school) he did not dare go out on the school grounds, where the other little boys, and some bigger ones, were waiting to chase him and corner him against the back fence and thrash him with tree branches. He had to stay with Myra. But at our school there were the two sides, the Boys' Side and the Girls' Side, and it was believed that if you so much as stepped on the side that was not your own you might easily get the strap. Jimmy could not go out on the Girls' Side and Myra could not go out on the Boys' Side, and no one was allowed to stay in the school unless it was raining or snowing. So Myra and Jimmy spent every recess standing in the little back porch between the two sides. Perhaps they watched the baseball games, the tag and skipping and building of leaf houses in the fall and snow forts in the winter; perhaps they did not watch at all. Whenever you happened to look at them their heads were slightly bent, their narrow bodies hunched in, quite still. They had long smooth oval faces, **melancholy** and **discreet**—dark, oily shining hair. The little boy's was long, clipped at home, and Myra's was worn in heavy braids coiled on top of her head so that she looked, from a distance, as if she was wearing a turban too big for her. Over their dark eyes, the lids were never fully raised; they had a weary look. But it was more than that. They were like children in a medieval painting, they were like small figures carved of wood, for worship or magic, with faces smooth and aged, and meekly, **cryptically** uncommunicative.

melancholy
sad; downhearted

discreet
cautious; guarded

cryptically
mysteriously; secretively

♦ ♦ ♦ ♦ ♦

Most of the teachers at our school had been teaching for a long time and at recess they would disappear into the teachers' room and not bother us. But our own teacher, the young woman of the fragile gold-rimmed glasses, was apt to watch us from a window and sometimes come out, looking brisk and uncomfortable, to stop a fight among the little girls or start a running game among the big ones, who had been huddled together playing Truth or Secrets. One day she came out and called, "Girls in Grade Six, I want to talk to you!" She smiled persuasively, earnestly, and with dreadful unease, showing fine gold rims around her teeth. She said, "There is a girl in Grade Six called Myra Sayla. She is in your grade, isn't she?"

We mumbled. But there was a coo from Gladys Healey. "Yes, Miss Darling!"

"Well, why is she never playing with the rest of you? Every day I see her standing in the back porch, never playing. Do you think she looks happy standing back there? Do you think you would be very happy, if *you* were left back there?"

Nobody answered; we faced Miss Darling, all respectful, self-possessed, and bored with the unreality of her question. Then Gladys said, "Myra can't come out with us, Miss Darling. Myra has to look after her little brother!"

"Oh," said Miss Darling dubiously. "Well you ought to try to be nicer to her anyway. Don't you think so? Don't you? You will try to be nicer, won't you? I *know* you will." Poor Miss Darling! Her campaigns were soon confused, her persuasions turned to bleating and uncertain pleas.

When she had gone Gladys Healey said softly, "You will try to be nicer, won't you? I know you will." and then drawing her lip back over her big teeth she yelled exuberantly, "I don't care if it rains or freezes."[1] She went through the whole verse and ended it with a spectacular twirl of her Royal Stuart tartan[2] skirt. Mr. Healey ran a Dry Goods and Ladies' Wear, and his daughter's leadership in our class was partly due to her flashing plaid skirts and organdie blouses and velvet jackets with brass buttons, but also to her early-maturing bust and the fine brutal force of her personality. Now we all began to imitate Miss Darling.

We had not paid much attention to Myra before this. But now a game was developed; it started with saying, "Let's be nice to Myra!" Then we would walk up to her in formal groups of three or four and at a signal, say together, "Hel-lo Myra, Hello My-ra!" and follow up with something like, "What do you wash your hair

---

1 **"I don't care . . . freezes.":** lyrics from a popular song

2 **Royal Stuart tartan:** a red Scottish plaid

in, Myra, it's so nice and shiny, My-ra." "Oh she washes it in cod-liver oil, don't you, Myra, she washes it in cod-liver oil, can't you smell it?"

And to tell the truth there was a smell about Myra, but it was a rotten-sweetish smell as of bad fruit. That was what the Saylas did, kept a little fruit store. Her father sat all day on a stool by the window, with his shirt open over his swelling stomach and tufts of black hair showing around his belly button; he chewed garlic. But if you went into the store it was Mrs. Sayla who came to wait on you, appearing silently between the limp print curtains hung across the back of the store. Her hair was crimped in black waves and she smiled with her full lips held together, stretched as far as they would go; she told you the price in a little rapping voice, daring you to challenge her and, when you did not, handed you the bag of fruit with open mockery in her eyes.

◆ ◆ ◆ ◆ ◆

One morning in the winter I was walking up the school hill very early; a neighbour had given me a ride into town. I lived about half a mile out of town, on a farm, and I should not have been going to the town school at all, but to a country school nearby where there were half a dozen pupils and a teacher a little demented since her change of life.[3] But my mother, who was an ambitious woman, had prevailed on the town trustees to accept me and my father to pay the extra tuition, and I went to school in town. I was the only one in the class who carried a lunch pail and ate peanut-butter sandwiches in the high, bare, mustard-coloured cloakroom, the only one who had to wear rubber boots in the spring, when the roads were heavy with mud. I felt a little danger, on account of this; but I could not tell exactly what it was.

I saw Myra and Jimmy ahead of me on the hill; they always went to school very early—sometimes so early that they had to stand outside waiting for the janitor to open the door. They were walking slowly, and now and then Myra half turned around. I had often loitered in that way, wanting to walk with some important girl who was behind me, and not quite daring to stop and wait.

---

3 **change of life:** menopause, a time when women experience the hormonal changes of midlife

Day of the Butterfly

Now it occurred to me that Myra might be doing this with me. I did not know what to do. I could not afford to be seen walking with her, and I did not even want to—but, on the other hand, the flattery of those humble, hopeful turnings was not lost on me. A role was shaping for me that I could not resist playing. I felt a great pleasurable rush of self-conscious benevolence; before I thought what I was doing I called, "Myra! Hey, Myra, wait up, I got some Cracker Jack!" and I quickened my pace as she stopped.

Myra waited, but she did not look at me; she waited in the withdrawn and rigid attitude with which she always met us. Perhaps she thought I was playing a trick on her, perhaps she expected me to run past and throw an empty Cracker Jack box in her face. And I opened the box and held it out to her. She took a little. Jimmy ducked behind her coat and would not take any when I offered the box to him.

"He's shy," I said reassuringly. "A lot of little kids are shy like that. He'll probably grow out of it."

"Yes," said Myra.

"I have a brother four," I said. "He's awfully shy." He wasn't. "Have some more Cracker Jack," I said. "I used to eat Cracker Jack all the time but I don't any more. I think it's bad for your complexion."

There was silence.

"Do you like Art?" said Myra faintly.

"No. I like Social Studies and Spelling and Health."

"I like Art and Arithmetic." Myra could add and multiply in her head faster than anyone else in the class.

"I wish I was as good as you. In Arithmetic," I said, and felt magnanimous.

"But I am no good at Spelling," said Myra. "I make the most mistakes, I'll fail maybe." She did not sound unhappy about this, but pleased to have such a thing to say. She kept her head turned away from me staring at the dirty snowbanks along Victoria Street, and as she talked she made a sound as if she was wetting her lips with her tongue.

"You won't fail," I said. "You are too good in Arithmetic. What are you going to be when you grow up?"

She looked bewildered. "I will help my mother," she said.

"And work in the store."

"Well I am going to be an airplane hostess," I said. "But don't mention it to anybody. I haven't told many people."

"No, I won't," said Myra. "Do you read Steve Canyon in the paper?"

"Yes." It was queer to think that Myra, too, read the comics, or that she did anything at all, apart from her role at the school. "Do you read Rip Kirby?"

"Do you read Orphan Annie?"

"Do you read Betsy and the Boys?"

"You haven't had hardly any Cracker Jack," I said. "Have some. Take a whole handful."

Myra looked into the box. "There's a prize in there," she said. She pulled it out. It was a brooch, a little tin butterfly, painted gold with bits of coloured glass stuck onto it to look like jewels. She held it in her brown hand, smiling slightly.

I said, "Do you like that?"

Myra said, "I like them blue stones. Blue stones are sapphires."

"I know. My birthstone is sapphire. What is your birthstone?"

"I don't know."

"When is your birthday?"

"July."

"Then yours is ruby."

"I like sapphire better," said Myra. "I like yours." She handed me the brooch.

"You keep it," I said. "Finders keepers."

Myra kept holding it out, as if she did not know what I meant. "Finders keepers." I said.

"It was your Cracker Jack," said Myra, scared and solemn. "You bought it."

"Well you found it."

"No—" said Myra.

"Go on!" I said. "Here, I'll *give* it to you." I took the brooch from her and pushed it back into her hand.

We were both surprised. We looked at each other; I flushed but

> **It was a brooch, a little tin butterfly, painted gold with bits of coloured glass stuck onto it to look like jewels.**

Myra did not. I realized the pledge as our fingers touched; I was panicky, but *all right.* I thought, I can come early and walk with her other mornings. I can go and talk to her at recess. Why not? *Why not?*

Myra put the brooch in her pocket. She said, "I can wear it on my good dress. My good dress is blue."

I knew it would be. Myra wore out her good dresses at school. Even in midwinter among the plaid wool skirts and serge tunics, she glimmered sadly in sky-blue taffeta, in dusty turquoise crepe, a grown woman's dress made over, weighted by a big bow at the v of the neck and folding empty over Myra's narrow chest.

And I was glad she had not put it on. If someone asked her where she got it, and she told them, what would I say?

It was the day after this, or the week after, that Myra did not come to school. Often she was kept at home to help. But this time she did not come back. For a week, then two weeks, her desk was empty. Then we had a moving day at school and Myra's books were taken out of her desk and put on a shelf in the closet. Miss Darling said, "We'll find a seat when she comes back." And she stopped calling Myra's name when she took attendance.

Jimmy Sayla did not come to school either, having no one to take him to the bathroom.

◆ ◆ ◆ ◆ ◆

In the fourth week or the fifth, that Myra had been away, Gladys Healey came to school and said, "Do you know what—Myra Sayla is sick in the hospital."

It was true. Gladys Healey had an aunt who was a nurse. Gladys put up her hand in the middle of Spelling and told Miss Darling. "I thought you might like to know," she said. "Oh yes," said Miss Darling, "I do know."

"What has she got?" we said to Gladys.

And Gladys said, "Akemia,[4] or something. And she has blood transfusions." She said to Miss Darling, "My aunt is a nurse."

So Miss Darling had the whole class write Myra a letter, in which everybody said, "Dear Myra, We are all writing you a letter.

---

4 **Akemia:** a mispronunciation of "leukemia"

We hope you will soon be better and be back to school, Yours truly . . . ." And Miss Darling said, "I've thought of something. Who would like to go up to the hospital and visit Myra on the twentieth of March, for a birthday party?"

I said, "Her birthday's in July."

"I know," said Miss Darling. "It's the twentieth of July. So this year she could have it on the twentieth of March, because she's sick."

"But her *birthday* is July."

"Because she's sick," said Miss Darling, with a warning shrillness. "The cook at the hospital would make a cake and you could all give a little present, twenty-five cents or so. It would have to be between two and four, because that's visiting hours. And we couldn't all go, it'd be too many. So who wants to go and who wants to stay here and do supplementary reading?"

We all put up our hands. Miss Darling got out the spelling records and picked out the first fifteen, twelve girls and three boys. Then the three boys did not want to go so she picked out the next three girls. And I do not know when it was, but I think it was probably at this moment that the birthday party of Myra Sayla became fashionable.

Perhaps it was because Gladys Healey had an aunt who was a nurse, perhaps it was the excitement of sickness and hospitals, or simply the fact that Myra was so entirely, impressively set free of all the rules and conditions of our lives. We began to talk of her as if she were something we owned, and her party became a cause; with womanly heaviness we discussed it at recess, and decided that twenty-five cents was too low.

◆ ◆ ◆ ◆ ◆

We all went up to the hospital on a sunny afternoon when the snow was melting, carrying our presents, and a nurse led us upstairs, single file, and down a hall past half-closed doors and dim conversations. She and Miss Darling kept saying, "Sh-sh," but we were going on tiptoe anyway; our hospital demeanor was perfect.

At this small country hospital there was no children's ward, and Myra was not really a child; they had put her in with two

grey old women. A nurse was putting screens around them as we came in.

Myra was sitting up in bed, in a bulky stiff hospital gown. Her hair was down, the long braids falling over her shoulders and down the coverlet. But her face was the same, always the same.

She had been told something about the party, Miss Darling said, so the surprise would not upset her; but it seemed she had not believed, or had not understood what it was. She watched us as she used to watch in the school grounds when we played.

44   The Americas

"Well, here we are!" said Miss Darling. "Here we are!"

And we said, "Happy birthday, Myra! Hello, Myra, happy birthday!" Myra said, "My birthday is in July." Her voice was lighter than ever, drifting, expressionless.

"Never mind when it is, really," said Miss Darling. "Pretend it's now! How old are you, Myra?"

"Eleven," Myra said. "In July."

Then we all took off our coats and emerged in our party dresses, and laid our presents, in their pale flowery wrappings on Myra's bed. Some of our mothers had made immense, complicated bows of fine satin ribbon, some of them had even taped on little bouquets of imitation roses and lilies of the valley. "Here Myra," we said, "here Myra, happy birthday." Myra did not look at us, but at the ribbons, pink and blue and speckled with silver, and the miniature bouquets; they pleased her, as the butterfly had done. An innocent look came into her face, a partial, private smile.

"Open them, Myra," said Miss Darling. "They're for you!"

Myra gathered the presents around her, fingering them, with this smile, and a cautious realization, an unexpected pride. She said, "Saturday I'm going to London[5] to St. Joseph's Hospital."

"That's where my mother was at," somebody said. "We went and saw her. They've got all nuns there."

"My father's sister is a nun," said Myra calmly.

She began to unwrap the presents, with an air that not even Gladys could have bettered, folding the tissue paper and the ribbons, and drawing out books and puzzles and cutouts as if they were all prizes she had won. Miss Darling said that maybe she should say thank you, and the person's name with every gift she opened, to make sure she knew whom it was from, and so Myra said, "Thank you, Mary Louise, thank you, Carol," and when she came to mine she said, "Thank you, Helen." Everyone explained their presents to her and there was talking and excitement and a little gaiety, which Myra presided over, though she was not gay. A cake was brought in with *Happy Birthday Myra* written on it, pink on white, and eleven candles. Miss Darling lit the candles and we all sang Happy Birthday to You, and cried,

---

5 **London:** a city in Ontario, central Canada

"Make a wish, Myra, make a wish—" and Myra blew them out. Then we all had cake and strawberry ice cream.

♦ ♦ ♦ ♦ ♦

At four o'clock a buzzer sounded and the nurse took out what was left of the cake and the dirty dishes, and we put on our coats to go home. Everybody said, "Goodbye, Myra," and Myra sat in bed watching us go, her back straight, not supported by any pillow, her hands resting on the gifts. But at the door I heard her call; she called, "Helen!" Only a couple of the others heard; Miss Darling did not hear, she had gone out ahead. I went back to the bed.

Myra said, "I got too many things. You take something."

"What?" I said. "It's for your birthday. You always get a lot at a birthday."

"Well you take something," Myra said. She picked up a leatherette case with a mirror in it, a comb and a nail file and a natural lipstick and a small handkerchief edged with gold thread. I had noticed it before. "You take that," she said.

"Don't you want it?"

"You take it." She put it into my hand. Our fingers touched again.

"When I come back from London," Myra said, "you can come and play at my place after school."

"Okay," I said. Outside the hospital window there was a clear carrying sound of somebody playing in the street, maybe chasing with the last snowballs of the year. This sound made Myra, her triumph and her bounty, and most of all her future in which she had found this place for me, turn shadowy, turn dark. All the presents on the bed, the folded paper and ribbons, those guilt-tinged offerings, had passed into this shadow, they were no longer innocent objects to be touched, exchanged, accepted without danger. I didn't want to take the case now but I could not think how to get out of it, what lie to tell. I'll give it away, I thought, I won't ever play with it. I would let my little brother pull it apart.

The nurse came back, carrying a glass of chocolate milk.

"What's the matter, didn't you hear the buzzer?"

So I was released, set free by the barriers which now closed about Myra, her unknown, **exalted**, ether-smelling[6] hospital world, and by the treachery of my own heart. "Well thank you," I said. "Thank you for the thing. Goodbye."

Did Myra ever say goodbye? Not likely. She sat in her high bed, her delicate brown neck, rising out of a hospital gown too big for her, her brown carved face immune to treachery, her offering perhaps already forgotten, prepared to be set apart for legendary uses, as she was even in the back porch at school.

exalted
elevated; glorified

Responding to the Selection

1. The reminiscent narrator uses an adult point of view to tell a story set in the past. What does the author gain by using this technique?

2. How does Helen's own status at school shape her relationship to Myra?

3. Identify the acts of cruelty in this story, both deliberate and unintentional. What do you think is the author's purpose in using them?

4. At what point in the story do you feel the most pity and sympathy for Myra? Explain why.

---

6 **ether-smelling:** smelling of the chemical compound used to anesthetize patients

No Dogs Bark

Juan Rulfo

WORLD LENS

•••

MEXICO

Mexican Juan Rulfo contributed to the Latin American writing known as magic realism, in which ordinary events can blend into the magical and fantastical. This vivid expression helps to capture the strangeness of everyday life, especially in places such as Mexico, where many people believe that the dead pay visits to their loved ones.

Each November, Mexicans celebrate *El Día de los Muertos*—The Day of the Dead. On this day, people pay homage to the deceased with homemade altars, prayer vigils, and nighttime processions to cemeteries. Papier-mâché skeletons, called *calaveras*, sprout up everywhere, mocking death and satirizing the living.

Y ou up there, Ignacio! Don't you hear something or see a light somewhere?"

"I can't see a thing."

"We ought to be near now."

'Yes, but I can't hear a thing."

"Look hard. Poor Ignacio."

The long black shadow of the men kept moving up and down, climbing over rocks, diminishing and increasing as it advanced along the edge of the arroyo.¹ It was a single, reeling shadow.

The moon came out of the earth like a round flare.

"We should be getting to that town, Ignacio. Your ears are uncovered, so try to see if you can't hear dogs barking. Remember they told us Tonaya was right behind the mountain. And we left the mountain hours ago. Remember, Ignacio?"

"Yes, but I don't see a sign of anything."

"I'm getting tired."

"Put me down."

---

1 **arroyo:** a narrow gulch, dry except during heavy rains

The Americas

The old man backed up to a thick wall and shifted his load but didn't let it down from his shoulders. Though his legs were buckling on him, he didn't want to sit down, because then he would be unable to lift his son's body, which they had helped to sling on his back hours ago. He had carried him all this way.

"How do you feel?"

"Bad."

Ignacio didn't talk much. Less and less all the time. Now and then he seemed to sleep. At times he seemed to be cold. He trembled. When the trembling seized him, his feet dug into his father's flanks like spurs. Then his hands, clasped around his father's neck, clutched at the head and shook it as if it were a rattle.

The father gritted his teeth so he wouldn't bite his tongue, and when the shaking was over, he asked, "Does it hurt a lot?"

"Some," Ignacio answered.

First Ignacio had said, "Put me down here—leave me here— you go on alone. I'll catch up with you tomorrow or as soon as I get a little better." He'd said this some fifty times. Now he didn't say it.

There was the moon. Facing them. A large red moon that filled their eyes with light and stretched and darkened its shadow over the earth.

"I can't see where I'm going anymore," the father said.

No answer.

The son up there was illumined by the moon. His face, discolored, bloodless, reflected the opaque light. And he here below.

"Did you hear me, Ignacio? I tell you, I can't see very well."

No answer.

Falteringly, the father continued. He hunched his body over, then straightened up to stumble on again.

"This is no road. They told us Tonaya was behind the hill. We've passed the hill. And you can't see Tonaya or hear any sound that would tell us it is close. Why won't you tell me what you see up there, Ignacio?"

"Put me down, Father."

"Do you feel bad?"

"Yes."

"I'll get you to Tonaya. There I'll find somebody to take care of you. They say there's a doctor in the town. I'll take you to him. I've already carried you for hours, and I'm not going to leave you lying here now for somebody to finish off."

He staggered a little. He took two or three steps to the side, then straightened up again.

"I'll get you to Tonaya."

"Let me down."

His voice was faint, scarcely a murmur. "I want to sleep a little."

"Sleep up there. After all, I've got a good hold on you."

The moon was rising, almost blue, in a clear sky. Now the old man's face, drenched with sweat, was flooded with light. He lowered his eyes so he wouldn't have to look straight ahead, since he couldn't bend his head, tightly gripped in his son's hands.

"I'm not doing all this for you. I'm doing it for your dead mother. Because you were her son. That's why I'm doing it. She would've haunted me if I'd left you lying where I found you and hadn't picked you up and carried you to be cured as I'm doing. She's the one who gives me courage, not you. From the first you've caused me nothing but trouble, humiliation, and shame."

He sweated as he talked. But the night wind dried his sweat. And over the dry sweat, he sweated again.

"I'll break my back, but I'll get to Tonaya with you so they can ease those wounds you got. I'm sure as soon as you feel well, you'll go back to your bad ways. But that doesn't matter to me anymore. As long as you go far away, where I won't hear anything more of you. As long as you do that—because as far as I'm concerned, you aren't my son anymore. I've cursed the blood you got from me. My part of it I've cursed. I said, 'Let the blood I gave him rot in his kidneys.' I said it when I heard you'd taken to the roads, robbing and killing people—good people. My old friend Tranquilino, for instance. The one who baptized you. The one who gave you your name. Even he had the bad luck to run into you. From that time on I said, 'That one cannot be my son.'

> **"From that time on I said, 'That one cannot be my son.'"**

"See if you can't see something now. Or hear something. You'll have to do it from up there, because I feel deaf."

"I don't see anything."

"Too bad for you, Ignacio."

"I'm thirsty."

"You'll have to stand it. We must be near now. Because it's now very late at night, they must've turned out the lights in the town. But at least you should hear dogs barking. Try to hear."

"Give me some water."

"There's no water here. Just stones. You'll have to stand it. Even if there was water, I wouldn't let you down to drink. There's nobody to help me lift you up again, and I can't do it alone."

"I'm awfully thirsty and sleepy."

"I remember when you were born. You were that way then. You woke up hungry and ate and went back to sleep. Your mother had to give you water because you'd finished all her milk. You couldn't be filled up. And you were always mad and yelling. I never thought that in time this madness would go to your head. But it did. Your mother, may she rest in peace, wanted you to grow up strong. She thought when you grew up, you'd look after her. She only had you. The other child she tried to give birth to killed her. And you would've killed her again if she'd lived till now."

The man on his back stopped gouging with his knees. His feet began to swing loosely from side to side. And it seemed to the father that Ignacio's head, up there, was shaking as if he were sobbing.

On his hair he felt thick drops fall.

"Are you crying, Ignacio? The memory of your mother makes you cry, doesn't it? But you never did anything for her. You always repaid us badly. Somehow your body got filled with evil instead of affection. And now you see? They've wounded it. What happened to your friends? They were all killed. Only they didn't have anybody. They might well have said, 'We have nobody to be concerned about.' But you, Ignacio?"

At last, the town. He saw roofs shining in the moonlight. He felt his son's weight crushing him as the back of his knees buckled in a final effort. When he reached the first dwelling, he leaned against the wall by the sidewalk. He slipped the body off, dangling, as if it had been wrenched from him.

With difficulty he unpried his son's fingers from around his neck. When he was free, he heard the dogs barking everywhere.

"And you didn't hear them, Ignacio?" he said. "You didn't even help me listen."

Translated by George D. Schade

Responding to the Selection

1. Dogs have been barking everywhere, yet Ignacio has not told his father. Why not?

2. Which concrete details contribute to the atmosphere in this story? Describe what mood they help to create.

3. Notice the many references to "not hearing" or "not seeing." What do you think this sensory deprivation suggests about Ignacio and his father?

4. How is the moon used to tell this story? Note its different stages and colors and how it reflects on the journey of father and son across the deserted landscape.

5. Do you believe Ignacio's father is a good parent? Name some of his feelings for and attitudes toward his son in the story.

Two Bodies

Octavio Paz

A Nobel laureate, Octavio Paz has been called, "Mexican by birth and cosmopolitan by education . . . this century's intellectual conscience." His book, *The Labyrinth of Solitude*, may be the most important work ever written about Mexico's culture, history, and people. In the following poem one sees the existentialism that informs so much of his writing. Human beings are alone in the universe and wholly responsible for themselves.

WORLD LENS
◆◆◆
MEXICO

Two bodies face to face
are at times two waves
and night is an ocean.

Two bodies face to face
are at times two stones
and night a desert.

Two bodies face to face
are at times two roots
laced into night.

Two bodies face to face
are at times two knives
and night strikes sparks.

Two bodies face to face
are two stars falling
in an empty sky.

Translated by Muriel Rukeyser

ABISMO
Fernando Holguin Cereceres

Responding to the Selection

1. Name some examples of repetition in "Two Bodies" and discuss what they contribute to the poem. How do you explain the omission of "at times" in the final stanza?

2. Choose one of the stanzas and explain what you think its metaphor, or central comparison, suggests about human beings and their relationship to the universe.

3. The unnamed people are placed "face to face" amid the immensity of the ocean, desert, night, and sky. What is the effect of this placement?

4. The bodies in this poem are always described at night. How would it change the poem to envision them in the daylight?

Crossroads: A Sad Vaudeville

Carlos Solórzano

WORLD LENS

◆◆◆

GUATEMALA/
MEXICO

Carlos Solórzano, a native Guatemalan, became a protégé of the famous French writer Albert Camus while living in Europe as a young man. He left Europe for Mexico, where he taught and wrote plays employing the artistic and philosophical trends of the European avant-garde. Some of the elements of this "cutting edge" artistic movement include surrealism and existentialism, which moved Latin American drama and fiction away from its roots in realism and naturalism. "Crossroads: A Sad Vaudeville" is one of a group of three one-act plays produced for the first time in 1966. The play exemplifies the author's use of symbolism and concern with humans striving to live with dignity and love in an unfeeling world.

Characters

THE FLAGMAN

THE TRAIN

THE MAN

THE WOMAN

Setting

Stage empty, dark. At one end, a semaphore that alternately flashes a green light and a red one. In the center, hanging from the ceiling, a big clock whose hands show five o'clock sharp.

(The characters will move mechanically, like characters in the silent movies. The MAN in fast motion; the WOMAN, in slow motion. As the curtain rises, the FLAGMAN is at the end of the stage, opposite the semaphore, with a lighted lantern in his hand. He is standing very stiffly and indifferently.)

FLAGMAN (*staring into space, in an impersonal voice*). The trains from the North travel toward the South, the trains from the North travel toward the South, the trains from the North travel toward the South. (*He repeats the refrain several times while the train crosses the back of the stage. The train will be formed by three men dressed in gray. As they pass by, they each mechanically perform a pantomime with one arm extended, the hand on the shoulder of the man in front, and the other arm making a circular motion, synchronized with the rhythm of the* FLAGMAN's *words.*) The trains from the North travel toward the South (etc.). (*Loud train whistle. The* MAN *who comes at the end of the train breaks free of it by making a movement as though he were jumping off. The train disappears on the right.*)

MAN (*carrying a small valise. He glances around the place, then looks at the clock, which he compares with his watch. He is young, serene of face, approximately twenty-five years old. He addresses the* FLAGMAN.). Good afternoon. (*As a reply, he receives the latter's refrain.*) Is this the place this ticket indicates? (*He places it in front of the* FLAGMAN's *eyes. The* FLAGMAN *nods.*) A train stops here, just about now, doesn't it?

FLAGMAN (*without looking at him*). Trains never stop here.

MAN. Are you the flagman?

FLAGMAN. They call me by many names.

MAN. Then, perhaps you've seen a woman around here.

FLAGMAN. I've seen no one.

MAN (*approaching him*). Do you know? The woman I'm looking for is . . .

FLAGMAN (*interrupting*). They all look alike.

MAN. Oh, no! She's different. She's the woman that I've been waiting for for many years. She'll be wearing a white flower on her dress. Or is it yellow? *(He searches nervously in his pockets and takes out a paper that he reads.)* No, it's white . . . that's what she says in her letter. *(The* FLAGMAN *takes a few steps, feeling ill at ease.)* Pardon me for telling you all this, but now you'll be able to understand how important it is for me to find this woman, because . . .

FLAGMAN *(interrupting again)*. What woman?

MAN. The one that I'm looking for.

FLAGMAN. I don't know what woman you're looking for.

MAN. The one that I've just told you about.

FLAGMAN. Ah . . . .

MAN. Perhaps she has passed by and you didn't see her. *(The* FLAGMAN *shrugs his shoulders.)* Well, I guess that I have to tell you everything to see if you can remember. She's tall, slender, with black hair and big blue eyes. She's wearing a white flower on her dress . . . . *(Anxiously)* Hasn't she been around here?

FLAGMAN. I can't know if someone I don't know has been around.

MAN. Excuse me. I know that I'm nervous but I have the impression that we aren't speaking the same language, that is, that you aren't answering my questions . . . .

FLAGMAN. That's not my job.

MAN. Nevertheless, I believe that a flagman ought to know how to answer questions. *(Transition.)* She wrote to me that she'd be here at five, at the railroad crossing of . . . *(He reads the ticket.)* I'll never know how to pronounce this name, but I know that it's here. We chose this point because it's halfway between our homes. Even for this kind of date, a romantic one, one must be fair. *(The* FLAGMAN *looks at him without understanding.)* Yes, romantic. *(With ingenuous pride:)* Maybe I'll bore you, but I must tell you that one day I saw an ad in a magazine. It was hers. How well written that ad was! She said that she needed a young man like me, to establish relations with so as not to live so alone. *(Pause.)* I wrote to her and she answered me. Then I sent her my photo and she sent me hers. You can't imagine what a beauty!

FLAGMAN *(who has not heard most of the account).* Is she selling something?

MAN *(surprised).* Who?

FLAGMAN. The woman who placed the ad?

MAN. No, for heaven's sake! She placed that ad because she said that she was shy, and she thought it might help and . . .

FLAGMAN. Everyone sells something.

MAN *(impatiently).* You just don't understand me.

FLAGMAN. It's possible . . . .

MAN. Well, I mean . . . understand how excited I am on coming to meet someone whom I don't know but who . . .

FLAGMAN. How's that?

MAN *(upset).* That is, I know her well, but I haven't seen her.

FLAGMAN. That's very common.

MAN. Do you think so?

FLAGMAN. The contrary's also common.

MAN. I don't understand.

FLAGMAN. It isn't necessary.

MAN. But you only speak nonsense! I should warn you that although I've an inclination toward romantic things, I'm a man who isn't pleased by jokes in bad taste. *(The* FLAGMAN *shrugs his shoulders again.)* Besides, this delay upsets me as does this dark place with that clock that doesn't run. It seems like a timeless place.

It seems like a timeless place.

(Suddenly a loud train whistle is heard. The semaphore comes to life flashing the green light. The FLAGMAN *again adopts his rigid posture; staring into space, he repeats his refrain.)*

FLAGMAN *(loudly).* The trains from the South travel toward the North. The trains from the South travel toward the North. The trains from the South travel toward the North *(etc.).*

(The train passes across the back of the stage, from right to left.)

MAN *(shouting).* There, on that train! . . . She should be on it. *(He rushes to meet the train which passes by without stopping, almost knocking him down. The* MAN *remains at stage center, his arms at his sides. Disillusioned:)* She wasn't on it.

FLAGMAN. It's only natural.

MAN. What do you mean?

FLAGMAN. He's never coming . . .

MAN. Who?

FLAGMAN. The man we're waiting for.

MAN. But it's a question of a woman.

FLAGMAN. It's the same.

MAN. How is a man going to be the same as a woman?

FLAGMAN. He isn't the same, but in a certain way he is.

MAN. You change your mind quickly.

FLAGMAN. I don't know.

MAN *(furiously).* Then, what is it that you do know?

FLAGMAN *(indifferently).* Where they're going.

MAN. The trains?

FLAGMAN. They all go to the same place.

MAN. What do you mean?

FLAGMAN. They come and go, but they end by meeting one another . . . .

MAN. That would be impossible.

FLAGMAN. But it's true. The impossible is always true.

MAN *(as if these last words brought him back to reality, he abandons his furious attitude and calms down).* You're right in what you say. *(Hesitating.)* For example, my meeting with that woman seems impossible and it's the only certain thing of my whole existence. *(Suddenly, with an unexpected tone of anguish:)* But it's five ten. *(He looks at his watch.)* And she isn't coming. *(He takes the arm of the* FLAGMAN *who remains indifferent.)* Help me, do all that is possible to remember! I'm sure that if you want to, you can tell me if you saw her or not . . . .

FLAGMAN. One can't know by just seeing a person whether it was the one who placed an ad in newspaper.

MAN (*once again containing his ill humor*). But I already described what she's like to you! . . .

FLAGMAN (*imperturbably*). I'm sorry. I forgot . . . .

(*Meanwhile a* WOMAN *dressed in black has come in behind the* MAN. *She is tall and slim. Her face is covered by a heavy veil. She walks softly with a pantomime motion. On her dress she wears a very large white flower. On seeing her the* FLAGMAN *raises his lantern and examines her. The* MAN, *blinded by light, covers his eyes. On seeing herself discovered, the* WOMAN *tears the white flower violently from her dress. She puts it in her purse and turns her back, remaining motionless.*)

MAN (*still covering his eyes*). Ooh! You're going to blind me with that lantern.

FLAGMAN (*returning to his habitual stiffness*). I beg your pardon . . . .

MAN (*to the* FLAGMAN). Someone has come in, right?

FLAGMAN. It's not important.

MAN (*recovering from the glare, he notices the presence of the* WOMAN *and runs toward her. He stops suddenly*). Ah . . . (*Timidly*) I beg you to . . . .

WOMAN (*her back turned*). Yes?

MAN (*embarrassed*). I thought that you . . . were someone . . .

WOMAN. Yes . . .

MAN (*with determination*). Someone I'm looking for. (*She does not move. Pause.*) Will you permit me to see you from the front?

WOMAN. From the front?

MAN *(upset)*. Yes . . . it's absolutely necessary that I see you . . .

WOMAN *(without turning)*. But . . . why? *(She begins to turn slowly.)*

MAN. Well . . . in order to . . . *(On seeing that her face is covered, he backs away.)* You aren't wearing anything on your dress . . . and nevertheless . . .

WOMAN *(trembling)*. And nevertheless?

MAN. You have the same stature and build . . . .

WOMAN *(with a jesting tone)*. Really?

MAN *(with distrust)*. Could you tell me how you got here? I didn't see a train.

WOMAN *(interrupting, stammering)*. I arrived . . . ahead of time . . . and I waited.

MAN. Ahead of what time?

WOMAN. We all wait for a time. Aren't you waiting for it?

MAN *(sadly)*. Yes.

WOMAN. I believe that there is but one moment to recognize one another, to extend our hands. One musn't let it pass by.

MAN. What do you mean by that? Who are you?

WOMAN. Now I'm the woman I've always wanted to be.

MAN *(timidly)*. Will you let me see your face?

WOMAN *(frightened)*. Why?

MAN. I need to find that one face, the special one, the different one.

WOMAN *(moving away)*. I am sorry. I can't.

MAN *(following her with a tortured motion)*. Excuse me. I'm stupid, I know. For a moment I thought that you could be she. But it's absurd. If it were so, you'd come straight to me, for we have called one another from afar.

WOMAN *(trembling)*. Perhaps she's more afraid of finding the one she seeks than of letting him pass by without stopping.

MAN. No, that would also be absurd. *(Transition.)* In any case, I beg your pardon. *(He moves away and sits down on his small suitcase, his back to the* WOMAN.*)* I'll wait here.

(In the meantime, while the man is not looking at her, the WOMAN *has raised her veil with long slow movements. When she uncovers her face, it is obvious that she is old. Her forehead is furrowed by deep wrinkles. She is like the mask of old age. This face contrasts obviously with her body, still slender, ageless.)*

WOMAN *(to the* FLAGMAN *who stares at her)*. You saw me from the beginning, didn't you? Why didn't you tell him?

FLAGMAN *(indifferently)*. Whom?

WOMAN *(pointing to the* MAN*)*. Him, the only one.

FLAGMAN. I'd forgotten him.

WOMAN *(in a surge of anguish)*. Shall I tell him that I'm that woman he's waiting for? Will he recognize in this old face the unsatisfied longing still in this body of mine? How can I tell him that I need him even more than when I was young, as young as I am in that touched-up photo that he's looking at?

(In the meantime, the man studies the photograph with fascination. The WOMAN *covers her face again with the veil and goes up to the* MAN.*)*

WOMAN. Is she very late?

MAN *(his back turned)*. Of course . . . .

WOMAN. It would hurt you a great deal if she wouldn't come!

MAN *(turning forcefully)*. She has to come.

WOMAN. Nevertheless, you must realize that perhaps she's afraid to reveal herself, that maybe she's waiting for you to discover her.

MAN. I don't understand.

WOMAN *(very close to the* MAN*)*. I have a friend . . . who always lived alone, thinking nevertheless that the best thing for her was to get together with someone. *(She pauses. The* MAN *listens to her, interested.)* She was ugly, very ugly, perhaps that was why she dreamed of a man instead of looking for him. She liked to have her pictures taken. She had the photographs touched up, so that the picture turned out to be hers, but at the same time it was someone else's. She used to write to young men, sending them her photograph. She called them close to her house, with loving words . . . . When they arrived, she'd wait behind the windows; she wouldn't let herself be seen. . . .

MAN. Why are you telling me all this?

WOMAN *(without hearing)*. She'd see them. She knew that they were there on account of her. Each day, a different one. She accumulated many memories, the faces, the bodies of those strong men who had waited for her.

MAN. How absurd! I think . . . .

WOMAN. You're also strong and young.

MAN *(confused)*. Yes, but . . .

WOMAN. And today she's one day older than yesterday.

MAN *(after allowing a pause)*. Really I don't see what relation all this can have to . . .

WOMAN *(drawing near and placing her hand on the* MAN's *head)*. Perhaps you'll understand now. Close your eyes. *(She passes her hand over the eyes of the* MAN *in a loving manner.)* Have you never felt fear?

MAN. Fear? Of what?

WOMAN. Of living, of being . . . as if all your life you'd been waiting for something that never comes?

MAN. No . . . . *(He opens his eyes.)*

WOMAN. Tell me the truth. Close your eyes, those eyes that are separating us now. Have you been afraid?

(The MAN *closes his eyes.)*

MAN *(hesitatingly)*. Well, a little . . . .

WOMAN *(with an absent voice)*. A suffering . . . in solitude . . .

MAN. Yes, at times . . . . *(He takes the* WOMAN's *hand.)*

WOMAN. Above all when you begin to fall asleep. The solitude of your body, a body alone, that inevitably ages.

MAN. Yes, but . . .

WOMAN. The solitude of the heart that tries hard every night to prolong its cry against silence.

MAN. I've felt something like that . . . but . . . not so clearly . . . not so pointedly.

WOMAN. It's that . . . perhaps you were waiting for that voice, the one of someone invented by you, to your measure. . . .

MAN. Yes . . . I think that's it.

WOMAN. Would you be able to recognize that voice with your eyes open?

MAN. I'm sure that I could . . . .

WOMAN. Even if it were a voice invented many years before, in the dark inmost recesses of time?

MAN. It wouldn't matter. I'd know how to recognize it.

WOMAN. Then, is that what you're waiting for?

MAN. Yes. I'm here for her sake, looking for her.

WOMAN. She's waiting for you also. *(The* WOMAN *raises the veil little by little until she leaves her withered face in the open.)* She'll be only a memory for you, if you don't allow yourself to be overcome by time. Time is her worst enemy. Will you fight it?

(They are seated very close to one another.)

MAN. Yes.

WOMAN. All right . . . . Open your eyes.

brusque
abrupt; curt

(The MAN *opens his eyes slowly and is surprised to find himself held by the* WOMAN*'s two hands. He stands up with a* **brusque** *movement.)*

MAN (*bewildered*). Excuse me, I'm confused . . .

WOMAN (**entreatingly**). Oh, no! . . . Don't tell me that . . .

MAN. It was a stupidity of mine . . .

WOMAN (**imploringly**). But you said . . .

MAN. It's ridiculous! For a moment I thought that you were she. Understand me. It was a wild dream.

WOMAN (*grieved*). Yes, yes . . .

MAN. I don't know how I could . . .

WOMAN (*calming herself*). I understand you. A wild dream and nothing more . . .

MAN. You're really very kind to pardon me. . . . *(Looking at his watch, astonished:)* It's five thirty! . . . *(Pause.)*

WOMAN (*sadly*). Yes . . . . Now I believe that she won't come.

MAN. How would that be possible?

WOMAN. It's better that way.

MAN. Who are you to tell me that?

WOMAN. No one. *(She opens her purse.)* Do you want this white flower?

MAN (*snatching it from her*). Where did you get it? Why are you giving it to me?

WOMAN. I picked it up . . . in passing . . .

MAN (*with great excitement*). But then, she has been here. Perhaps she has gotten lost or mistaken the place. Or perhaps, while I was here talking with you, she has passed by without stopping.

WOMAN *(covering her face).* I already told you that there is but a moment to recognize oneself, to close one's eyes . . .

MAN. But now . . . what can I do in order to . . . find her?

WOMAN. Wait . . . as everyone does . . . Wait . . . *(She takes the flower again.)*

MAN. But, what about you?

WOMAN. I'll continue searching, calling them, seeing them pass by. When you're old, you'll understand. *(The train whistle is heard. The* WOMAN *moves away from the* MAN, *with sorrowful movements.)* Good-bye, good-bye . . .

MAN *(to himself).* Who can this woman be who speaks to me as if she knew me? *(He runs toward her. He checks himself.)* Good-bye . . .

(The semaphore flashes the green light. The FLAGMAN *becomes stiff in order to repeat his refrain.)*

FLAGMAN. The trains from the North travel toward the South, the trains from the North travel toward the South, the trains from the North travel toward the South, the trains from the North travel toward the South *(etc.).*

(The train crosses the back of the stage. The WOMAN *waves the flower sadly and with long movements approaches the train. She gets on it. The* FLAGMAN *repeats his refrain while the train leaves dragging the* WOMAN, *who goes off with writhing and anguished pantomime movements.)*

MAN *(with a certain sadness, to the* FLAGMAN *who remains indifferent).* There was something in her that . . . anyhow, I believe it's better that that woman has left.

FLAGMAN. Which one, sir?

MAN. That one, the one who had picked up a white flower . . .

FLAGMAN. I didn't notice that . . . .

MAN. No? *(He looks at the* FLAGMAN *dejectedly.)* But, really, haven't you seen the other one?

FLAGMAN. What other one?

MAN. The one that I'm looking for.

FLAGMAN. I don't know who it can be . . . .

MAN. One who is wearing a white flower, but who isn't the one that you saw a moment ago.

FLAGMAN *(harshly)*. I saw the one that you aren't looking for, and the one you're looking for I didn't see!

MAN *(irritated)*. Can't you be useful for anything? What the devil are you good for?

(Loud train whistle.)

FLAGMAN. What did you say?

MAN *(shouting)*. What the devil are you good for!

(Green light of the semaphore. The train crosses the back of the stage very slowly.)

FLAGMAN *(in a distant voice)*. The trains from the North travel toward the South, the trains from the North travel toward the South, the trains from the North travel toward the South, the trains from the North travel toward the South *(etc.)*.

(The MAN *covers his head with his hands, desperate. The* FLAGMAN *repeats his refrain while the train passes by slowly. Before it leaves the stage, the curtain falls gently.)*

Curtain

Translated by Francesca Colecchia and Julio Matas

Responding to the Selection

1. The techniques Solórzano uses in this play are avant-garde—modern and experimental. Note the various ways in which it detours from a straightforward, realistic drama. Can you cite some examples?

2. One of the play's themes is the conflict people have between conformity and freedom. How does this play illustrate that theme?

3. Dramatic irony occurs when the audience knows more about the characters and events of a play than the characters do themselves. Find an example of dramatic irony in the play. What purpose do you think it serves?

4. Do you believe the woman when she says: "... there is but one moment to recognize one another, to extend our hands. One mustn't let it pass by"?

5. The characters in this play do not communicate with each other successfully. Find a passage of dialogue that illustrates this and explain what the playwright's intentions might be.

Love after Love

Derek Walcott

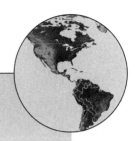

WORLD LENS

♦♦♦

ST. LUCIA

The American poetry critic Helen Vendler once described Nobel laureate Derek Walcott this way: "He is a black descended from both European and black ancestors; a St. Lucian, yet educated beyond the island norm; a painter-poet deeply attached to the Caribbean landscape, yet living for much of the year in New England; a rebellious colonial, yet deeply involved, imaginatively, in English poetry."

It is easy to imagine a writer of Walcott's stature and background having the issues of identity that are addressed in the following poem.

The time will come
when, with elation,
you will greet yourself arriving
at your own door, in your own mirror,
and each will smile at the other's welcome,

and say, sit here. Eat.
You will love again the stranger who was your self.
Give wine. Give bread. Give back your heart
to itself, to the stranger who has loved you

all your life, whom you ignored
for another, who knows you by heart.
Take down the love letters from the bookshelf,

the photographs, the desperate notes,
peel your own image from the mirror.
Sit. Feast on your life.

STILL LIFE WITH HAM, Andre Dunoyer de Segonzac, 1924

Responding to the Selection

1. What significance do you think the words "wine" and "bread" have for this poem?

2. Notice the everyday language of this poem. Given the theme, why do you think the poet uses such language?

3. There is one word—"elation"—that suggests something about the speaker's past relationship to himself. Say what that might be.

4. Why do you think it's important for the speaker to "take down the letters, the photographs, and the desperate notes"?

5. Name some things that can turn a person into a stranger, unrecognizable to him or herself.

The Americas

When Greek Meets Greek

Samuel Selvon

WORLD LENS
◆◆◆
TRINIDAD AND
TOBAGO

Like the characters in his story, the Trinidadian author Samuel Selvon lived for a long time in England before eventually becoming a Canadian citizen. In the late 1950s and early 1960s, over 113,000 immigrants from the former British colonies of India, Pakistan, and the West Indies came to Great Britain for jobs. As their numbers grew, so did racial tension, and in 1958 there were race riots in England between West Indians and the local white population.

One of the most popular Caribbean writers, Selvon treats important themes—nationality, cultural blending, and rootlessness—with humor and affection. In this selection, much of the comedy and liveliness come from its West Indian dialect—the regional usage of speech and idiom.

One morning Ramkilawansingh (after this, we calling this man Ram) was making a study of the noticeboards along Westbourne Grove what does advertise rooms to let. Every now and then he writing down an address or a telephone number, though most of the time his eyes colliding up with *No Colours, Please,* or *Sorry, No Kolors.*

"Red, white and blue, all out but you," Ram was humming a little ditty what children say when they playing whoop. Just as he get down by Bradley's Corner he met Fraser.

"You look like a man who looking for a place to live," Fraser say.

"You look like a man who could tell me the right place to go," Ram say.

"You try down by Ladbroke Grove?"[1] Fraser ask.

"I don't want to go down in that criminal area," Ram say, "at

---

1 **Westbourne Grove . . . Ladbroke Grove:** municipal districts in London, England

least, not until they find the man who kill Kelso."

"Then you will never live in the Grove," Fraser say.

"You are a contact man,"[2] Ram say, "Which part you think I could get a room, boy?"

Fraser scratch his head. "I know of a landlord up the road who vow that he ain't ever taking anybody who come from the West Indies.[3] But he don't mind taking Indians. He wouldn't know the difference when he see you is a Indian . . . them English people so foolish they believe every Indian come from India."

"You think I stand a chance?" Ram ask.

"Sure, you stand a chance. All you have to do is put on a turban."

"I never wear a turban in my life; I am a born Trinidadian,[4] a real Creole.[5] All the same, you best hads give me the address, I will pass around there later."

So Fraser give him the address, and Ram went on reading a few more boards, but he got discourage after a while and went to see the landlord.

The first thing the landlord ask him was: "What part of the world do you come from?"

"I am an Untouchable from the heart of India." Ram say. "I am looking for a single room. I dwelt on the banks of the Ganges. Not too expensive."

"But you are not in your national garments," the landlord say.

"When you are in Rome," Ram say, making it sound like an original statement, "do as the Romans do."

While the landlord sizing up Ram, an Indian tenant come up the steps to go inside. This fellar was Chandrilaboodoo (after this, we calling this man Chan) and he had a big beard with a hairnet over it, and he was wearing a turban. When he see Ram, he clasp his hands with the palms touching across his chest by way of greeting.

The old Ram catch on quick and do the same thing.

---

2 **contact man:** a go-between; someone "in the know"

3 **West Indies:** the Caribbean islands made up of the Greater Antilles, Lesser Antilles, and the Bahamas

4 **Trinidadian:** a citizen of the West Indies republic of Trinidad and Tobago

5 **Creole:** in the West Indies refers to anyone from the Caribbean island cultures

"*Acha, Hindustani,*"[6] Chan say.

"*Acha, pilau, papadom, chickenvindaloo,*"[7] Ram say desperately, hoping for the best.

Chan nod his head, say good morning to the landlord and went inside.

"That was a narrow shave," Ram thought, "I have to watch out for that man,"

"That was Mr. Chan," the landlord say, "he is the only other Indian tenant I have at the moment. I have a single room for two pounds. Are you a student?"

"Who is not a student?" Ram say, getting into the mood of the thing. "Man is forever studying ways and means until he passes into the hands of Allah."[8]

Well, to cut a long story short, Ram get a room on the first floor, right next door to Chan, and he move in that same evening.

But as the days going by, Ram had to live like cat-and-mouse with Chan. Every time he see Chan, he have to hide in case this man start up this Hindustani talk again, or start to ask him questions about Mother India. In fact, it begin to get on Ram nerves, and he decide that he had to do something.

"This house too small for the two of we," Ram say to himself, "one will have to go."

So Ram went down in the basement to see the landlord.

"I have the powers of the **occult**," Ram say, "and I have come to warn you of this man Chan. He is not a good tenant. He keeps the bathroom dirty, he does not tidy up his room at all, and he is always chanting and saying his prayers loudly and disturbing the other tenants."

occult
supernatural; magic arts

"I have had no complaints," the landlord say.

"But I am living next door to him," Ram say, "and if I concentrate my powers I can see through the wall. That man is a menace, and the best thing you can do is to give him notice. You have a good house here and it would be a pity to let one man spoil it for the other tenants."

"I will have a word with him about it," the landlord say.

---

6 **Acha, Hindustani:** Hindi for "Yes, I'm Indian."

7 **pilau, papadom, chickenvindaloo:** a rice dish, a type of cracker, a spicy chicken dish

8 **Allah:** the Supreme Being in the Islamic religion

Well, the next evening Ram was in his room when he hear a knock at the door. He run in the corner quick and stand upon his head, and say, "Come in."

The landlord come in.

"I am just practicing my yogurt," Ram say.

"I have had a word with Mr. Chan," the landlord say, "and I have reason to suspect that you have deceived me. You are not from India, you are from the West Indies."

Ram turn right-side up. "I am a citizen of the world," he say.

"You are flying false colors," the landlord say. "You do not burn incense like Mr. Chan, you do not dress like Mr. Chan, and you do not talk like Mr. Chan."

"Give me a break, old man," Ram say, falling back on the good old West Indian dialect.

"It is too late. You have already started to make trouble. You must go."

Well, the very next week find Ram out scouting again, giving the boards a **perusal**, and who he should chance to meet but Fraser.

He start to tell how life hard, how he had to keep dodging from this Chan fellar all the time, and it was pure torture.

"Listen," Fraser say, "you don't mean a big fellar with a beard, and he always wearing a turban?"

"That sound like him," Ram say. "You know him?"

"Know him!" Fraser say. "Man, that is a fellar from Jamaica who I send to that house to get a room!"

perusal
close look; study

Responding to the Selection

1. Find some examples of humor in the plot, characters, and language of this story.

2. What kind of a man is Ram? As proof of your opinion, describe him using details from the story.

3. Explain how the West Indian dialect adds to or detracts from "When Greek Meets Greek."

Girls Can We Educate We Dads?

James Berry

In his stories and poetry, James Berry writes with an expressive, lyrical voice about ordinary Caribbeans, often the Jamaican people with whom he grew up. His special forte is the reproduction and use of Jamaican dialect, giving his writing a distinctive lilt and energy, as well as authenticity.

WORLD LENS
◆ ◆ ◆
JAMAICA

Listn the male chauvinist in mi dad—
a girl walkin night street mus be bad.
He dohn sey, the world's a free place
for a girl to keep her unmolested space.
Instead he sey—a girl is a girl.

He sey a girl walkin swingin hips about
call boys to look and shout.
He dohn sey, if a girl have style
she wahn to sey, look
I okay from top to foot.
Instead he sey—a girl is a girl.

Listn the male chauvinist in mi dad—
a girl too laughy-laughy look too glad-glad
jus like a girl too looky-looky roun
will get a pretty satan at her side.
He dohn sey—a girl full of go
dohn wahn stifle talent comin on show.
Instead he sey—a girl is a girl.

Responding to the Selection

1. Think about how this poem would change if it was written in standard English. How does dialect add to its overall effect?

2. Read this poem out loud, more than once if possible. What are some of the elements that make it better suited to spoken English than written English?

3. The last line remains the same throughout each stanza ("Instead he sey—a girl is a girl."). What does that repetition possibly imply about the father?

4. In many cultures, young people assert their independence through the way they dress and present themselves. Do you think fathers in the Jamaican culture are different from most fathers in the way they react to their daughters? Explain.

NUBIAN KNOTS
Samere Tansley

In Trying Times

Herberto Padilla

The people of Cuba suffered under totalitarian politics for most of the 20th century. Herberto Padilla supported the 1959 revolution that toppled the repressive Batista regime. A journalist and award-winning writer for many years, his criticisms of the communist Castro government eventually landed him in prison. He was exiled to the United States in 1980.

WORLD LENS

♦♦♦

CUBA

They asked that man for his time
so that he could link it to History.
They asked him for his hands,
because for trying times
nothing is better than a good pair of hands.
They asked him for his eyes
that once had tears
so that he should see the bright side
(the bright side of life, especially)
because to see horror one startled eye is enough.
They asked him for his lips,
parched and split, to affirm,
to belch up, with each affirmation, a dream
(the great dream)
they asked him for his legs
hard and knotted
(his wandering legs)
because in trying times
is there anything better than a pair of legs
for building or digging ditches?
They asked him for the grove that fed him as a child,
with its obedient tree.
They asked him for his breast, heart, his shoulders.

They told him
that that was absolutely necessary.
they explained to him later
that all this gift would be useless
unless he turned his tongue over to them,
because in trying times
nothing is so useful in checking hatred or lies.
and finally they begged him,
please, to go take a walk.
Because in trying times
that is, without debate, the decisive test.

Translated by Alastair Reid and Andrew Hurley

Responding to the Selection

1. In order to understand this poem fully, you need to know the main facts about the author's relationship to the Cuban government, both before, during, and in the later years of the communist revolution. Using the headnote as a guide, try to determine the poet's attitude toward the communist regime from what the speaker says in this poem.

2. What do you think the title means?

3. What do you think is one of the themes of this poem? Use evidence in the poem to support your view.

4. Why do you think "History" is capitalized in the poem?

The Youngest Doll

Rosario Ferré

WORLD LENS

◆◆◆

PUERTO RICO

Puerto Rican Rosario Ferré is notable for writing about the role of women in Latin America, where historically the status of male children has been more powerful than that of girls. As the daughter of a wealthy and powerful family, the author herself fought against this discrimination, only pursuing her career as a writer after divorcing her husband. Her family background has also given her firsthand knowledge of the immense power of the South American elites, a theme also implicit in the following story. "The Youngest Doll" comes from Ferré's first book, a response to the Pandora myth, which she considers anti-female. In the Greek myth, Pandora's curiosity leads her to open a box from the gods, unloosing all the evils on the world.

Early in the morning the maiden aunt took her rocking chair out onto the porch facing the cane fields, as she always did whenever she woke up with the urge to make a doll. As a young woman, she had often bathed in the river, but one day when the heavy rains had fed the dragontail current, she had a soft feeling of melting snow in the marrow of her bones. With her head nestled among the black rocks' reverberations, she could hear the slamming of salty foam on the beach rolled up with the sound of waves, and she suddenly thought that her hair had poured out to sea at last. At that very moment, she felt a sharp bite in her calf. Screaming, she was pulled out of the water and, writhing in pain, was taken home on a stretcher.

The doctor who examined her assured her it was nothing, that she had probably been bitten by an angry river prawn.[1] But days passed and the scab wouldn't heal. A month later the doctor concluded that the prawn had worked its way into the soft flesh of her calf and had nestled there to grow. He prescribed a mustard

---

1 **prawn:** a shellfish resembling shrimp

plaster[2] so that the heat would force it out. The aunt spent a whole week with her leg covered with mustard from thigh to ankle, but when the treatment was over, they found that the ulcer had grown even larger and that it was covered with a slimy, stonelike substance that couldn't be removed without endangering the whole leg. She then resigned herself to living with the prawn permanently curled up in her calf.

She had been very beautiful, but the prawn hidden under the long, gauzy folds of her skirt stripped her of all vanity. She locked herself up in her house, refusing to see any suitors. At first she devoted herself entirely to bringing up her sister's children, dragging her enormous leg around the house, quite nimbly. In those days, the family was nearly ruined; they lived surrounded by a past that was breaking up around them with the same impassive musicality with which the dining room chandelier crumbled on the frayed linen cloth of the dining room table. Her nieces adored her. She would comb their hair, bathe and feed them, and when she read them stories, they would sit around her and **furtively** lift the starched ruffle of her skirt so as to sniff the aroma of ripe sweetsop[3] that oozed from her leg when it was at rest.

As the girls grew up, the aunt devoted herself to making dolls for them to play with. At first they were just plain dolls, with cotton stuffing from the gourd tree and stray buttons sewn on for eyes. As time passed, though, she began to refine her craft, gaining the respect and admiration of the whole family. The birth of a doll was always cause for a ritual celebration, which explains why it never occurred to the aunt to sell them for profit, even when the girls had grown up and the family was beginning to fall into need. The aunt had continued to increase the size of the dolls so that their height and other measurements conformed to those of each of the girls. There were nine of them, and the aunt made one doll for each per year, so it became necessary to set aside a room for the dolls alone. When the eldest turned eighteen, there were one hundred and twenty-six dolls of all ages in the room. Opening the door gave the impression of entering a

margin note:
furtively
secretly; surreptitiously

---

2 **plaster:** a covering for a wound

3 **sweetsop:** an aromatic tropical fruit

dovecote or the ballroom in the Czarina's[4] palace or a warehouse in which someone had spread out a row of tobacco leaves to dry. But the aunt did not enter the room for any of these pleasures. Instead, she would unlatch the door and gently pick up each doll, murmuring a lullaby as she rocked it: "This is how you were when you were a year old, this is you at two, and like this at three," measuring out each year of their lives against the hollow they left in her arms.

The day the eldest had turned ten, the aunt sat down in her rocking chair facing the cane fields and never got up again. She would rock away entire days on the porch, watching the patterns of rain shift in the cane fields, coming out of her stupor only when the doctor paid a visit or whenever she awoke with the desire to make a doll. Then she would call out so that everyone in the house would come and help her. On that day, one could see the hired help making repeated trips to town like cheerful Inca[5] messengers, bringing wax, porcelain clay, lace, needles, spools of thread of every color. While these preparations were taking place, the aunt would call the niece she had dreamt about the night before into her room and take her measurements. Then she would make a wax mask of the child's face, covering it with plaster on both sides, like a living face wrapped in two dead ones. She would draw out an endless flaxen thread of melted wax through a pinpoint on its chin. The porcelain of the hands and face was always translucent; it had an ivory tint to it that formed a great contrast with the curdled whiteness of the bisque faces. For the body, the aunt would send out to the garden for twenty glossy gourds. She would hold them in one hand, and with an expert twist of her knife, would slice them up against the railing of the balcony, so that the sun and breeze would dry out the cottony *guano*[6] brains. After a few days, she would scrape off the dried fluff with a teaspoon and, with infinite patience, feed it into the doll's mouth.

The only items the aunt would agree to use that were not made by her were the glass eyeballs. They were mailed to her from

4 **Czarina:** the czar's wife; the wife of a dictator

5 **Inca:** the South American Indians who ruled before the Spanish conquest

6 **guano:** a kind of palm tree

Europe in all colors, but the aunt considered them useless until she had left them submerged at the bottom of the stream for a few days, so that they could learn to recognize the slightest stirring of the prawns' antennae. Only then would she carefully rinse them in ammonia water and place them, glossy as gems and nestled in a bed of cotton, at the bottom of one of her Dutch cookie tins. The dolls were always dressed in the same way, even though the girls were growing up. She would dress the younger ones in Swiss embroidery and the older ones in silk *guipure*,[7] and on each of their heads she would tie the same bow, wide and white and trembling like the breast of a dove.

The girls began to marry and leave home. On their wedding day, the aunt would give each of them their last doll, kissing them on the forehead and telling them with a smile, "Here is your Easter Sunday." She would reassure the grooms by explaining to them that the doll was merely a sentimental ornament, of the kind that people used to place on the lid of grand pianos in the old days. From the porch, the aunt would watch the girls walk down the staircase for the last time. They would carry a modest checkered cardboard suitcase in one hand, the other hand slipped around the waist of the exuberant doll made in their image and likeness, still wearing the same old-fashioned kid slippers and gloves, and with Valenciennes[8] bloomers barely showing under their snowy, embroidered skirts. But the hands and faces of these new dolls looked less transparent than those of the old: they had the consistency of skim milk. This difference concealed a more subtle one: the wedding doll was never stuffed with cotton but filled with honey.

All the older girls had married and only the youngest was left at home when the doctor paid his monthly visit to the aunt, bringing along his son, who had just returned from studying medicine up north. The young man lifted the starched ruffle of the aunt's skirt and looked intently at the huge, swollen ulcer which oozed a perfumed sperm from the tip of its greenish scales. He pulled out his stethoscope and

. . . the wedding doll was never stuffed with cotton but filled with honey.

---

7 *guipure:* lace

8 *Valenciennes:* lace from Valenciennes, France

The Americas

listened to her carefully. The aunt thought he was listening for the breathing of the prawn to see if it was still alive, and she fondly lifted his hand and placed it on the spot where he could feel the constant movement of the creature's antennae. The young man released the ruffle and looked fixedly at his father. "You could have cured this from the start," he told him. "That's true," his father answered, "but I just wanted you to come and see the prawn that has been paying for your education these twenty years."

From then on it was the young doctor who visited the old aunt every month. His interest in the youngest was evident from the start, so the aunt was able to begin her last doll in plenty of time. He would always show up wearing a pair of brightly polished shoes, a starched collar, and an **ostentatious** tiepin of extravagantly poor taste. After examining the aunt, he would sit in the parlor, lean his paper silhouette against the oval frame of the chair and, each time, hand the youngest an identical bouquet of purple forget-me-nots. She would offer him ginger cookies, taking the bouquet squeamishly with tips of her fingers, as if she were handling a sea urchin turned inside out. She made up her mind to marry him because she was intrigued by his sleepy profile and also because she was deathly curious to see what the dolphin flesh was like.

On her wedding day, as she was about to leave the house, the youngest was surprised to find that the doll her aunt had given her as a wedding present was warm. As she slipped her arm around its waist, she looked at it curiously, but she quickly forgot about it, so amazed was she at the excellence of its craft. The doll's face and hands were made of the most delicate Mikado porcelain.[9] In the doll's half-open and slightly sad smile she recognized her full set of baby teeth. There was also another notable detail: the aunt had embedded her diamond eardrops inside the doll's pupils.

The young doctor took her off to live in town, in a square house that made one think of a cement block. Each day he made her sit out on the balcony, so that passersby would be sure to see that he had married into high society. Motionless inside her

ostentatious
showy; pretentious

---

9   **Mikado porcelain:** ceramic material from Japan

cubicle of heat, the youngest began to suspect that it wasn't only her husband's silhouette that was made of paper, but his soul as well. Her suspicions were soon confirmed. One day, he pried out the doll's eyes with the tip of his scalpel and pawned them for a fancy gold pocket watch with a long embossed chain. From then on the doll remained seated on the lid of the grand piano, but with her gaze modestly lowered.

A few months later, the doctor noticed the doll was missing from her usual place and asked the youngest what she'd done with it. A sisterhood of pious ladies had offered him a healthy sum for the porcelain hands and face, which they thought would be perfect for the image of the Veronica in the next Lenten procession.[10]

The youngest answered that the ants had at last discovered the doll was filled with honey and, streaming over the piano, had devoured it in a single night. "Since its hands and face were of Mikado porcelain," she said, "they must have thought they were made of sugar and at this very moment they are most likely wearing down their teeth, gnawing furiously at its fingers and eyelids in some underground burrow." That night the doctor dug up all the ground around the house, to no avail.

---

10 **the Veronica . . . procession:** The Veronica is the image of Jesus's bloody face on a cloth offered to him by Saint Veronica on his way to the Crucifixion. The Lenten procession is a spectacle held to mark Lent, the forty days on the Christian calendar leading up to Easter.

As the years passed, the doctor became a millionaire. He had slowly acquired the whole town as his clientele, people who didn't mind paying **exorbitant** fees in order to see a genuine member of the extinct sugar cane aristocracy up close. The youngest went on sitting in her rocking chair on the balcony, motionless in her muslin and lace, and always with lowered eyelids. Whenever her husband's patients, draped with necklaces and feathers and carrying elaborate canes, would seat themselves beside her, shaking their self-satisfied rolls of flesh with a jingling of coins, they would notice a strange scent that would involuntarily remind them of a slowly oozing sweetsop. They would then feel an uncomfortable urge to rub their hands together as though they were paws.

> **exorbitant**
> *excessive; unreasonably high*

There was only one thing missing from the doctor's otherwise perfect happiness. He noticed that although he was aging, the youngest still kept that same firm, porcelained skin she had had when he would call on her at the big house on the plantation. One night he decided to go into her bedroom to watch her as she slept. He noticed that her chest wasn't moving. He gently placed his stethoscope over her heart and heard a distant swish of water. Then the doll lifted her eyelids, and out of the empty socket of her eyes came the frenzied antennae of all those prawns.

Translated by Diana Velez

Responding to the Selection

1. Which events and details in this story could be true (realism), and which things could never be true (magic realism)?

2. What do the aunt's actions reveal about her needs and desires?

3. Think about all the ways that girls are likened to dolls in our language ("She's a real doll."). What do you think the effects of this are, if any?

The Handsomest Drowned Man in the World
A Tale for Children

Gabriel García Márquez

WORLD LENS

◆◆◆

COLOMBIA

Nobel Prize-winning author Gabriel García Márquez may be the foremost living Latin American writer. In his journalism and fiction, the author addresses the great trinity of Latin American themes: politics, religion, and history. He is often associated with magic realism, in which realistic events blend easily into the fantastical and surreal. Some believe this method is a more accurate description of real life, particularly in South America, where myths can seem indistinguishable from facts.

Traditionally in this region women have been expected to be submissive and nurturing and men to be virile and authoritative. In Marquez' most famous book, *One Hundred Years of Solitude*, he employs the idea of the handsome and charismatic man—the born leader—whose spirit attracts women and garners the admiration of men, a theme that is echoed in the following story.

T he first children who saw the dark and slinky bulge approaching through the sea let themselves think it was an enemy ship. Then they saw it had no flags or masts and they thought it was a whale. But when it washed up on the beach, they removed the clumps of seaweed, the jellyfish tentacles, and the remains of fish and flotsam, and only then did they see that it was a drowned man.

They had been playing with him all afternoon, burying him in the sand and digging him up again, when someone chanced to see them and spread the alarm in the village. The men who carried him to the nearest house noticed that he weighed more than any dead man they had ever known, almost as much as a horse, and they said to each other that maybe he'd been floating too long and the water had got into his bones. When they laid him on the floor they said he'd been taller than all other men because there was barely enough room for him in the house, but they thought that maybe the ability to keep on growing after death was part of the nature of certain drowned men. He had the smell of the sea about him and only his shape gave one to suppose that it was the corpse of a human being, because the skin was covered with a crust of mud and scales.

They did not even have to clean off his face to know that the dead man was a stranger. The village was made up of only twenty-odd wooden houses that had stone courtyards with no flowers and which were spread about on the end of a desertlike cape. There was so little land that mothers always went about with the fear that the wind would carry off their children and the few dead that the years had caused among them had to be thrown off the cliffs. But the sea was calm and bountiful and all the men fit into seven boats. So when they found the drowned man they simply had to look at one another to see that they were all there. That night they did not go out to work at sea. While the men went to find out if anyone was missing in neighboring villages, the women stayed behind to care for the drowned man. They took the mud off with grass swabs, they removed the underwater stones entangled in his hair, and they scraped the crust off with tools used for scaling fish. As they were doing that they noticed that the vegetation on him came from faraway oceans and deep water and that his clothes were in tatters, as if he had sailed through **labyrinths** of coral. They noticed too that he bore his death with pride, for he did not have the lonely look of other drowned men who came out of the sea or that **haggard**, needy look of men who drowned in rivers. But only when they finished cleaning him off did they become aware of the kind of man he was and it left them breathless. Not only was he the tallest, strongest, most **virile**, and best built man they had ever seen, but even though they were looking at him there was no room for him in their imagination.

labyrinths
mazes; complex passageways

haggard
gaunt; excessively thin

virile
manly; potent

They could not find a bed in the village large enough to lay him on nor was there a table solid enough to use for his wake. The tallest men's holiday pants would not fit him, not the fattest ones' Sunday shirts, nor the shoes of the one with the biggest feet. Fascinated by his huge size and his beauty, the women then decided to make him some pants from a large piece of sail and a shirt from some bridal brabant linen[1] so that he could continue through his death with dignity. As they sewed, sitting in a circle and gazing at the corpse between stitches, it seemed to them that the wind had never been so steady nor the sea so restless as on that night and they supposed that the change had something to do with the dead man. They thought that if that magnificent man had lived in the village, his house would have had the widest doors, the highest ceiling, and the strongest floor, his bedstead would have been made from a midship frame held together by iron bolts, and his wife would have been the happiest woman. They thought that he would have had so much authority that he could have drawn fish out of the sea simply by calling their names and that he would have put so much work into his land that springs would have burst forth from among the rocks so that he would have been able to plant flowers on the cliffs. They secretly compared him to their own men, thinking that for all their lives theirs were incapable of doing what he could do in one night, and they ended up dismissing them deep in their hearts as the weakest, meanest, and most useless creatures on earth. They were wandering through that maze of fantasy when the oldest woman, who as the oldest had looked upon the drowned man with more compassion than passion, sighed:

"He has the face of someone called Esteban."

It was true. Most of them had only to take another look at him to see that he could not have any other name. The more stubborn among them, who were the youngest, still lived for a few hours with the illusion that when they put his clothes on and he lay among the flowers in patent leather shoes his name might be Lautaro. But it was a vain illusion. There had not been enough canvas, the poorly cut and worse sewn pants were too tight, and the hidden strength of his heart popped the buttons on his shirt.

---

1 **brabant linen:** linen from what is now southern Netherlands and northern Belgium

After midnight the whistling of the wind died down and the sea fell into its Wednesday drowsiness. The silence put an end to any last doubts: he was Esteban. The women who had dressed him, who had combed his hair, had cut his nails and shaved him were unable to hold back a shudder of pity when they had to resign themselves to his being dragged along the ground. It was then that they understood how unhappy he must have been with that huge body since it bothered him even after death. They could see him in life, condemned to going through doors sideways, cracking his head on crossbeams, remaining on his feet during visits, not knowing what to do with his soft, pink, sea lion hands

VILLAGE SCENE
ON THE RIVER
Antoine Montas

while the lady of the house looked for her most resistant chair and begged him, frightened to death, sit here, Esteban, please, and he, leaning against the wall, smiling, don't bother, ma'am, I'm fine where I am, his heels raw and his back roasted from having done the same thing so many times whenever he paid a visit, don't bother, ma'am, I'm fine where I am, just to avoid the embarrassment of breaking up the chair, and never knowing perhaps that the ones who said don't go, Esteban, at least wait till the coffee's ready, were the ones who later on would whisper the big boob finally left, how nice, the handsome fool has gone. That was what the women were thinking beside the body a little before dawn. Later, when they covered his face with a handkerchief so that the light would not bother him, he looked so forever dead, so defenseless, so much like their men that the first furrows of tears opened in their hearts. It was one of the younger ones who began the weeping. The others, coming to, went from sighs to wails, and the more they sobbed the more they felt like weeping, because the drowned man was becoming all the more Esteban for them, and so they wept so much, for he was the most destitute, most peaceful, and most obliging man on earth, poor Esteban. So when the men returned with the news that the drowned man was not from the neighboring villages either, the women felt an opening of jubilation in the midst of their tears.

"Praise the Lord," they sighed, "he's ours!"

The men thought the fuss was only womanish **frivolity**. Fatigued because of the difficult nighttime inquiries, all they wanted was to get rid of the bother of the newcomer once and for all before the sun grew strong on that arid, windless day. They improvised a litter with the remains of foremasts and gaffs,[2] tying it together with rigging[3] so that it would bear the weight of the body until they reached the cliffs. They wanted to tie the anchor from a cargo ship to him so that he would sink easily into the deepest waves, where fish are blind and divers die of nostalgia, and bad currents would not bring him back to shore, as had happened with other bodies. But the more they hurried, the more

---

2 **foremasts and gaffs:** the foremast is in the ship's bow, or forward area, and gaffs are attachments to the mast

3 **rigging:** a ship's sails and masts

The Americas

the women thought of ways to waste time. They walked about like startled hens, pecking with the sea charms on their breasts, some interfering on one side to put a scapular[4] of the good wind on the drowned man, some on the other side to put a wrist compass on him, and after a great deal of *get away from there, woman, stay out of the way, look, you almost made me fall on top of the dead man*, the men began to feel mistrust in their livers and started grumbling about why so many main-altar decorations for a stranger, because no matter how many nails and holy-water jars he had on him, the sharks would chew him all the same, but the women kept piling on their junk relics, running back and forth, stumbling, while they released in sighs what they did not in tears, so that the men finally exploded with *since when has there ever been such a fuss over a drifting corpse, a drowned nobody, a piece of cold Wednesday meat.* One of the women, **mortified** by so much lack of care, then removed the handkerchief from the dead man's face and the men were left breathless too.

mortified
ashamed; chagrined

He was Esteban. It was not necessary to repeat it for them to recognize him. If they had been told Sir Walter Raleigh,[5] even they might have been impressed with his gringo[6] accent, the macaw[7] on his shoulder, his cannibal-

. . . since when has there ever been such a fuss over a drifting corpse, a drowned nobody, a piece of cold Wednesday meat.

killing blunderbuss,[8] but there could be only one Esteban in the world and there he was, stretched out like a sperm whale, shoeless, wearing the pants of an undersized child, and with those stony nails that had to be cut with a knife. They only had to take the handkerchief off his face to see that he was ashamed, that it was not his fault that he was so big or so heavy or so handsome, and if he had known that this was going to happen, he would

---

4 **scapular:** a band of cloth

5 **Sir Walter Raleigh:** (1522–1618), an English writer and explorer

6 **gringo:** a disparaging term for an English or American foreigner

7 **macaw:** a parrot from central or south America

8 **blunderbuss:** an old-fashioned firearm

discreet
unobtrusive; convenient

have looked for a more **discreet** place to drown in, seriously, I even would have tied the anchor off a galleon[9] around my neck and staggered off a cliff like someone who doesn't like things in order not to be upsetting people now with this Wednesday dead body, as you people say, in order not to be bothering anyone with this filthy piece of cold meat that doesn't have anything to do with me. There was so much truth in his manner that even the most mistrustful men, the ones who felt the bitterness of endless nights at sea fearing that their women would tire of dreaming about them and begin to dream of drowned men, even they and others who were harder still shuddered in the marrow of their bones at Esteban's sincerity.

That was how they came to hold the most splendid funeral they could conceive of for an abandoned drowned man. Some women who had gone to get flowers in the neighboring villages returned with other women who could not believe what they had been told, and those women went back for more flowers when they saw the dead man, and they brought more and more until there were so many flowers and so may people that it was hard to walk about. At the final moment it pained them to return him to the waters as an orphan and they chose a father and mother from among the best people, and aunts and uncles and cousins, so that through him all the inhabitants of the village became kinsmen. Some sailors who heard weeping from a distance went off course and people heard of one who had himself tied to the mainmast, remembering ancient fables about sirens.[10] While they fought for the privilege of carrying him on their shoulders along the steep escarpment[11] by the cliffs, men and women became aware for the first time of the desolation of their streets, the dryness of their courtyards, the narrowness of their dreams as they faced the splendor and beauty of their drowned man. They let him go without an anchor so that he could come back if he wished and whenever he wished, and they all held their breath for the fraction of centuries the body took to fall into the **abyss**. They did not need to look at one another to realize that they were no

abyss
gulf; depths

---

9 **galleon:** a large sailing ship used at war and for cargo by the Spanish

10 **sirens:** in Greek mythology, female creatures whose seductive songs lured sailors to their deaths

11 **escarpment:** a cliff or slope

longer all present, that they would never be. But they also knew that everything would be different from then on, that their houses would have wider doors, higher ceilings, and stronger floors so that Esteban's memory could go everywhere without bumping into beams and so that no one in the future would dare whisper the big boob finally died, too bad, the handsome fool has finally died, because they were going to paint their house fronts gay colors to make Esteban's memory eternal and they were going to break their backs digging for springs among the stones and planting flowers on the cliffs so that in future years at dawn the passengers on great liners would awaken, suffocated by the smell of gardens on the high seas, and the captain would have to come down from the bridge in his dress uniform, with his astrolabe,[12] his pole star,[13] and his row of war medals and, pointing to the **promontory** of roses on the horizon, he would say in fourteen languages, look there, where the wind is so peaceful now that it's gone to sleep beneath the beds, over there, where the sun's so bright that the sunflowers don't know which way to turn, yes, that's Esteban's village.

promontory
headland; high point

Translated by Gregory Rabassa and S. J. Bernstein

Responding to the Selection

1. Why do the women entertain such fantasies about the drowned man?

2. What makes the men begin to believe in Esteban's specialness?

3. What does this story seem to reveal about Latin Americans' attitudes toward death?

4. It is said that "A Stranger Comes to Town" is one of the most basic of story plots. Looking at this story, explain why you think this plot line is so fruitful for a storyteller and audience.

5. What do you think the subtitle means?

---

12 **astrolabe:** an instrument that was used to measure the heavenly bodies

13 **pole star:** the North or guiding star

The Third Bank of the River

João Guimarães Rosa

WORLD LENS

◆◆◆

BRAZIL

The Mexican writer Juan Rulfo claimed that João Guimarães Rosa was "the greatest author to have emerged from the Americas in this century." Certainly Rosa was one of the most important Brazilian metaphysical writers (one who is concerned with the nature of existence). His unique voice has presented such a challenge to translators that his reputation has been slow to build.

Rosa was a polyglot, mastering several languages as diverse as Russian and Japanese, a medical doctor who often traveled by horseback in the great Brazilian backlands, and a foreign diplomat. His novel *The Devil to Pay in the Backlands* somewhat anticipates the theme of the following story. In this sprawling novel, characters make a pact with Satan and wrestle with the forces of God and the Devil.

M y father was a dutiful, orderly, straightforward man. And according to several reliable people of whom I enquired, he had had these qualities since adolescence or even childhood. By my own recollection, he was neither jollier nor more melancholy than the other men we knew. Maybe a little quieter. It was Mother, not Father, who ruled the house. She scolded us daily—my sister, my brother, and me. But it happened one day that Father ordered a boat.

He was very serious about it. It was to be made specially for him, of mimosa[1] wood. It was to be sturdy enough to last twenty or thirty years and just large enough for one person. Mother carried on plenty about it. Was her husband going to become a

---

1 **mimosa:** a type of tree or shrub from the tropics

fisherman all of a sudden? Or a hunter? Father said nothing. Our house was less than a mile from the river, which around there was deep, quiet, and so wide you couldn't see across it.

I can never forget the day the rowboat was delivered. Father showed no joy or other emotion. He just put on his hat as he always did and said goodbye to us. He took along no food or bundle of any sort. We expected Mother to rant and rave, but she didn't. She looked very pale and bit her lip, but all she said was: "If you go away, stay away. Don't ever come back!"

Father made no reply. He looked gently at me and motioned me to walk along with him. I feared Mother's wrath, yet I eagerly obeyed. We headed towards the river together. I felt bold and exhilarated, so much so that I said: "Father, will you take me with you in your boat?"

He just looked at me, gave me his blessing, and, by a gesture, told me to go back. I made as if to do so but, when his back was turned, I ducked behind some bushes to watch him. Father got into the boat and rowed away. Its shadow slid across the water like a crocodile, long and quiet.

Father did not come back. Nor did he go anywhere, really. He just rowed and floated across and around, out there in the river. Everyone was appalled. What had never happened, what could not possibly happen, was happening. Our relatives, neighbours, and friends came over to discuss the phenomenon.

Mother was ashamed. She said little and conducted herself with great composure. As a consequence, almost everyone thought (though no one said it) that Father had gone insane. A few, however, suggested that Father might be fulfilling a promise he had made to God or to a saint, or that he might have some horrible disease, maybe leprosy, and that he left for the sake of the family, at the same time wishing to remain fairly near them.

Travellers along the river and people living near the bank on one side or the other reported that Father never put foot on land, by day or night. He just moved about on the river, solitary, aimless, like a **derelict**. Mother and our relatives agreed that the food which he had doubtless hidden in the boat would soon give out and that then he would either leave the river and travel off somewhere (which would be at least a little more respectable) or

derelict
vagrant; drifter

he would repent and come home.

How far from the truth they were! Father had a secret source of provisions: me. Every day I stole food and brought it to him. The first night after he left, we all lit fires on the shore and prayed and called to him. I was deeply distressed and felt a need to do something more. The following day I went down to the river with a loaf of corn bread, a bunch of bananas, and some bricks of raw brown sugar. I waited impatiently a long, long hour. Then I saw the boat, far off, alone, gliding almost imperceptibly on the smoothness of the river. Father was sitting in the bottom of the boat. He saw me but he did not row towards me or make any gesture. I showed him the food and then I placed it in a hollow rock on the river bank; it was safe there from animals, rain, and dew. I did this day after day, on and on and on. Later I learned, to my surprise, that Mother knew what I was doing and left food around where I could easily steal it. She had a lot of feelings she didn't show.

Mother sent for her brother to come and help on the farm and in business matters. She had the schoolteacher come and tutor us children at home because of the time we had lost. One day, at her request, the priest put on his vestments,[2] went down to the shore, and tried to **exorcise** the devils that had got into my father. He shouted that Father had a duty to cease his unholy obstinacy. Another day she arranged to have two soldiers come and try to frighten him. All to no avail. My father went by in the distance, sometimes so far away he could barely be seen. He never replied to anyone and no one ever got close to him. When some newspapermen came in a launch to take his picture, Father headed his boat to the other side of the river and into the marshes, which he knew like the palm of his hand but in which other people quickly got lost. There in his private maze, which extended for miles, with heavy foliage overhead and rushes[3] on all sides, he was safe.

We had to get accustomed to the idea of Father's being out on the river. We had to but we couldn't, we never could. I think I was the only one who understood to some degree what our father

exorcise
banish; send away

---

2 **vestments:** religious garments

3 **rushes:** grass-like plants found in marsh areas

wanted and what he did not want. The thing I could not understand at all was how he stood the hardship. Day and night, in sun and rain, in heat and in terrible mid-year cold spells, with his old hat on his head and very little other clothing, week after week, month after month, year after year, unheedful of the waste and emptiness in which his life was slipping by. He never set foot on earth or grass, on isle or mainland shore. No doubt he sometimes tied up the boat at a secret place, perhaps at the tip of some island, to get a little sleep. He never lit a fire or even struck a match and he had no flashlight. He took only a small part of the food that I left in the hollow rock—not enough, it seemed to me, for survival. What could his state of health have been? How about the continual drain on his energy, pulling and pushing the oars to control the boat? And how did he survive the annual floods, when the river rose and swept along with it all sorts of dangerous objects—branches of trees, dead bodies of animals—that might suddenly crash against his little boat?

He never talked to a living soul. And we never talked about him. We just thought. No, we could never put our father out of mind. If for a short time we seemed to, it was just a lull from which we would be sharply awakened by the realization of his frightening situation.

My sister got married, but Mother didn't want a wedding party. It would have been a sad affair, for we thought of him every time we ate some especially tasty food. Just as we thought of him in our cosy beds on a cold, stormy night—out there, alone and unprotected, trying to bail out the boat with only his hands and a gourd. Now and then someone would say that I was getting to look more and more like my father. But I knew that by then his hair and beard must have been shaggy and his nails long. I pictured him thin and sickly, black with hair and sunburn, and almost naked despite the articles of clothing I occasionally left for him.

He didn't seem to care about us at all. But I felt affection and respect for him, and, whenever they praised me because I had done something good, I said: "My father taught me to act that way."

It wasn't exactly accurate but it was a truthful sort of lie. As I said, Father didn't seem to care about us. But then why did he stay around there? Why didn't he go up the river or down the river, beyond the possibility of seeing us or being seen by us? He alone knew the answer.

My sister had a baby boy. She insisted on showing Father his grandson. One beautiful day we all went down to the riverbank, my sister in her white wedding dress, and she lifted the baby high. Her husband held a parasol[4] above them. We shouted to Father and waited. He did not appear. My sister cried; we all cried in each other's arms.

My sister and her husband moved far away. My brother went to live in a city. Times changed, with their usual **imperceptible** rapidity. Mother finally moved too; she was old and went to live with her daughter. I remained behind, a leftover. I could never think of marrying. I just stayed there with the impedimenta[5] of my life. Father, wandering alone and forlorn on the river, needed me. I knew he needed me, although he never even told me why he was doing it. When I put the question to people bluntly and insistently, all they told me was that they heard that Father had explained it to the man who made the boat. But now this man was dead and nobody knew or remembered anything. There was just some foolish talk, when the rains were especially severe and persistent, that my father was wise like Noah and had the boat built in anticipation of a new flood; I dimly remember people saying this. In any case, I would not condemn my father for what he was doing. My hair was beginning to turn grey.

I have only sad things to say. What bad had I done, what was my great guilt? My father always away and his absence always with me. And the river, always the river, perpetually renewing itself. The river, always. I was beginning to suffer from old age, in which life is just a sort of lingering. I had attacks of illness and of anxiety. I had a nagging rheumatism.[6] And he? Why, why was he doing it? He must have been suffering terribly. He was so old. One day, in his failing strength, he might let the boat capsize; or he might let the current carry it downstream, on and on, until it

imperceptible
unobservable; untraceable

---

4 **parasol:** a type of umbrella used for sun protection

5 **impedimenta:** things that get in the way

6 **rheumatism:** a health condition marked by muscle and joint pain

plunged over the waterfall to the boiling turmoil below. It pressed upon my heart. He was out there and I was forever robbed of my peace. I am guilty of I know not what, and my pain is an open wound inside me. Perhaps I would know—if things were different. I began to guess what was wrong.

Out with it! Had I gone crazy? No, in our house that word was never spoken, never through all the years. No one called anybody crazy, for nobody is crazy. Or maybe everybody. All I did was go there and wave a handkerchief so he would be more likely to see me. I was in complete command of myself. I waited. Finally he appeared in the distance, there, then over there, a vague shape sitting in the back of the boat. I called to him several times. And I said what I was so eager to say, to state formally and under oath. I said it as loud as I could:

> **No one called anybody crazy, for nobody is crazy. Or maybe everybody.**

"Father, you have been out there long enough. You are old . . . Come back, you don't have to do it anymore . . . Come back and I'll go instead. Right now, if you want. Any time. I'll get into the boat. I'll take your place."

And when I had said this my heart beat more firmly.

He heard me. He stood up. He **manoeuvred** with his oars and headed the boat towards me. He had accepted my offer. And suddenly I trembled, down deep. For he had raised his arm and waved—the first time in so many, so many years. And I couldn't . . . In terror, my hair on end, I ran, I fled madly. For he seemed to come from another world. And I'm begging forgiveness, begging, begging.

manoeuvred
handled; moved skillfully

I experienced the dreadful sense of cold that comes from deadly fear, and I became ill. Nobody ever saw or heard about him again. Am I a man, after such a failure? I am what never should have been. I am what must be silent. I know it is too late. I must stay in the deserts and unmarked plains of my life, and I fear I shall shorten it. But when death comes I want them to take me and put me in a little boat in this perpetual water between the long shores; and I, down the river, lost in the river, inside the river . . . the river . . .

Translated by William L. Grossman

Responding to the Selection

1. What are some possible explanations for why the father left his family to live on a boat on the river? Name as many as you can.

2. How does the narrator react, both intellectually and emotionally, to his father's leaving the family for the river?

3. The son is very distraught at not being able to take over his father's mission. Why do you think he is unable to make this sacrifice? Consider why he wants to be placed on a boat in the river after he is dead.

4. In this story, there are many references to journeys, time, and the everlasting nature of the river. How do these elements contribute to the story's theme?

5. What do you think is the significance of the narrator's comments: "... for nobody is crazy. Or maybe everybody"?

The Book of Sand

Jorge Luis Borges

WORLD LENS

♦♦♦

ARGENTINA

Jorge Luis Borges's influence on literature, especially in Latin America, is incomparable. He wrote in all genres, but preferred short stories because of the way in which they compress connections and meaning. Like many Latin American writers, he uses fantasy as a way to invest the ordinary with the extraordinary. He wrote about dreams, the connection between reality and the imagination, and the magic of ordinary objects. As a director of the National Library in Buenos Aires, he could indulge his love of books and the notion of the "infinite library" that is another of his repeated themes.

Borges once wrote, "Through the years, a man peoples a space with images of provinces, kingdoms, mountains, bays, ships, islands, fishes, rooms, tools, stars, horses, and people. Shortly before his death, he discovers that the patient labyrinth of lines traces the images of his own face."

> . . . thy rope of sands . . .
> George Herbert (1593–1623)

The line consists of an infinite number of points; the plane, of an infinite number of lines; the volume, of an infinite number of planes; the hypervolume, of an infinite number of volumes . . . No—this, *more geometrico*, is decidedly not the best way to begin my tale. To say that the story is true is by now a convention of every fantastic tale; mine, nevertheless, is true.

I live alone, in a fifth-floor apartment on Calle Belgrano. One evening a few months ago, I heard a knock at my door. I opened it, and a stranger stepped in. He was a tall man, with blurred, vague features, or perhaps my nearsightedness made me see him that way. Everything about him spoke of honest poverty: he was dressed in gray, and carried a gray valise.[1] I immediately sensed that he was a foreigner. At first I thought he was old; then I noticed that I had been misled by his sparse hair, which was blond, almost white, like the Scandinavians'. In the course of our conversation, which I doubt lasted more than an hour, I learned that he hailed from the Orkneys.[2]

I pointed the man to a chair. He took some time to begin talking. He gave off an air of melancholy, as I myself do now.

"I sell Bibles," he said at last.

"In this house," I replied, not without a somewhat stiff, **pedantic** note, "there are several English Bibles, including the first one, Wyclif's.[3] I also have Cipriano de Valera's, Luther's (which is, in literary terms, the worst of the lot), and a Latin copy of the Vulgate.[4] As you see, it isn't exactly Bibles I might be needing."

After a brief silence he replied.

"It's not only Bibles I sell. I can show you a sacred book that might interest a man such as yourself. I came by it in northern India, in Bikaner."

He opened his valise and brought out the book. He laid it on the table. It was clothbound octavo[5] volume that had clearly passed through many hands. I examined it; the unusual heft of it surprised me. On the spine was printed *Holy Writ*, and then *Bombay*.

"Nineteenth century, I'd say," I observed.

"I don't know," was the reply. "Never did know."

I opened it at random. The characters were unfamiliar to me. The pages, which seemed worn and badly set, were printed in double columns, like a Bible. The text was cramped, and composed into versicles.[6] At the upper corner of each page were Arabic numerals. I was struck by an odd fact: the even-numbered page would carry the number 40,514, let us say, while the odd-numbered page that followed it would be 999. I turned the page;

---

1 **valise:** a piece of handheld luggage

2 **Orkneys:** a group of islands off of northeastern Scotland

3 **Wyclif:** John Wyclif (1328–1384), an English reformer, who inspired the first complete English translation of the Latin Bible

4 **Vulgate:** the Latin Bible used by Roman Catholics

5 **octavo:** a size of book, printed on sheets which fold to form 8 leaves, or 16 pages

6 **versicles:** short verses used in worship services

the next page bore an eight-digit number. It also bore a small illustration, like those one sees in dictionaries: an anchor drawn in pen and ink, as though by the unskilled hand of a child.

It was at that point that the stranger spoke again.

"Look at it well. You will never see it again."

There was a threat in the words, but not in the voice.

I took note of the page, and then closed the book. Immediately I opened it again. In vain I searched for the figure of the anchor, page after page. To hide my discomfiture, I tried another tack.

"This is a version of Scripture in some Hindu language, isn't that right?"

"No," he replied.

Then he lowered his voice, as though entrusting me with a secret.

"I came across this book in a village on the plain, and I traded a few rupees and a Bible for it. The man who owned it didn't know how to read. I suspect he saw the Book of Books as an amulet.[7] He was of the lowest caste;[8] people could not so much as step on his shadow without being defiled. He told me his book was called the Book of Sand because neither sand nor this book has a beginning or an end."

He suggested I try to find the first page.

I took the cover in my left hand and opened the book, my thumb and forefinger almost touching. It was impossible: several pages always lay between the cover and my hand. It was as though they grew from the very book.

"Now try to find the end."

I failed there as well.

"This can't be," I stammered, my voice hardly recognizable as my own.

"It can't be, yet it is," the Bible peddler said, his voice little more than a whisper. "The number of pages in this book is literally infinite. No page is the first page; no page is the last. I don't know why they're numbered in this **arbitrary** way, but perhaps it's to give one to understand that the terms of an infinite series can be numbered any way whatever."

arbitrary
random; discretionary

---

7 **amulet:** an object which is supposed to protect against harm

8 **caste:** a person's inherited social class in the Hindu religion

Then, as though thinking out loud, he went on.

"If space is infinite, we are anywhere, at any point in space. If time is infinite, we are at any point in time."

His musings irritated me.

"You," I said, "are a religious man, are you not?"

"Yes, I'm Presbyterian. My conscience is clear. I am certain I didn't cheat that native when I gave him the Lord's Word in exchange for his **diabolic** book."

I assured him he had nothing to reproach himself for, and asked whether he was just passing through the country. He replied that he planned to return to his own country within a few days. It was then that I learned he was a Scot, and that his home was in the Orkneys. I told him I had great personal fondness of Scotland because of my love for Stevenson[9] and Hume.[10]

"And Robbie Burns,"[11] he corrected.

As we talked I continued to explore the infinite book.

"Had you intended to offer this curious specimen to the British Museum, then?" I asked with feigned indifference.

"No," he replied. "I am offering it to you," and he mentioned a great sum of money.

I told him, with perfect honesty, that such an amount of money was not within my ability to pay. But my mind was working; in a few moments I had devised my plan.

"I propose a trade," I said. "You purchased the volume with a few rupees and the Holy Scripture; I will offer you the full sum of my pension, which I have just received, and Wyclif's black-letter Bible. It was left to me by my parents."

"A black-letter Wyclif!" he murmured.

I went to my bedroom and brought back the money and the book. With a bibliophile's[12] zeal he turned the pages and studied the binding.

"Done," he said.

I was astonished that he did not haggle. Only later was I to realize that he had entered my house already determined to sell

---

9 **Stevenson:** Robert Louis Stevenson (1850–1894), a famous Scottish novelist

10 **Hume:** David Hume (1711–1776), a Scottish philosopher and historian of renown

11 **Robbie Burns:** Robert Burns (1759–1796), the well-known Scottish poet

12 **bibliophile:** one who loves books

The Americas

the book. He did not count the money, but merely put the bills into his pocket.

We chatted about India, the Orkneys, and the Norwegian jarls[13] that had once ruled those islands. Night was falling when the man left. I have never seen him since, nor do I know his name.

I thought of putting the Book of Sand in the space left by the Wyclif, but I chose at last to hide it behind some imperfect volumes of the *Thousand and One Nights*.[14]

I went to bed but could not sleep. At three or four in the morning I turned on the light. I took out the impossible book and turned its pages. On one, I saw an engraving of a mask. There was a number in the corner of the page—I don't remember now what it was—raised to the ninth power.

I showed no one my treasure. To the joy of possession was added the fear that it would be stolen from me, and to that, the suspicion that it might not be truly infinite. Those two points of anxiety aggravated my already habitual **misanthropy**. I had but few friends left, and those, I stopped seeing. A prisoner of the Book, I hardly left my house, I examined the worn binding and the covers with a magnifying glass, and rejected the possibility of some artifice. I found that the small illustrations were spaced at two-thousand-page intervals. I began noting them down in an alphabetized notebook, which was very soon filled. They never repeated themselves. At night, during the rare intervals spared me by insomnia, I dreamed of the book.

> **misanthropy**
> *dislike of humanity*

Summer was drawing to a close, and I realized that the book was monstrous. It was cold consolation to think that I, who looked upon it with my eyes and fondled it with my ten flesh-and-bone fingers, was no less monstrous than the book. I felt it was a nightmare thing, an obscene thing, and that it defiled and corrupted reality.

I felt it was a nightmare thing, an obscene thing, and that it defiled and corrupted reality.

---

13 **jarls:** Scandinavian noblemen

14 ***Thousand and One Nights:*** a famous collection of Indian, Persian, and Arabic tales, arranged together in about 1450

I considered fire, but I feared that the burning of an infinite book might be similarly infinite, and suffocate the planet in smoke.

I remembered reading once that the best place to hide a leaf is in the forest. Before my retirement I had worked in the National Library, which contained nine hundred thousand books; I knew that to the right of the lobby a curving staircase descended into the shadows of the basement, where the maps and periodicals are kept. I took advantage of the librarians' distraction to hide the Book of Sand on one of the library's damp shelves; I tried not to notice how high up, or how far from the door.

I now feel a little better, but I refuse even to walk down the street the library's on.

Translated by Andrew Hurley

Responding to the Selection

1. Why do you think the narrator begins the story as he does? Explain what you think the mathematical equations might have to do with this story and its subject.

2. An epigraph is an opening quote that sets a story's theme. What theme is established by the line from the poet George Herbert, whose metaphysical poetry is concerned with the philosophy of life?

3. What is it about the Book of Sand that makes its owners so melancholic and dispirited?

4. Some people might recall the melodramatic tones of Edgar Allen Poe in this short story. Find a passage of language that seems heightened in tone and explain how it fits this story's purpose.

The Censors

Luisa Valenzuela

WORLD LENS

♦♦♦

ARGENTINA

This short story of Luisa Valenzuela's is famous, both for its artfulness as well as the way it captures the spirit of many Argentines during the military dictatorship of the 1970s. The "Process of National Reorganization," as it was euphemistically called, lasted from 1976 to 1983 and was remarkable for its violence. The military filled concentration camps and later mass graves with its victims, who were characterized as enemies of the state. Ordinary citizens lived in terror, and many fled the country in fear for their lives.

Since the cessation of European colonialism in Latin America, the tensions between the indigenous poor, the powerful military forces, and the elite, often corrupt, ruling classes have continued in several countries, not only Argentina.

Poor Juan! One day they caught him with his guard down before he could even realize that what he had taken as a stroke of luck was really one of fate's dirty tricks. These things happen the minute you're careless and you let down your guard, as one often does. Juancito let happiness—a feeling you can't trust—get the better of him when he received from a confidential source Mariana's new address in Paris and he knew that she hadn't forgotten him. Without thinking twice, he sat down at his table and wrote her a letter. The letter that keeps his mind off his job during the day and won't let him sleep at night (what had he scrawled, what had he put on that sheet of paper he sent to Mariana?).

Juan knows there won't be a problem with the letter's contents, that it's **irreproachable**, harmless. But what about the rest? He knows that they examine, sniff, feel, and read between the lines of each and every letter, and check its tiniest comma and most accidental stain. He knows that all letters pass from hand to

irreproachable
blameless; impeccable

hand and go through all sorts of tests in the huge censorship offices and that, in the end, very few continue on their way. Usually it takes months, even years, if there aren't any snags; all this time the freedom, maybe even the life, of both sender and receiver is in jeopardy. And that's why Juan's so down in the dumps: thinking that something might happen to Mariana because of his letters. Of all people, Mariana, who must finally feel safe there where she always dreamed she'd live. But he knows that the *Censor's Secret Command* operates all over the world and cashes in on the discount in air rates; there's nothing to stop them from going as far as that hidden Paris neighborhood, kidnapping Mariana, and returning to their cozy homes, certain of having fulfilled their noble mission.

Well, you've got to beat them to the punch, do what everyone tries to do: sabotage the machinery, throw sand in its gears, get to the bottom of the problem so as to stop it.

This was Juan's sound plan when he, like many others, applied for a censor's job—not because he had a calling or needed a job: no, he applied simply to intercept his own letter, a consoling but unoriginal idea. He was hired immediately, for each day more and more censors are needed and no one would bother to check on his references.

Ulterior motives couldn't be overlooked by the *Censorship Division*, but they needn't be too strict with those who applied. They knew how hard it would be for those poor guys to find the letter they wanted and even if they did, what's a letter or two when the new censor would snap up so many others? That's how Juan managed to join the *Post Office's Censorship Division*, with a certain goal in mind.

The building had a festive air on the outside which contrasted with its inner staidness. Little by little, Juan was absorbed by his job and he felt at peace since he was doing everything he could to get his letter for Mariana. He didn't even worry when, in his first month, he was sent to *Section K*, where envelopes were very carefully screened for explosives.

It's true that on the third day, a fellow worker had his right hand blown off by a letter, but the division chief claimed it was sheer negligence on the victim's part. Juan and the other employees were allowed to go back to their work, albeit feeling less secure. After work, one of them tried to organize a strike to demand higher wages for unhealthy work, but Juan didn't join in; after thinking it over, he reported him to his superiors and thus got promoted.

You don't form a habit by doing something once, he told himself as he left his boss's office. And when he was transferred to *Section J*, where letters are carefully checked for poison dust, he felt he had climbed a rung in the ladder.

By working hard, he quickly reached *Section E* where the work was more interesting, for he could now read and analyze the letters' contents. Here he could even hope to get hold of his letter which, judging by the time that had elapsed, had gone through the other sections and was probably floating around in this one.

Soon his work became so absorbing that his noble mission blurred in his mind. Day after day he crossed out whole paragraphs in red ink, pitilessly chucking many letters into the censored basket. These were horrible days when he was shocked by the subtle and conniving ways employed by people to pass on subversive messages; his instincts were so sharp that he found behind a simple "the weather's unsettled" or "prices continue to soar" the wavering hand of someone secretly scheming to overthrow the Government.

His zeal brought him swift promotion. We don't know if this made him happy. Very few letters reached him in *Section B*—only a handful passed the other hurdles—so he read them over and over again, passed them under a magnifying glass, searched for microprint with an electronic microscope, and tuned his sense of smell so that he was beat by the time he made it home. He'd barely manage to warm up his soup, eat some fruit, and fall into bed, satisfied with having done his duty. Only his darling mother worried, but she couldn't get him back on the right road. She'd say, though it wasn't always true: Lola called, she's at the bar with the girls, they miss you, they're waiting for you. Or else she'd leave a bottle of red wine on the table. But Juan wouldn't overdo it: any distraction could make him lose his edge and the perfect censor had to be alert, keen, attentive, and sharp to nab cheats. He had a truly patriotic task, both self-denying and uplifting.

His basket for censored letters became the best fed as well as the most cunning basket in the whole *Censorship Division*. He was about to congratulate himself for having finally discovered his true mission, when his letter to Mariana reached his hands. Naturally, he censored it without regret. And just as naturally, he couldn't stop them from executing him the following morning, another victim of his devotion to his work.

Translated by David Unger

Responding to the Selection

1. What do you think is the author's message about the nature of state censorship?

2. Is this a realistic story? Explain your answer using examples from the text.

3. How can a man who is afraid of censorship become a censor? What is Valenzuela saying about human nature?

4. Can you think of any other situations in which people end up hurting themselves because they participate in something corrupt?

Tonight I Can Write

Pablo Neruda

WORLD LENS

◆◆◆

CHILE

Chilean Nobel laureate Pablo Neruda may be the most famous poet in the world. One critic called him "a surrealist who is never out of touch with reality . . . ."

Neruda wrote passionately about such major themes as love, loneliness, and death, while chronicling political upheavals in Civil War Spain and past-and-present South America. Besides championing the poor, he composed whimsical and appreciative odes to such diverse common objects as lemons, onions, and socks. In the poet's vast body of work, he paid special tribute to Chile—its dramatic landscapes, the destruction of native cultures, and the strife between the ruling elite and common Chileans.

Tonight I can write the saddest lines.

Write, for example, "The night is starry
and the stars are blue and shiver in the distance."

The night wind revolves in the sky and sings.

Tonight I can write the saddest lines.
I loved her, and sometimes she loved me too.

Through nights like this one I held her in my arms.
I kissed her again and again under the endless sky.

She loved me, sometimes I loved her too.
How could one not have loved her great still eyes.

Tonight I can write the saddest lines.
To think that I do not have her. To feel that I have lost her.

To hear the immense night, still more immense without her.
And the verse falls to the soul like dew to the pasture.

What does it matter that my love could not keep her.
The night is starry and she is not with me.

This is all. In the distance someone is singing. In the distance.
My soul is not satisfied that it has lost her.

My sight tries to find her as though to bring her closer
My heart looks for her, and she is not with me.

The same night whitening the same trees.
We, of that time, are no longer the same.

I no longer love her, that's certain, but how I loved her.
My voice tried to find the wind to touch her hearing.

Another's. She will be another's. As she was before my kisses.
Her voice, her bright body. Her infinite eyes.

I no longer love her, that's certain, but maybe I love her.
Love is so short, forgetting is so long.

Because through nights like this I held her in my arms
my soul is not satisfied that it has lost her.

Though this be the last pain that she makes me suffer
and these the last verses that I write for her.

Translated by W. S. Merwin

Responding to the Selection

1. What do you think is meant by the line, "Love is so short, forgetting is so long"?

2. Pablo Neruda is noted for writing musical lines of poetry. Find some examples of melody in this poem.

Serenity

Gabriela Mistral

Gabriela Mistral was the first Latin American woman to receive the Nobel Prize in literature. In a land that prizes its poets, Mistral is viewed with special affection for her strong identity with the poor and the indigenous people of South America. Her poems are noteworthy for their portrayals of the bonds between women and their children, as depicted in many of her lullabies and poems of motherly love.

WORLD LENS

♦♦♦

CHILE

When I am singing to you,
on earth all evil ends:
as smooth as your forehead
are the gulch and the bramble.

When I am singing to you,
for me all cruel things end:
as gentle as your eyelids,
the lion with the jackal.

Translated by Doris Dana

Responding to the Selection

1. To whom is the speaker singing?

2. In what ways does this poem seem like a lullaby?

3. What emotions are expressed or implied in this poem?

4. Love between a mother and her children—the theme of so much of Mistral's writing—is a subject that often lends itself to sentimentality. Look up the word "sentimental" in a dictionary and decide for yourself if this poem fits that definition.

And of Clay Are We Created

Isabel Allende

WORLD LENS
•••
CHILE

Isabel Allende resides among the front ranks of Latin American authors, bringing a woman's perspective to matters of class, family, and sexual politics. Like Gabriel García Márquez, Allende often uses magic realism in her fiction, a technique that seems to go naturally with the fantastic and tumultuous events in Latin American history.

In the following story, Allende addresses two classic conflicts in South America: Humans against Nature (avalanches and other catastrophes having brought so much suffering to the region) and Modern Civilization against Traditional Cultures. Due to poverty, ethnic differences, and the severe geographical features of its mountain ranges, deserts, and rainforests, many South American cultures are still isolated from modern life.

Allende's inspiration for this story came from the ordeal of a 13-year-old Colombian girl trapped in the mud after a 1985 avalanche. The author watched on television as a reporter comforted the dying girl.

They discovered the girl's head protruding from the mud pit, eyes wide open, calling soundlessly. She had a First Communion name,[1] Azucena. Lily. In that vast cemetery where the odor of death was already attracting vultures from far away, and where the weeping of orphans and wails of the injured filled the air, the little girl obstinately clinging to life became the symbol of the tragedy. The television cameras transmitted so often the unbearable image of the head budding like a black squash from the clay that there was no one who did not recognize her and know her name. And every time we saw her on the screen,

---

1 **First Communion name:** the name a Roman Catholic child takes when receiving this religious sacrament

right behind her was Rolf Carlé, who had gone there on assignment, never suspecting that he would find a fragment of his past, lost thirty years before.

First a **subterranean** sob rocked the cotton fields, curling them like waves of foam. Geologists had set up their seismographs[2] weeks before and knew that the mountain had awakened again. For some time they had predicted that the heat of the eruption could detach the eternal ice from the slopes of the volcano, but no one heeded their warnings; they sounded like the tales of frightened old women. The towns in the valley went about their daily life, deaf to the moaning of the earth, until that fateful Wednesday night in November when a prolonged roar announced the end of the world, and walls of snow broke loose, rolling in an avalanche of clay, stones, and water that descended on the villages and buried them beneath unfathomable meters of telluric[3] vomit. As soon as the survivors emerged from the paralysis of that first awful terror, they could see that houses, plazas, churches, white cotton plantations, dark coffee forests, cattle pastures—all had disappeared. Much later, after soldiers and volunteers had arrived to rescue the living and try to assess the magnitude of the **cataclysm**, it was calculated that beneath the mud lay more than twenty thousand human beings and an indefinite number of animals **putrefying** in a **viscous** soup. Forests and rivers had also been swept away, and there was nothing to be seen but an immense desert of mire.

When the station called before dawn, Rolf Carlé and I were together. I crawled out of bed, dazed with sleep, and went to prepare coffee while he hurriedly dressed. He stuffed his gear in the green canvas backpack he always carried, and we said goodbye, as we had so many times before. I had no **presentiments**. I sat in the kitchen, sipping my coffee and planning the long hours without him, sure that he would be back the next day.

He was one of the first to reach the scene, because while other reporters were fighting their way to the edges of that **morass** in jeeps, bicycles, or on foot, each getting there however he could,

subterranean
underground;
below the surface

cataclysm
disaster; catastrophe

putrefying
rotting; decaying

viscous
sticky; gluey

presentiments
foreshadowing;
premonitions

morass
swamp; quagmire

---

2 **seismographs:** instruments for measuring earth tremors

3 **telluric:** earthly

And of Clay Are We Created

bedlam
chaos; place of uproar

tenacity
persistence; mental toughness

equanimity
calm; poise

fictive
imaginary; fictional

quagmire
bog; quicksand

Rolf Carlé had the advantage of the television helicopter, which flew him over the avalanche. We watched on our screens the footage captured by his assistant's camera, in which he was up to his knees in muck, a microphone in his hand, in the midst of a **bedlam** of lost children, wounded survivors, corpses, and devastation. The story came to us in his calm voice. For years he had been a familiar figure in newscasts, reporting live at the scene of battles and catastrophes with awesome **tenacity**. Nothing could stop him, and I was always amazed at his **equanimity** in the face of danger and suffering; it seemed as if nothing could shake his fortitude or deter his curiosity. Fear seemed never to touch him, although he had confessed to me that he was not a courageous man, far from it. I believe that the lens of a camera had a strange effect on him; it was as if it transported him to a different time from which he could watch events without actually participating in them. When I knew him better, I came to realize that this **fictive** distance seemed to protect him from his own emotions.

Rolf Carlé was in on the story of Azucena from the beginning. He filmed the volunteers who discovered her, and the first persons who tried to reach her; his camera zoomed in on the girl, her dark face, her large desolate eyes, the plastered-down tangle of her hair. The mud was like quicksand around her, and anyone attempting to reach her was in danger of sinking. They threw a rope to her that she made no effort to grasp until they shouted to her to catch it; then she pulled a hand from the mire and tried to move but immediately sank a little deeper. Rolf threw down his knapsack and the rest of his equipment and waded into the **quagmire**, commenting for his assistant's microphone that it was cold and that one could begin to smell the stench of corpses.

"What's your name?" he asked the girl, and she told him her flower name. "Don't move, Azucena," Rolf Carlé directed, and kept talking to her, without a thought for what he was saying, just to distract her, while slowly he worked his way forward in mud up to his waist. The air around him seemed as murky as the mud.

It was impossible to reach her from the approach he was attempting, so he retreated and circled around where there seemed to be firmer footing. When finally he was close enough, he took the rope and tied it beneath her arms, so they could pull her out. He smiled at her with that smile that crinkles his eyes and makes him look like a little boy; he told her that everything was fine, that he was here with her now, that soon they would have her out. He signaled the others to pull, but as soon as the cord tensed, the girl screamed. They tried again, and her shoulders and arms appeared, but they could move her no farther; she was trapped. Someone suggested that her legs might be caught in the collapsed walls of her house, but she said it was not just rubble, that she was also held by the bodies of her brothers and sisters clinging to her legs.

"Don't worry, we'll get you out of here," Rolf promised. Despite the quality of the transmission, I could hear his voice break, and I loved him more than ever. Azucena looked at him but said nothing.

During those first hours Rolf Carlé exhausted all the resources of his ingenuity to rescue her. He struggled with poles and ropes, but every tug was an intolerable torture for the imprisoned girl. It occurred to him to use one of the poles as a lever but got no result and had to abandon the idea. He talked a couple of soldiers into working with him for a while, but they had to leave because so many other victims were calling for help. The girl could not move, she barely could breathe, but she did not seem desperate, as if an ancestral resignation allowed her to accept her fate. The reporter, on the other hand, was determined to snatch her from death. Someone brought him a tire, which he placed beneath her arms like a life buoy, and then laid a plank near the hole to hold his weight and allow him to stay closer to her. As it was impossible to remove the rubble blindly, he tried once or twice to dive toward her feet but emerged frustrated, covered with mud, and spitting gravel. He concluded that he would have to have a pump to drain the water, and radioed a request for one but received in return a message that there was no available transport and it could not be sent until the next morning.

"We can't wait that long!" Rolf Carlé shouted, but in the pandemonium no one stopped to commiserate. Many more hours would go by before he accepted that time had **stagnated** and reality had been irreparably distorted.

stagnated
stilled; stopped moving

A military doctor came to examine the girl and observed that her heart was functioning well and that if she did not get too cold she could survive the night.

"Hang on, Azucena, we'll have the pump tomorrow," Rolf Carlé tried to console her.

"Don't leave me alone," she begged.

"No, of course I won't leave you."

Someone brought him coffee, and he helped the girl drink it, sip by sip. The warm liquid revived her, and she began telling him about her small life, about her family and her school, about how things were in that little bit of world before the volcano erupted. She was thirteen, and she had never been outside her village. Rolf Carlé, buoyed by a premature optimism, was convinced that

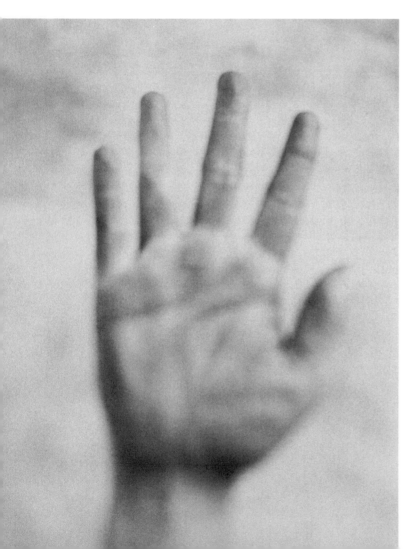

everything would end well: the pump would arrive, they would drain the water, move the rubble, and Azucena would be transported by helicopter to a hospital where she would recover rapidly and where he could visit her and bring her gifts. He thought, She's already too old for dolls, and I don't know what would please her; maybe a dress. I don't know much about women, he concluded, amused, reflecting that although he had known many women in his lifetime, none had taught him these details. To pass the hours he began to tell Azucena about his travels and adventures as a news

The Americas

hound, and when he exhausted his memory, he called upon imagination, inventing things he thought might entertain her. From time to time she dozed, but he kept talking in the darkness, to assure her that he was still there and to overcome the menace of uncertainty.

That was a long night.

◆◆◆◆◆

Many miles away, I watched Rolf Carlé and the girl on a television screen. I could not bear the wait at home, so I went to National Television, where I often spent entire nights with Rolf editing programs. There, I was near his world, and I could at least get a feeling of what he lived through during those three decisive days. I called all the important people in the city, senators, commanders of the armed forces, the North American ambassador, and the president of National Petroleum, begging them for a pump to remove the silt, but obtained only vague promises. I began to ask for urgent help on radio and television, to see if there wasn't *someone* who could help us. Between calls I would run to the newsroom to monitor the satellite transmissions that periodically brought new details of the catastrophe. While reporters selected scenes with most impact for the new report, I searched for footage that featured Azucena's mud pit. The screen reduced the disaster to a single plane and accentuated the tremendous distance that separated me from Rolf Carlé; nonetheless, I was there with him. The child's every suffering hurt me as it did him; I felt his frustration, his **impotence**. Faced with the impossibility of communicating with him, the fantastic idea came to me that if I tried, I could reach him by force of mind and in that way give him encouragement. I concentrated until I was dizzy—a frenzied and futile activity. At times I would be overcome with compassion and burst out crying; at other times, I was so drained I felt as if I were staring through a telescope at the light of a star dead for a million years.

I watched that hell on the first morning broadcast, **cadavers** of people and animals awash in the current of new rivers formed overnight from the melted snow. Above the mud rose the tops of trees and the bell towers of a church where several people had

impotence
powerlessness;
helplessness

cadavers
bodies; corpses

taken refuge and were patiently awaiting rescue teams. Hundreds of soldiers and volunteers from the civil defense were clawing through rubble searching for survivors, while long rows of ragged **specters** awaited their turn for a cup of hot broth. Radio networks announced that their phones were jammed with calls from families offering shelter to orphaned children. Drinking water was in scarce supply, along with gasoline and food. Doctors, resigned to amputating arms and legs without anesthesia, pled that at least they be sent **serum** and painkillers and antibiotics; most of the roads, however, were impassable, and worse were the bureaucratic obstacles that stood in the way. To top it all, the clay contaminated by decomposing bodies threatened the living with an outbreak of epidemics.

Azucena was shivering inside the tire that held her above the surface. Immobility and tension had greatly weakened her, but she was conscious and could still be heard when a microphone was held out to her. Her tone was humble, as if apologizing for all the fuss. Rolf Carlé had a growth of beard, and dark circles beneath his eyes; he looked near exhaustion. Even from that enormous distance I could sense the quality of his weariness, so different from the fatigue of other adventures. He had completely forgotten the camera; he could not look at the girl through a lens any longer. The pictures we were receiving were not his assistant's but those of other reporters who had appropriated Azucena, bestowing on her the pathetic responsibility of embodying the horror of what had happened in that place. With the first light Rolf tried again to dislodge the obstacles that held the girl in her tomb, but he had only his hands to work with; he did not dare use a tool for fear of injuring her. He fed Azucena a cup of the cornmeal mush and bananas the army was distributing, but she immediately vomited it up. A doctor stated that she had a fever but added that there was little he could do: antibiotics were being reserved for cases of gangrene. A priest also passed by and blessed her, hanging a medal of the Virgin around her neck. By evening a gentle, persistent drizzle began to fall.

"The sky is weeping," Azucena murmured, and she, too, began to cry.

"Don't be afraid," Rolf begged. "You have to keep your

specters
ghosts; shadows

serum
blood serum; the liquid part of blood

strength up and be calm. Everything will be fine. I'm with you, and I'll get you out somehow."

Reporters returned to photograph Azucena and ask her the same questions, which she no longer tried to answer. In the meanwhile, more television and movie teams arrived with spools of cable, tapes, film, videos, precision lenses, recorders, sound consoles, lights, reflecting screens, auxiliary motors, cartons of supplies, electricians, sound technicians, and cameramen: Azucena's face was beamed to millions of screens around the world. And all the while Rolf Carlé kept pleading for a pump. The improved technical facilities bore results, and National Television began receiving sharper pictures and clearer sound, the distance seemed suddenly compressed, and I had the horrible sensation that Azucena and Rolf were by my side, separated from me by impenetrable glass. I was able to follow events hour by hour; I knew everything my love did to wrest the girl from her prison and help her endure her suffering; I overheard fragments of what they said to one another and could guess the rest; I was present when she taught Rolf to pray and when he distracted her with the stories I had told him in a thousand and one nights beneath the white mosquito netting of our bed.

When darkness came on the second day, Rolf tried to sing Azucena to sleep with old Austrian folk songs he had learned from his mother, but she was far beyond sleep. They spent most of the night talking, each in a stupor of exhaustion and hunger and shaking with cold. That night, imperceptibly, the unyielding floodgates that had contained Rolf Carlé's past for so many years began to open, and the torrent of all that had lain hidden in the deepest and most secret layers of memory poured out, leveling before it the obstacles that had blocked his consciousness for so long. He could not tell it all to Azucena; she perhaps did not know there was a world beyond the sea or time previous to her own; she was not capable of imagining Europe in the years of the war. So he could not tell her of defeat, nor of the afternoon the Russians had led them to the concentration camp to bury prisoners dead from starvation. Why should he describe to her how the naked bodies piled like a mountain of firewood resembled fragile china? How could he tell this dying child about ovens and gallows? Nor did he mention the night that he had seen his mother naked, shod in stiletto-heeled red boots, sobbing with humiliation. There was much he did not tell, but in those hours he relived for the first time all the things his mind had tried to erase. Azucena had surrendered her fear to him and so, without wishing it, had obliged Rolf to confront his own. There, beside that hellhole of mud, it was impossible for Rolf to flee from himself any longer, and the **visceral** terror he had lived as a boy suddenly invaded him. He reverted to the years when he was the age of Azucena and younger, and, like her, found himself trapped in a pit without escape, buried in life, his head barely above ground; he saw before his eyes the boots and legs of his father, who had removed his belt and was whipping it in the air with the neverforgotten hiss of a viper coiled to strike. Sorrow flooded through him, intact and precise, as if it had lain always in his mind, waiting. He was once again in the armoire[4] where his father locked him to punish him for imagined misbehavior, there where for eternal hours he had crouched with his eyes closed, not to see the darkness, with his hands over his ears to shut out the beating of his heart, trembling, huddled like a cornered animal. Wandering in the mist of his memories he found his sister, Katharina, a sweet, retarded child who spent her life hiding, with the hope that her father would forget the disgrace of her having been born. With Katharina, Rolf crawled beneath the dining room table, and with her hid there under the long white tablecloth, two children forever embraced, alert to footsteps and voices. Katharina's scent melded with his own sweat, with aromas of cooking, garlic, soup, freshly baked bread, and the unexpected odor of **putrescent** clay. His sister's hand in his, her frightened breathing, her silk hair against his cheek, the candid gaze of the eyes. Katharina . . . Katharina materialized before him, floating on the air like a flag, clothed in the white tablecloth, now a winding sheet, and at last he could weep for her death and for the guilt of having abandoned her. He understood then that all his exploits as a reporter, the feats that had won him such recognition and fame, were merely an attempt to keep his most ancient fears at bay, a stratagem for taking refuge behind a lens to test whether

---

4 **armoire:** a kind of cupboard or wardrobe

visceral
deep; instinctive

putrescent
rotting; stinking

The Americas

reality was more tolerable from that perspective. He took excessive risks as an exercise of courage, training by day to conquer the monsters that tormented him by night. But he had to come face to face with the moment of truth; he could not continue to escape his past. He was Azucena; he was buried in the clayey mud; his terror was not the distant emotion of an almost forgotten childhood, it was a claw sunk in his throat. In the flush of his tears he saw his mother, dressed in black and clutching her imitation-crocodile pocketbook to her bosom, just as he had last seen her on the dock when she had come to put him on the boat to South America. She had not come to dry his tears, but to tell him to pick up a shovel: the war was over and now they must bury the dead.

"Don't cry. I don't hurt anymore. I'm fine," Azucena said when dawn came.

"I'm not crying for you," Rolf Carlé smiled. "I'm crying for myself. I hurt all over."

◆ ◆ ◆ ◆ ◆

The third day in the valley of the cataclysm began with a pale light filtering through storm clouds. The president of the republic visited the area in his tailored safari jacket to confirm that this was the worst catastrophe of the century; the country was in mourning; sister nations had offered aid; he had ordered a state of siege; the armed forces would be merciless; anyone caught stealing or committing other offenses would be shot on sight. He added that it was impossible to remove all the corpses or count the thousands who had disappeared; the entire valley would be declared holy ground, and bishops would come to celebrate a solemn mass for the souls of the victims. He went to the army field tents to offer relief in the form of vague promises to crowds of the rescued, then to the improvised hospital to offer a word of encouragement to doctors and nurses worn down from so many hours of **tribulations**. Then he asked to be taken to see Azucena, the little girl the whole world had seen. He waved to her with a limp statesman's hand, and microphones recorded his emotional voice and paternal tone as he told her that her courage had served as an example to the nation. Rolf Carlé interrupted to ask for a

tribulations
great sufferings; afflictions

And of Clay Are We Created

pump, and the president assured him that he personally would attend to the matter. I caught a glimpse of Rolf for a few seconds kneeling beside the mud pit. On the evening news broadcast, he was still in the same position; and I, glued to the screen like a fortuneteller to her crystal ball, could tell that something fundamental had changed in him. I knew somehow that during the night his defenses had crumbled and he had given in to grief; finally he was vulnerable. The girl had touched a part of him that he himself had no access to, a part he had never shared with me. Rolf had wanted to console her, but it was Azucena who had given him consolation.

I recognized the precise moment at which Rolf gave up the fight and surrendered to the torture of watching the girl die. I was with them, three day and two nights, spying on them from the other side of life. I was there when she told him that in all her thirteen years no boy had ever loved her and that it was a pity to leave this world without knowing love. Rolf assured her that he loved her more than he could ever love anyone, more than he loved his mother, more than his sister, more than all the women who had slept in his arms, more than he loved me, his life companion, who would have given anything to be trapped in that well in her place, who would have exchanged her life for Azucena's, and I watched as he leaned down to kiss her poor forehead, consumed by a sweet, sad emotion he could not name. I felt how in that instant both were saved from despair, how they were freed from the clay, how they rose above the vultures and helicopters, how together they flew above the vast swamp of corruption and laments. How, finally, they were able to accept death. Rolf Carlé prayed in silence that she would die quickly, because such pain cannot be borne.

By then I had obtained a pump and was in touch with a general who had agreed to ship it the next morning on a military cargo plane. But on the night of that third day, beneath the unblinking focus of quartz lamps and the lens of a hundred cameras, Azucena gave up, her eyes locked with those of the friend who had sustained her to the end. Rolf Carlé removed the life buoy, closed her eyelids, held her to his chest for a few moments, and then let her go. She sank slowly, a flower in the mud.

You are back with me, but you are not the same man. I often accompany you to the station, and we watch the videos of Azucena again; you study them intently, looking for something you could have done to save her, something you did not think of in time. Or maybe you study them to see yourself as if in a mirror, naked. Your cameras lie forgotten in a closet; you do not write or sing; you sit long hours before the window, staring at the mountains. Beside you, I wait for you to complete the voyage into yourself, for the old wounds to heal. I know that when you return from your nightmares, we shall again walk hand in hand, as before.

Translated by Margaret Sayers Peden

Responding to the Selection

1. In the first sentence you learn that this is going to be a dramatic story about a terrible catastrophe. Make a list of the nouns (both concrete and abstract) in the first paragraph to see how the author establishes her theme and tone from the very beginning.

2. At the end, Rolf Carlé seems destroyed by Azucena's death and the personal memories it has called up. Why does the narrator have a sense of optimism about his eventual recovery?

3. Find a passage of vivid description and try to explain what makes it effective for you. What sense imagery (sight, sound, smell, taste, or touch) or figurative language (similes, metaphors, personification) does it employ?

4. Why do you think the local population ignores the warnings from scientists that the volcano is going to erupt?

UNIT REVIEW

The Americas

Discussing

1. Magic realism is often referred to in the unit on the Americas. Find an example of this blend of the magical and the realistic in one of the selections. Why might an author choose this form of expression? Explain whether you do or do not like this style of writing.

2. Tone is the author's attitude toward the subject he or she is writing about. For example, a writer may express irony or pessimism through a piece of writing. Review one of the selections in this unit and decide on its overall tone. Select two or three lines that you feel best express this attitude and prepare to explain your choice.

3. "I am a citizen of the world" is a key line in the story "When Greek Meets Greek." What does it mean to you? How does it fit the events of this story or any other selection in this unit?

4. One thing the poems in this unit share is the theme of love: love of self, love of family, love of country, and love of a significant other. After deciding what kind of love is being addressed in each poem, list the sensory details the poet uses to evoke this powerful emotion. Which poem affects you most? Explain why you think that is.

5. Explain how Azucena is used as a symbol of the disaster in "And of Clay Are We Created," the story by Isabel Allende. Consider other examples of large-scale tragedies where one or more people have been chosen by the media to represent the catastrophe. Why do you think this happens?

Writing

6. Write "No Dogs Bark" from a different point of view: perhaps through the eyes of the son, Ignacio; a stranger observing the father carrying his son across the Mexican landscape at night; or a doctor called to the scene at the end. You may choose to fill in many more facts and details or, like Rulfo, write a story that is mysterious and does not provide clear answers.

7. Gabriela Mistral believed that artists are to society what the soul is to the individual. Extend this idea in a short essay of your own. What functions do artists serve in society? Who do they speak for? Who are some of the artists—writers, painters, sculptors, or actors—who have given you the most inspiration and satisfaction in your daily life?

Speaking/Listening

8. Have a spoken-word festival by bringing together and sharing more selections of prose and poetry by these or other writers from the Americas. Practice reading your piece in private before sharing it with the class. Also, in order to enrich the audience's understanding, preface your selections with a biographical sketch of the writer(s) and define any word or concept that might be unfamiliar to most people.

Hands-on Project

Do some research on the Mexican celebration known as *El Día de los Muertos*—The Day of the Dead. On this day, *calaveras*—whimsical papier-maché skeletons—spring up everywhere, mocking the dead and satirizing the living. Look at as many photos or real examples of calaveras as you can in order to understand the character of this popular folk art form. A calavera can be found in almost any pose—ironing, walking a dog, even getting married—and is always grinning wickedly. Try your hand at constructing a calavera of your own.

Personal Connections

After reading the selections in this unit, choose one of the following questions to write about in your journal.

1. Which characters or selections helped open your eyes to a new way of seeing the world?

2. What new understanding do you have about American culture, your family, or yourself?

3. Which differences among cultures do you think really matter? Explain.

RESEARCHING THE WORLD

General Research Subjects

The following general subjects are merely starting points for research. After choosing one that interests you, you will have to narrow your topic considerably.

Belief Systems
Celebrations and
  Ceremonies
Children and Family
Coming of Age
Courtship and Marriage
Crime and Justice
The Economy
Education

The Environment
Famous Figures
Food
Geography
Globalism
Important Events
Language
Literature and the Arts
The Media

Oppression and Exile
Popular Culture
Rural and Urban Life
Sports
Technology
Travel
Work and Leisure

Specific Research Topics

Pick from the following topics or use them as starting points for your research. Some topics can be applied to more than one country in this region; others pertain to a single country or group of people. Note that in order to be a manageable size, many of these topics will require further narrowing.

Arts/Leisure

- Winter sports in Canada
- Film (Canada, Mexico, Brazil)
- Mexican muralists (Rivera, Orozco, Siqueiros)
- Latin and Caribbean music and dance (salsa, samba, reggae)
- Andean arts (textiles, pipe music)

Culture/Geography

- Unique geography (the Arctic Circle, rainforests, *pampas*)
- Language in the Caribbean (dialects, pidgin, creole)
- Celebrations (Day of the Dead or Lenten Carnivals)
- Astronomy and the Mayan Indians
- Street children in Brazil

History/Politics

- First Nation peoples in Canada
- Latin American revolutionaries (Pancho Villa, Che Guevara)
- 1968 Summer Olympics in Mexico
- Pre-Columbian civilizations (Incas, Mayan, Aztecs)
- Civil wars (Argentina, Cuba, Chile)

AUTHOR BIOGRAPHIES

Isabel Allende (1942–) In her native country of Chile, Isabel Allende was a journalist. She went into exile soon after her uncle, Chilean president Salvador Allende, was assassinated in 1973. She has traveled to many parts of the world and now lives in the United States. At various times, Allende found herself in frightening situations. But as she said in an interview for *Mother Jones*, "The wonderful quality of human beings is that we can overcome even absolute terror, and we do." Allende has written novels, short stories, newspaper and magazine articles, plays, television shows, and children's literature. Her books include the international bestseller, *The House of the Spirits*, as well as *Eva Luna, The Infinite Plan,* and *Paula*.

Margaret Atwood (1939–) Atwood is a Canadian author of fiction, poetry, social history, criticism, and children's books. Her many international literary awards include the British Booker Prize for her novel *The Blind Assassin*. Atwood writes with a sharp sense of irony, often directed toward specific political and cultural notions. In an interview for *Mother Jones*, she said that her political positions developed out of "looking into things . . . out of that comes your view—not that you have the view first and then squash everything to make it fit." Among Atwood's other novels are *The Handmaid's Tale, Cat's Eye,* and *Alias Grace*.

James Berry (1924–) Born in Jamaica, James Berry spent a few years in the United States and then settled in Britain. In London, he first wrote short stories and then poetry. In 1990, Berry was awarded the O.B.E. (Officer of the British Empire, an honor similar to knighthood) for his services to poetry. Berry says, "My advice to young developing writers is: find stories that engage you and read, read and read. Find the poems that really engage you, and silently and aloud, read, read and read them. Write every day, if at all possible. Find a helpful teacher." His works include short stories for children (*A Thief in the Village and Other Stories of Jamaica*) as well as poetry for children and adults.

Jorge Luis Borges (1899–1986) Born in Argentina, Jorge Luis Borges grew up in a Spanish/English bilingual household. He would later live in several other countries and travel around the world. He was a prolific writer of stories, poems, and essays. His best-known stories—such as "Pierre Menard, Author of Don Quixote," "Tlön, Uqbar, Orbis Tertius," and "The Garden of Forking Paths"—mix philosophy, fantasy, and mystery. In 1961 Borges shared the International Publishers Prize with Samuel Beckett, making him internationally famous. Borges always had poor vision, and he eventually became blind, but continued to study languages, write, and travel. In a 1977 lecture he said: "Everything that happens, including humiliations, embarrassments, misfortunes, all has been given like clay, like material for one's art . . . If a blind man thinks this way, he is saved."

Rosario Ferré (1938–) Puerto Rican poet, novelist, and literary critic Rosario Ferré has studied and taught in the United States and in her home country. In the early 1970s, Ferré and other students published a literary magazine, *Zona de Carga y Descarga,* featuring new Puerto Rican authors and discussing politics. Stories Ferré wrote for her own children are included in the short story collection *Sonatinas.* She has written several novels in English, including *House on the Lagoon.* Her decision to publish in English as well as her belief that the Commonwealth of Puerto Rico should become the United States' 51st state has made her a controversial figure in Puerto Rico.

Gabriel García Márquez (1928–) The essayist, novelist, and short-story writer Gabriel García Márquez was born in Colombia and has lived in many parts of the Spanish-speaking world. His early years of poverty led to his lifelong sympathy with Marxism. A longtime friend of Fidel Castro, García Márquez has quietly used his influence with the Cuban dictator to free political prisoners and help dissidents leave Cuba. His most famous novels include *One Hundred Years of Solitude, Love in the Time of Cholera,* and *The General in His Labyrinth.* Such works have made him the best-known writer of the magic realist movement. His use of the fantastic helps to convey the troubled realities of Latin America. As he explained upon accepting the Nobel Prize in 1982, "our crucial problem has been a lack of conventional means to render our lives believable."

Thomas King (1943–) King, who is part Cherokee and a Canadian citizen, writes witty, insightful fiction about Native Americans. His novels, *Medicine River, Green Grass, Running Water,* and *Truth and Bright Water* have all won literary awards. For young readers, he wrote *A Coyote Columbus Story* and *Coyote Sings to the Moon.* At Canada's University of Guelph, where King teaches English, he noted that he gives special attention to the sound and rhythm of his words: "I look at my novels as musical pieces, symphonies." He is also a fine arts photographer and has a weekly radio show called "The Dead Dog Cafe Comedy Hour."

Gabriela Mistral (1889–1957) Lucila Godoy Alcayaga was born in Chile, where she became a village schoolteacher. After the suicide of a man she was romantically involved with, she began writing poetry, which she published under the pseudonym Gabriela Mistral. She is credited with founding the modern poetry movement in Chile and was a mentor to the great Pablo Neruda. A longtime classroom teacher, in later life she became a pioneer in modernizing public education throughout Latin America. She also served as the Chilean consul in Naples, Madrid, and Lisbon and taught Spanish literature at major colleges and universities in the United States and Puerto Rico. In 1945, Mistral was the first woman in Latin America to be awarded the Nobel Prize in literature for, the Nobel committee said, her "lyric poetry which, inspired by powerful emotions, has made her name a symbol of the idealistic aspirations of the entire Latin American world."

Alice Munro (1931–) Canadian author Alice Munro began writing when she was 12. In a 1984 interview, she said that although she was always an outsider, she "felt able to cope with everything" when she wrote. Munro's one novel and eight collections of stories, mostly set in southwestern Ontario, have won literary awards and have been translated into 13 languages. Sometimes she starts writing from her own experiences, with "a memory, an anecdote, but that gets lost and is usually unrecognizable in the final story." Her work is known for sharp observations about everyday people and situations.

Pablo Neruda (1904–1973) Neftalí Ricardo Reyes Basoalto was born in Chile. He used the pen name Pablo Neruda in memory of Czechoslovakian poet Jan Neruda. Troubled by the Spanish Civil War and the murder of writer Federico García Lorca, Neruda became politically active in Spain. In the 1940s, he returned to Chile, where he was elected senator. Neruda had to flee from his homeland, however, after joining the Communist Party and protesting harsh government policies toward workers. He was able to return to Chile in 1952. Neruda produced a large body of poetry and won the 1971 Nobel Prize in literature. In his acceptance speech he said, "The poet is not a 'little god' . . . the best poet is he who prepares our daily bread . . . kneading the dough, consigning it to the oven, baking it in golden colors and handing [it to us] as a duty of fellowship."

Herberto Padilla (1932–2000) The Cuban poet and novelist was a supporter of the Castro revolution, but later became critical of the Communist government. In 1971, Padilla was accused of treason and jailed. His arrest aroused international protest. A group of intellectuals—including Italo Calvino, Mario Vargas Llosa, Gabriel García Márquez, Alberto Moravia, and Octavio Paz—wrote a letter to Fidel Castro demanding Padilla's release. Thirty-seven days later, Padilla read a public statement of self-criticism and was freed. For the next ten years, he worked in Cuba as a translator of foreign literature. After García Márquez and other writers again appealed to Castro, Padilla was allowed to leave Cuba in 1981. He moved to the United States, where his work published in English includes his memoir, *Self-Portrait of the Other*.

Octavio Paz (1914–1998) Mexican poet, essayist, and literary critic Octavio Paz grew up in a house with a "jungle-like garden and a great room full of books." Paz studied modernist poetry in the United States on a Guggenheim Fellowship. He traveled to France as a member of the Mexican diplomatic service, and was also ambassador to India. However, Paz resigned from diplomatic life when government troops fired on a student protest during the 1968 Olympic Games in Mexico. In addition to his own international experiences, his work reflects pre-Columbian Indian and Spanish Conquistador cultures. His most famous work, *The Labyrinth of Solitude*, is a meditation on Mexican history. In his acceptance speech for the 1990 Nobel Prize in literature, Paz said, "Modernity led me to the source of my beginning . . . . I thus found out that the poet is a pulse in the rhythmic flow of generations."

João Guimarães Rosa (1908–1967) Born in rural Brazil, author João Guimarães Rosa studied medicine and practiced as a physician in the sparsely-populated *sertao* (backcountry) where he grew up. He later became a Brazilian diplomat, serving in several world capitals. Although his short stories are widely respected, his novel, *The Devil to Pay in the Backlands*, is the work that brought him international renown. "The Third Bank of the River," perhaps his most famous short story, is typical of Rosa's work in its "magical realist" blending of fantasy and naturalism, as well as its sertao setting. It shows a variety of influences, ranging from Brazilian oral storytelling to the work of American authors such as Nathaniel Hawthorne and Edgar Allan Poe.

Juan Rulfo (1918–1986) Juan Rulfo was born into a wealthy Mexican family, but the Mexican Revolution (1926–1929) and other uprisings swept away his parents' lives and fortunes. By 1927, Rulfo was an orphan. Educated in religious schools, he later moved to Mexico City, where he wrote two novels, a collection of short stories, and several film scripts. Rulfo's most famous novel, *Pedro Páramo* (1955), is narrated by the dead inhabitants of a mythical village. According to Mexican historian Enrique Krauze, student revolutionaries of the 1960s were "dazzled by the mysterious and magical pages of Juan Rulfo, where the power and weight of authority . . . was carved into images of massive but also crumbling stone." Rulfo's mixture of fantasy with keen observations of the everyday world strongly influenced the development of magic realism.

Samuel Selvon (1923–) Born in Trinidad to East Indian parents, Samuel Selvon is the author of novels, plays, and scripts for film, television, and radio. He served in the Royal Navy Reserve during World War II, after which he began publishing his work in Caribbean magazines. In 1950, Selvon moved to

England, became a freelance writer, and was soon internationally famous. His novels, *A Brighter Sun* and *The Lonely Londoners,* are mostly humorous tales about Caribbean migrants in Britain. Selvon's later novels, *Moses Ascending* (1975) and *Moses Migrating* (1983) express sharp social criticism in a mixture of Trinidad's Creole English and standard English. Selvon moved to Canada in 1978.

Carlos Solórzano (1922–) Playwright and director Carlos Solórzano was born in Guatemala and has made his home in Mexico. He has introduced the Mexican theater to modern European dramatists, including Eugene Ionesco, but his writing also shows a strong Latin American influence. Described as "mythic theater," his plays are sometimes derived from Mexican folk traditions. For example, one of his most famous plays, "The Puppets," was inspired by a Mexican ceremony in which papier-maché effigies of Judas are exploded with firecrackers on Easter Sunday. In addition to writing plays, he has written a novel and edited anthologies of Latin American drama.

Luisa Valenzuela (1938–) Argentine journalist and fiction writer Luisa Valenzuela was born in Buenos Aires, but has spent years in other countries—Spain, Mexico, and the United States—mostly due to political turmoil in her home country. Much of her writing reflects Argentina's strife-torn political and military situations. Her stories are sometimes told with dark humor and a touch of the grotesque. Valenzuela has said, "I think that the separation between what we usually call reality and fiction is more tenuous than we can imagine." Her novels include *Cola de lagartija (*The lizard's tail*)*, and *Novela negra con argentinos (*Black novel with Argentines*)*.

Derek Walcott (1930–) The West Indian poet and playwright Derek Walcott was born in St. Lucia and has spent much of his life in Trinidad. His books of poetry include *The Castaway, The Gulf,* and *Midsummer.* Although he writes in English, Walcott's poetry reflects the rhythms of Caribbean speech. Of Dutch, English, and African ancestry, Walcott has made diversity one of his most important themes and is known to quote sources ranging from Homer to the Beatles. "I am only one-eighth the writer I might have been had I contained all the fragmented languages of Trinidad," he wrote upon receiving the Nobel Prize for literature in 1992.

UNIT TWO

The Literature of Europe

Petra Fiero
Professor of English, Western Washington University, Bellingham, Washington

In the 20th century, Europe was ravaged by two world wars, saw the rise and fall of fascism and communism, and began to live with the threat of the atomic bomb. The impact of these events on all areas of human life, including literature, was enormous.

A movement called modernism emerged in the first decades of the 20th century, its representatives seeking a radical break with traditional Western ideas. After the catastrophe of World War I (1914–18) and the collapse of European monarchies, many writers felt they could no longer describe the world's harsh new realities in the time-honored ways. Modernist literature substitutes the traditional techniques of storytelling with innovations such as stream of consciousness, fragmentation, and unconventional ways of representing characters.

The term "postmodernism" is often applied to literature and art after World War II (1939–45). Influences on literature included the experience of the Holocaust, the rapid development of technology—including nuclear weapons—and the continuing spoilage of the natural environment. These things eroded Western morale even more than the first war had done. Works of postmodern literature blend literary genres and mix the serious with the playful, resisting classification along traditional lines.

The literature of the absurd, one branch of postmodern writing, depicts a world without continuity or meaning. Absurdist writers often use black humor, combining the genres of tragedy and comedy to convey this attitude.

Not all literary works since World War II can be characterized as postmodern. The aim of neorealism, especially prominent in Italy, was to describe the human condition authentically.

Neorealistic works often convey a tragic view of human existence, marked by solitude and alienation.

The 1950s signaled an era of high hopes and deep disappointments. Writers began to attack what they perceived as the materialism, complacency, and shabby values of the middle class. The 1960s saw renewed political and social concern among the young, prompted by the Vietnam War, the emergence of the "third world," and the rise in western democracies of both liberating and reactionary factions. Well into the 1990s, many postwar writers concentrated on their own time period and its conditions. The contemporary European reading public expects writers to confront the problems of society, not sit in the ivory tower of art.

In Eastern Europe, World War II and its aftermath made a deep impact. The euphoria of liberation was soon followed by radical changes in the political and social structure. Communist regimes were established, with the Cold War well under way by mid-century. The Stalinist doctrine of socialist realism demanded uncritical optimism about progress toward a "classless society." These governments insisted that writers create purely positive heroes who were healthy and active, never questioning their roles in society. This constituted a sharp break with earlier literature, in which protagonists were generally male, alienated from society, and unable to find a useful purpose in life. Many Eastern European writers had trouble adhering to this formula and openly resisted it; as a result, their work was censored and suppressed, some were imprisoned, and others were sent into exile.

Mikhail Gorbachev, president of the former Soviet Union, introduced the policies of *glasnost* (openness) and *perestroika* (reconstruction) in the early '90s, freeing up the communist societies of Eastern Europe and leading to the demise of Soviet-style communism. Previously suppressed books and new works of long-silenced authors could now be published. The end of the Cold War in the late 1980s brought Eastern and Western European countries much closer together. In the larger picture, how an increasingly global economy and the threat of worldwide terrorism will affect Europe remains to be seen. What is certain is that human tragedy and comedy will continue to shape European literature.

The Literature of Europe

Literary Map of Europe

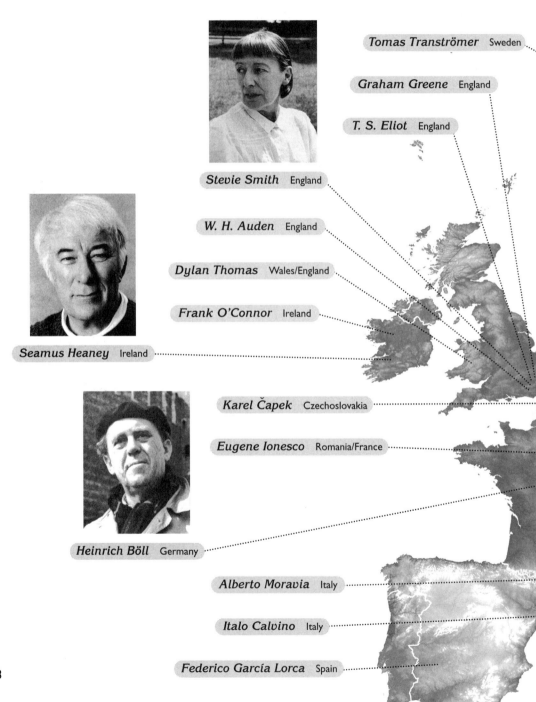

Tomas Tranströmer   Sweden

Graham Greene   England

T. S. Eliot   England

Stevie Smith   England

W. H. Auden   England

Dylan Thomas   Wales/England

Frank O'Connor   Ireland

Seamus Heaney   Ireland

Karel Čapek   Czechoslovakia

Eugene Ionesco   Romania/France

Heinrich Böll   Germany

Alberto Moravia   Italy

Italo Calvino   Italy

Federico García Lorca   Spain

Andre Voznesensky Russia

Fazil Iskander Republic of Abkhazia/Russia

Czeslaw Milosz Poland/United States

Wislawa Szymborska Poland

Boris Pasternak Russia

SCANDINAVIA

WESTERN EUROPE

EASTERN EUROPE

RUSSIA

First Confession[1]

Frank O'Connor

"First Confession" blends family politics with religion, two topics of considerable interest to the Irish.

About 95 percent of citizens in the Irish Republic are baptized Catholic. After centuries of Protestant British rule, the Catholic church came to be a powerful source of Irish national identity. It also offered spiritual comfort to a country downtrodden by colonialism and crushing poverty. To this day, Catholic ceremonies such as first confession and first Communion are considered major events in Irish Catholic families. Even the poorest families often manage to afford the fancy white dresses customary for a girl's first Communion.

All the trouble began when my grandfather died and my grandmother—my father's mother—came to live with us. Relations in the one house are a strain at the best of times, but, to make matters worse, my grandmother was a real old country woman and quite unsuited to the life in town. She had a fat, wrinkled old face, and, to Mother's great indignation, went round the house in bare feet—the boots had her crippled, she said. For dinner she had a jug of porter[2] and a pot of potatoes with—sometimes—a bit of salt fish, and she poured out the potatoes on the table and ate them slowly, with great relish, using her fingers by way of a fork.

Now, girls are supposed to be **fastidious**, but I was the one who suffered most from this. Nora, my sister, just sucked up to the old woman for the penny she got every Friday out of the old-age pension, a thing I could not do. I was too honest, that was my

fastidious
dainty; squeamish

---

1 **confession:** one of the Roman Catholic sacraments that requires church members to confess their sins to a priest and ask for forgiveness from God

2 **porter:** a heavy malt beer

trouble; and when I was playing with Bill Connell, the sergeant-major's son, and saw my grandmother steering up the path with a jug of porter sticking out from beneath her shawl I was **mortified**. I made excuses not to let him come into the house, because I could never be sure what she would be up to when we went in.

When Mother was at work and my grandmother made the dinner I wouldn't touch it. Nora once tried to make me, but I hid under the table from her and took the bread-knife with me for protection. Nora let on to be very indignant (she wasn't, of course, but she knew Mother saw through her, so she sided with Gran) and came after me. I lashed out at her with the bread-knife, and after that she left me alone. I stayed there till Mother came in from work and made my dinner, but when Father came in later Nora said in a shocked voice: "Oh, Dadda, do you know what Jackie did at dinnertime?" Then, of course, it all came out; Father gave me a flaking; Mother interfered, and for days after that he didn't speak to me and Mother barely spoke to Nora. And all because of that old woman! God knows, I was heart-scalded.

Then, to crown my misfortunes, I had to make my first confession and Communion.[3] It was an old woman called Ryan who prepared us for these. She was about the one age with Gran; she was well-to-do, lived in a big house on Montenotte, wore a black cloak and bonnet, and came every day to school at three o'clock when we should have been going home, and talked to us of Hell. She may have mentioned the other place as well, but that could only have been by accident, for Hell had the first place in her heart.

She lit a candle, took out a new half-crown, and offered it to the first boy who would hold one finger—only one finger!—in the flame for five minutes by the school clock. Being always very ambitious I was tempted to volunteer, but I thought it might look greedy. Then she asked were we afraid of holding one finger—only one finger!—in a little candle flame for five minutes and not afraid of burning all over in roasting hot furnaces for all eternity. "All eternity! Just think of that! A whole lifetime goes by and it's nothing, not even a drop in the ocean of your sufferings." The

---

3 **Communion:** the Christian sacrament that involves receiving bread and wine, which symbolizes the body and blood of Christ

woman was really interesting about Hell, but my attention was all fixed on the half-crown. At the end of the lesson she put it back in her purse. It was a great disappointment; a religious woman like that, you wouldn't think she'd bother about a thing like a half-crown.

Another day she said she knew a priest who woke one night to find a fellow he didn't recognize leaning over the end of his bed. The priest was a bit frightened—naturally enough—but he asked the fellow what he wanted, and the fellow said in a deep, husky voice that he wanted to go to Confession. The priest said it was an awkward time and wouldn't it do in the morning, but the fellow said that last time he went to Confession, there was one sin he kept back, being ashamed to mention it, and now it was always on his mind. Then the priest knew it was a bad case, because the fellow was after making a bad confession and committing a mortal sin. He got up to dress, and just then the cock crew in the yard outside, and—lo and behold!—when the priest looked round there was no sign of the fellow, only a smell of burning timber, and when the priest looked at his bed didn't he see the print of two hands burned in it? That was because the fellow had made a bad confession. This story made a shocking impression on me.

But the worst of all was when she showed us how to examine our conscience. Did we take the name of the Lord, our God, in vain? Did we honor our father and our mother? (I asked her did this include grandmothers and she said it did.) Did we love our neighbor as ourselves? Did we **covet** our neighbor's goods? (I thought of the way I felt about the penny that Nora got every Friday.) I decided that, between one thing and another, I must

covet
want; desire what belongs to another

have broken the whole ten commandments, all on account of that old woman, and so far as I could see, so long as she remained in the house I had no hope of ever doing anything else.

I was scared to death of Confession. The day the whole class went I let on to have a toothache, hoping my absence wouldn't be noticed; but at three o'clock, just as I was feeling safe, along comes a chap with a message from Mrs. Ryan that I was to go to Confession myself on Saturday and be at the chapel for Communion with the rest. To make it worse, Mother couldn't come with me and sent Nora instead.

Now, that girl had ways of tormenting me that Mother never knew of. She held my hand as we went down the hill, smiling sadly and saying how sorry she was for me, as if she were bringing me to the hospital for an operation.

"Oh, God help us!" she moaned. "Isn't it a terrible pity you weren't a good boy? Oh, Jackie, my heart bleeds for you! How will you ever think of all your sins? Don't forget you have to tell him about the time you kicked Gran on the shin."

"Lemme go!" I said, trying to drag myself free of her. "I don't want to go to Confession at all."

"But sure, you'll have to go to Confession, Jackie," she replied in the same regretful tone. "Sure, if you didn't, the parish priest would be up to the house, looking for you. 'Tisn't, God knows, that I'm not sorry for you. Do you remember the time you tried to kill me with the bread-knife under the table? And the language you used to me? I don't know what he'll do with you at all, Jackie. He might have to send you up to the Bishop.[4]

I remember thinking bitterly that she didn't know the half of what I had to tell—if I told it. I knew I couldn't tell it, and understood perfectly why the fellow in Mrs. Ryan's story made a bad confession; it seemed to me a great shame that people wouldn't stop criticizing him. I remember that steep hill down to the church, and the sunlit hillsides beyond the valley of the river, which I saw in the gaps between the houses like Adam's last glimpse of Paradise.

Then, when she had manoeuvered me down the long flight of steps to the chapel yard, Nora suddenly changed her tone. She

---

4 **Bishop:** one of the highest-ranking members of the Roman Catholic church

became the raging malicious devil she really was.

"There you are!" she said with a yelp of triumph, hurling me through the church door. "And I hope he'll give you the penitential psalms,[5] you dirty little caffler."[6]

I knew then I was lost, given up to eternal justice. The door with the colored-glass panels swung shut behind me, the sunlight went out and gave place to deep shadow, and the wind whistled outside so that the silence within seemed to crackle like ice under my feet. Nora sat in front of me by the confession box. There were a couple of old women ahead of her, and then a miserable-looking poor devil came and wedged me in at the other side, so that I couldn't escape even if I had the courage. He joined his hands and rolled his eyes in the direction of the roof, muttering aspirations[7] in an anguished tone, and I wondered had he a grandmother too. Only a grandmother could account for a fellow behaving in that heartbroken way, but he was better off than I, for he at least could go and confess his sins; while I would make a bad confession and then die in the night and be continually coming back and burning people's furniture.

Nora's turn came, and I heard the sound of something slamming, and then her voice as if butter wouldn't melt in her mouth, and then another slam, and out she came. God, the hypocrisy of women! Her eyes were lowered, her head was bowed, and her hands were joined very low down on her stromach, and she walked up the aisle to the side altar looking like a saint. You never saw such an exhibition of devotion; and I remembered the devilish malice with which she had tormented me all the way from our door, and wondered were all religious people like that, really. It was my turn now. With the fear of damnation in my soul I went in, and the confessional door closed of itself behind me.

It was pitch-dark and I couldn't see priest or anything else. Then I really began to be frightened. In the darkness it was a matter between God and me, and He had all the odds. He knew what my intentions were before I even started; I had no chance.

---

5 **penitential psalms:** verses from the Biblical book of Psalms about seeking the Lord's forgiveness

6 **caffler:** Irish slang term for "idiot"

7 **aspirations:** short prayers

All I had ever been told about Confession got mixed up in my mind, and I knelt to one wall and said: "Bless me, father, for I have sinned; this is my first confession." I waited for a few minutes, but nothing happened, so I tried it on the other wall.

"Bless me, father, for I have sinned; this is my first confession."

Nothing happened there either. He had me spotted all right.

It must have been then that I noticed the shelf at about one height with my head. It was really a place for grown-up people to rest their elbows, but in my distracted state I thought it was probably the place you were supposed to kneel. Of course, it was on the high side and not very deep, but I was always good at climbing and managed to get up all right. Staying up was the trouble. There was room only for my knees, and nothing you could get a grip on but a sort of wooden molding a bit above it. I held on to the molding and repeated the words a little louder, and this time something happened all right. A slide was slammed back; a little light entered the box, and a man's voice said: "Who's there?"

"'Tis me, father," I said for fear he mightn't see me and go away again. I couldn't see him at all. The place the voice came from was under the molding, about level with my knees, so I took a good grip of the molding and swung myself down till I saw the astonished face of a young priest looking up at me. He had to put his head on one side to see me, and I had to put mine on one side to see him, so we were more or less talking to one another upside-down. It struck me as a queer way of hearing confessions, but I didn't feel it my place to criticize.

"Bless me, father, for I have sinned; this is my first confession," I rattled off all in one breath, and swung myself down the least shade more to make it easier for him.

"What are you doing up there?" he shouted in an angry voice, and the strain the politeness was putting on my hold of the molding, and the shock of being addressed in such an uncivil tone, were too much for me. I lost my grip, tumbled, and hit the door an unmerciful wallop before I found myself flat on my back in the middle of the aisle. The people who had been waiting stood up with their mouths open. The priest opened the door of the middle box and came out, pushing his biretta back from his forehead; he looked something terrible. Then Nora came scampering down the aisle.

"Oh, you dirty little caffler!" she said. "I might have known you'd do it. I might have known you'd disgrace me. I can't leave you out of my sight for one minute."

Before I could even get to my feet to defend myself she bent down and gave me a clip across the ear. This reminded me that I was so stunned I had even forgotten to cry, so that people might think I wasn't hurt at all, when in fact I was probably maimed for life. I gave a roar out of me.

"What's all this about?" the priest hissed, getting angrier than ever and pushing Nora off me. "How dare you hit the child like that, you little **vixen**?"

"But I can't do my penance with him, father," Nora cried, cocking an outraged eye up at him.

"Well, go and do it, or I'll give you some more to do," he said, giving me a hand up. "Was it coming to Confession you were, my poor man?" he asked me.

"'Twas, father," said I with a sob.

"Oh," he said respectfully, "a big hefty fellow like you must have terrible sins. Is this your first?"

"'Tis, father," said I.

"Worse and worse," he said gloomily. "The crimes of a lifetime. I don't know will I get rid of you at all today. You'd better wait now till I'm finished with these old ones. You can see by the looks of them they haven't much to tell."

"I will, father," I said with something approaching joy.

The relief of it was really enormous. Nora stuck out her tongue at me from behind his back, but I couldn't even be bothered retorting. I knew from the very moment that man opened his mouth that he was intelligent above the ordinary. When I had time to think, I saw how right I was. It only stood to reason that a fellow confessing after seven years would have more to tell than people that went every week. The crimes of a lifetime, exactly as he said. It was only what he expected, and the rest was a cackle of old women and girls with their talk of Hell, the Bishop, and the penitential psalms. That was all they knew. I started to make my examination of conscience, and barring the one bad business of my grandmother it didn't seem so bad.

The next time, the priest steered me into the confession box himself and left the shutter back the way I could see him get in and sit down at the further side of the grille from me.

"Well, now," he said, "what do they call you?"

"Jackie, father," said I.

"And what's a-trouble to you, Jackie?"

"Father," I said, feeling I might as well get it over while I had him in good humor, "I had it all arranged to kill my grandmother."

He seemed a bit shaken by that, all right, because he said nothing for quite a while.

"My goodness," he said at last, "that'd be a shocking thing to do. What put that into your head?"

"Father," I said, feeling very sorry for myself, "she's an awful woman."

"Is she?" he asked. "What way is she awful?"

"She takes porter, father," I said, knowing well from the way Mother talked of it that this was a mortal sin, and hoping it would make the priest take a more favorable view of my case.

"Oh, my!" he said, and I could see he was impressed.

"And snuff, father," said I.

"That's a bad case, sure enough, Jackie," he said.

"And she goes round in her bare feet, father," I went on in a rush of self-pity, "and she knows I don't like her, and she gives pennies to Nora and none to me, and my da sides with her and flakes me, and one night I was so heart-scalded I made up my mind I'd have to kill her."

"And what would you do with the body?" he asked with great interest.

"I was thinking I could chop that up and carry it away in a barrow I have," I said.

"Begor,[8] Jackie," he said, "do you know you're a terrible child?"

"I know, father," I said, for I was just thinking the same thing myself. "I tried to kill Nora too with a bread-knife under the table, only I missed her."

---

8 **Begor:** short for "begorrah," an Irish oath that stands for "by God"

"Is that the little girl that was beating you just now?" he asked.

"'Tis, father."

cryptically
obscurely; mysteriously

"Someone will go for her with a bread-knife one day, and he won't miss her," he said rather **cryptically**. "You must have great courage. Between ourselves, there's a lot of people I'd like to do the same to but I'd never have the nerve. Hanging is an awful death."

"Is it, father?" I asked with the deepest interest—I was always very keen on[9] hanging. "Did you ever see a fellow hanged?"

"Dozens of them," he said solemnly. "And they all died roaring."

"Jay!" I said.

"Oh, a horrible death!" he said with great satisfaction. "Lots of the fellows I saw killed their grandmothers too, but they all said 'twas never worth it."

He had me there for a full ten minutes talking, and then walked out of the chapel yard with me. I was genuinely sorry to part with him, because he was the most interesting character I'd ever met in the religious line. Outside, after the shadow of the church, the sunlight was like a roaring of waves on a beach; it dazzled me; and when the frozen silence melted and I heard the screech of trams on the road my heart soared. I knew now I wouldn't die in the night and come back, leaving marks on my mother's furniture. It would be a great worry to her, and the poor soul had enough.

Nora was sitting on the railing, waiting for me, and she put on a very sour puss when she saw the priest with me. She was mad jealous because a priest had never come out of the church with her.

"Well," she asked coldly, after he left me, "what did he give you?"

"Three Hail Marys,"[10] I said.

incredulously
skeptically; unbelievingly

"Three Hail Marys," she repeated **incredulously**. "You mustn't have told him anything."

"I told him everything," I said confidently.

"About Gran and all?"

"About Gran and all."

---

9 **keen on:** interested in

10 **Hail Marys:** Catholic prayers devoted to Mary, mother of Jesus

(All she wanted was to able to go home and say I'd made a bad confession.)

"Did you tell him you went for me with a bread-knife?" she asked with a frown.

"I did to be sure."

"And he only gave you three Hail Marys?"

"That's all."

She slowly got down from the railing with a baffled air. Clearly, this was beyond her. As we mounted the steps back to the main road she looked at me suspiciously.

"What are you sucking?" she asked.

"Bullseyes."[11]

"Was it the priest gave them to you?"

"'Twas."

"Lord God," she wailed bitterly, "some people have all the luck! 'Tis no advantage to anybody trying to be good. I might just as well be a sinner like you."

Responding to the Selection

1. How does this story convey the importance of the Catholic faith to the Irish?

2. The voice of the narrator in "First Confession" is especially vivid. Use adjectives and details from the story to help you sum up his character.

3. Family life is full of potential conflict, and many Irish writers turn that conflict into humor. If you remove the humor from "First Confession," what different story emerges? (Clue: look at every point in the story where there is conflict and show how the writer chooses to portray it in a humorous light.)

4. Frank O'Connor is considered one of Ireland's finest short story writers, and "First Confession" is thought to be one of his best stories. Name some of the elements of this story that may have made it so enduringly popular.

---

11 **Bullseyes:** a kind of hard candy

from Clearances

Seamus Heaney

WORLD LENS

♦♦♦

IRELAND

Seamus Heaney's poem is very Irish in its warm remembrance of the poet's mother. In Irish culture the mother is the binding emotional force in a family, appreciated for her selflessness and strength. Another recurring national image here is the potato, a great staple of the Irish diet. The potato crops' failure in the 1840s spelled disaster for Ireland. During the famine called the Great Hunger, over one million Irish died from starvation or disease, and millions more emigrated.

When all the others were away at Mass
I was all hers as we peeled potatoes.
They broke the silence, let fall one by one
Like solder weeping off the soldering iron:[1]
Cold comforts set between us, things to share
Gleaming in a bucket of clean water.
And again let fall. Little pleasant splashes
From each other's work would bring us to our senses.

So while the parish priest at her bedside
Went hammer and tongs at the prayers for the dying
And some were responding and some crying
I remembered her head bent towards my head,
Her breath in mine, our fluent dipping knives—
Never closer the whole rest of our lives.

---

1 **solder . . . soldering iron:** the substance and tool used to fuse metals

Responding to the Selection

1. In this poem, there is more than one meaning to such phrases as "bring us to our senses" and "cold comfort." What do you think the poet intends these phrases to mean?

2. The potato is an important symbol in Ireland because of its value as a food staple and reminder of the terrible potato famine in the 19th century. What personal symbolic value does it have in this poem?

3. Instead of *telling* us how important it was to peel potatoes with his mother, the poet *shows* us using vivid images, or word pictures. Name the images in the poem that you think are most powerful.

4. What is implied about the parish priest?

5. How does this poem benefit by portraying the poet and his mother in action?

from Clearances

Do Not Go Gentle into That Good Night

Dylan Thomas

WORLD LENS

◆◆◆

WALES/ENGLAND

Dylan Thomas's themes—birth, sex, and death—his exuberant language, and mix of surrealistic and realistic images made him an important force in 20th century poetry. "Do Not Go Gentle into That Good Night" was written during the final illness of the Welsh poet's father. It famously exemplifies the poet's "personal religion"—a joy and rage for life.

Do not go gentle into that good night,
Old age should burn and rave at close of day;
Rage, rage against the dying of the light.

Though wise men at their end know dark is right,
Because their words had forked no lightning they
Do not go gentle into that good night.

Good men, the last wave by, crying how bright
Their frail deeds might have danced in a green bay,
Rage, rage against the dying of the light.

Wild men who caught and sang the sun in flight,
And learn, too late, they grieved it on its way,
Do not go gentle into that good night.

Grave men, near death, who see with blinding sight
Blind eyes could blaze like meteors and be gay,
Rage, rage against the dying of the light.

And you, my father, there on the sad height,
Curse, bless, me now with your fierce tears, I pray.
Do not go gentle into that good night.
Rage, rage against the dying of the light.

Responding to the Selection

1. Lyric poetry is verse that conveys the poet's feelings, often in a way that is musically expressive. Unlike epic poetry, it does not tell a story explicitly. Find a line or phrase, other than the refrains, that captures for you the emotions of someone losing his father or that seem to have a musical quality.

2. Thomas appears to have been fond of the metaphor of "light." He once said, "My poetry is the record of my individual struggle from darkness towards some measure of light." How is light used metaphorically in this poem?

3. What do you think is meant by the phrase in line 5: "Because their words had forked no lightning . . ."?

4. What lessons does the poet try to impart to all the "men" invoked in this poem?

Do Not Go Gentle into That Good Night

Not Waving but Drowning

Stevie Smith

ENGLAND

Nobody heard him, the dead man,
But still he lay moaning:
I was much further out than you thought
And not waving but drowning.

Poor chap, he always loved larking[1]
And now he's dead
It must have been too cold for him his heart gave way,
They said.

Oh, no no no, it was too cold always
(Still the dead one lay moaning)
I was much too far out all my life
And not waving but drowning.

Responding to the Selection

1. Who is talking in this poem? Explain the possible effect of the switches in point of view.

2. Have you ever heard of some other gesture or action being misinterpreted with such a calamitous effect? Explain.

3. British writers are known for their irony and sense of the macabre. In what ways is this poem a good example of these types of expression?

4. Smith claimed not to know "whether other people find Death as merry" as she did. What about this poem, in tone and wording, shows her attitude about death?

---

1 **larking:** frolicking

The Love Song of J. Alfred Prufrock

T. S. Eliot

WORLD LENS

◆◆◆

ENGLAND

Nobel laureate T. S. Eliot is credited with propelling English poetry into the 20th century. The poet substituted the "poetic-sounding" language of earlier poetry with the free verse pioneered by French and Italian poets. Eliot approximated the sound of educated, but natural speech, and replaced abstractions with sensory imagery. Nevertheless, his poetry is intellectual and full of references to classical literature and history.

Critics believe the anxiety and moodiness of "The Love Song of J. Alfred Prufrock" is characteristic of the 20th century state of mind. The speaker's inclusion of the passage from Dante's *Inferno* lends weight to his claim that he is in hell.

S'io credesse che mia risposta fosse
a persona che mai tornasse al mondo,
questa fiamma staria senza piu scosse.
Ma per ciò che giammai di questo fondo
non tornò vivo alcun, s'i' odo il vero,
senza tema d'infamia ti rispondo.[1]

Let us go then, you and I,
When the evening is spread out against the sky

---

1 ***S'io . . . rispondo:*** An excerpt from Dante's *Inferno* (Canto 27, lines 61–66):
  If I thought my answer were given
  to anyone who would ever return to the world,
  this flame would stand still without moving any further.
  But since never from this abyss
  has anyone ever returned alive, if what I hear is true,
  without fear of infamy I answer thee.

Like a patient etherised[2] upon a table;
Let us go, through certain half-deserted streets,
The muttering retreats
Of restless nights in one-night cheap hotels
And sawdust restaurants with oyster-shells:
Streets that follow like a tedious argument
Of insidious intent
To lead you to an overwhelming question . . .
Oh, do not ask, "What is it?"
Let us go and make our visit.

In the room the women come and go
Talking of Michelangelo.[3]

The yellow fog that rubs its back upon the window-panes,
The yellow smoke that rubs its muzzle on the window-panes
Licked its tongue into the corners of the evening,
Lingered upon the pools that stand in drains,
Let fall upon its back the soot that falls from chimneys,
Slipped by the terrace, made a sudden leap,
And seeing that it was a soft October night,
Curled once about the house, and fell asleep.

And indeed there will be time
For the yellow smoke that slides along the street
Rubbing its back upon the window-panes;
There will be time, there will be time
To prepare a face to meet the faces that you meet;
There will be time to murder and create,
And time for all the works and days of hands
That lift and drop a question on your plate;
Time for you and time for me,
And time yet for a hundred indecisions
And for a hundred visions and revisions,
Before the taking of a toast and tea.

---

2 **etherised:** anaesthetized

3 **Michelangelo:** (1475–1564), Michelangelo Buonarroti, the famous Italian architect,
   artist, and sculptor, renowned especially for his painting of the Sistine Chapel in the
   Vatican

In the room the women come and go
Talking of Michelangelo.

And indeed there will be time
To wonder, "Do I dare?" and, "Do I dare?"
Time to turn back and descend the stair,
With a bald spot in the middle of my hair—
(They will say: "How his hair is growing thin!")
My morning coat, my collar mounting firmly to the chin,
My necktie rich and modest, but asserted by a simple pin—
(They will say: "But how his arms and legs are thin!")
Do I dare
Disturb the universe?
In a minute there is time
For decisions and revisions which a minute will reverse.

For I have known them all already, known them all—
Have known the evenings, mornings, afternoons,
I have measured out my life with coffee spoons;
I know the voices dying with a dying fall
Beneath the music from a farther room.
      So how should I presume?

And I have known the eyes already, known them all—
The eyes that fix you in a formulated phrase,
And when I am formulated, sprawling on a pin,
When I am pinned and wriggling on the wall,
Then how should I begin
To spit out all the butt-ends of my days and ways?
      And how should I presume?

And I have known the arms already, know them all—
Arms that are braceleted and white and bare
(But in the lamplight, downed with light brown hair!)
Is it perfume from a dress
That makes me so digress?
Arms that lie along a table, or wrap about a shawl.
      And should I then presume?
      And how should I begin?

The Love Song of J. Alfred Prufrock   157

♦ ♦ ♦ ♦

Shall I say, I have gone at dusk through narrow streets
And watched the smoke that rises from the pipes
Of lonely men in shirt-sleeves, leaning out of windows? . . .

I should have been a pair of ragged claws
Scuttling across the floors of silent seas.

♦ ♦ ♦ ♦

And the afternoon, the evening, sleeps so peacefully!
Smoothed by long fingers,
Asleep . . . tired . . . or it malingers,
Stretched on the floor, here beside you and me.
Should I, after tea and cakes and ices,
Have the strength to force the moment to its crisis?
But though I have wept and fasted, wept and prayed,
Though I have seen my head (grown slightly bald) brought in
    upon a platter,
I am no prophet—and here's no great matter;
I have seen the moment of my greatness flicker,
And I have seen the eternal Footman hold my coat, and snicker
And in short, I was afraid.

And would it have been worth it, after all,
After the cups, the marmalade, the tea,
Among the porcelain, among some talk of you and me,
Would it have been worth while,
To have bitten off the matter with a smile,
To have squeezed the universe into a ball
To roll it towards some overwhelming question,
To say: "I am Lazarus,[4] come from the dead,
Come back to tell you all, I shall tell you all"—
If one, settling a pillow by her head,
    Should say: "That is not what I meant at all.
    That is not it, at all."

---

4 **Lazarus:** in the Bible, he is resurrected from the dead by Jesus

And would it have been worth it, after all,
Would it have been worth while,
After the sunsets and the dooryards and
    the sprinkled streets,
After the novels, after the teacups, after
    the skirts that trail along the floor—
And this, and so much more?—
It is impossible to say just what I mean!
But as if a magic lantern threw the nerves
    in patterns on a screen:
Would it have been worth while
If one, settling a pillow or throwing off
    a shawl,
And turning toward the window, should
    say:
    "That is not it at all,
    That is not what I meant, at all."

★★★★★

No! I am not Prince Hamlet,[5] nor was
    meant to be;
Am an attendant lord, one that will do
To swell a progress, start a scene or two,
Advise the prince; no doubt, an easy tool,
Deferential, glad to be of use,
Politic, cautious, and meticulous;
Full of high sentence, but a bit obtuse;
At times, indeed, almost ridiculous—
Almost, at times, the Fool.

I grow old . . . I grow old . . .
I shall wear the bottoms of my trousers rolled.

Shall I part my hair behind? Do I dare to eat a peach?
I shall wear white flannel trousers, and walk upon the beach.
I have heard the mermaids singing, each to each.

THE NARCISSISTIC MAN, Marc Chagall, 1976

---

5 **Prince Hamlet:** the young royal from Shakespeare's play of the same name

The Love Song of J. Alfred Prufrock

I do not think that they will sing to me.

I have seen them riding seaward on the waves
Combing the white hair of the waves blown back
When the wind blows the water white and black.

We have lingered in the chambers of the sea
By sea-girls wreathed with seaweed red and brown
Till human voices wake us, and we drown.

Responding to the Selection

1. This is one of the most famous poems of the 20th century. Name one element that you feel makes it memorable.

2. Notice all the references to time in the poem ("I have measured out my life in coffee spoons"). How do these references contribute to the poem's theme?

3. If this is a love song, as the title claims, where is the evidence of that?

4. Notice how many stanzas begin with a simple conjunction, such as the words "and" or "for." What do you think the poet gains from this repetition?

5. This poem is replete with vivid, concrete images. Draw a picture of some image that has caught your eye and explain what you like about it.

from Ten Songs

W. H. Auden

In his writing, W. H. Auden addressed head-on the political and cultural crises of the 20th century. The British writer believed that in times of poverty, political extremism can flourish. In his day, Italy and Germany fell under Hitler's spell not only because of hatred for minorities and Jews, but because of the economic depression which followed World War I. In the 1930s, many people—especially the wealthy—saw Hitler's fascism as an antidote to the spread of communism.

WORLD LENS

◆ ◆ ◆

ENGLAND

I
Say this city has ten million souls,
Some are living in mansions, some are living in holes:
Yet there's no place for us, my dear, yet there's no place for us.

Once we had a country and we thought it fair,
Look in the atlas and you'll find it there:
We cannot go there now, my dear, we cannot go there now.

In the village churchyard there grows an old yew,
Every spring it blossoms anew:
Old passports can't do that, my dear, old passports can't do that.

The consul banged that table and said:
"If you've got no passport you're officially dead":
But we are still alive, my dear, but we are still alive.

Went to a committee; they offered me a chair;
Asked me politely to return next year:
But where shall we go to-day, my dear, but where shall we go to-day?

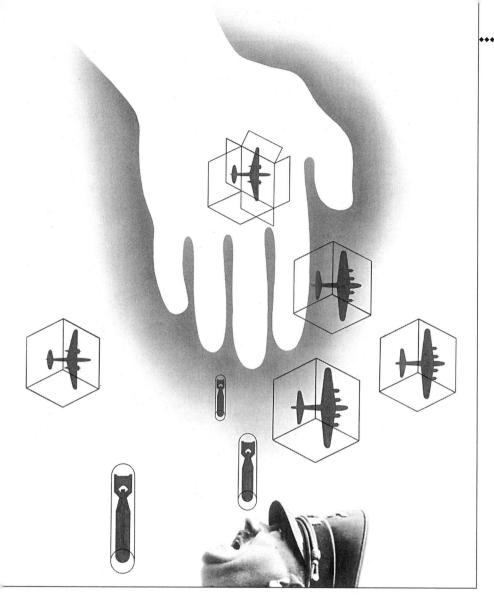

GIFT PACKAGES
FOR HITLER
Jean Carlu
1942

Came to a public meeting; the speaker got up and said:
"If we let them in, they will steal our daily bread";
He was talking of you and me, my dear, he was talking of you and me.

Thought I heard the thunder rumbling in the sky;
It was Hitler over Europe, saying: "They must die";
We were in his mind, my dear, we were in his mind.

Saw a poodle in a jacket fastened with a pin,
Saw a door opened and a cat let in:
But they weren't German Jews, my dear, but they weren't German Jews.

Went down to the harbour and stood upon the quay,[1]
Saw the fish swimming as if they were free:
Only ten feet away, my dear, only ten feet away.

Walked through a wood, saw the birds in the trees;
They had no politicians and sang at their ease:
They weren't the human race, my dear, they weren't the human race.

Dreamed I saw a building with a thousand floors,
A thousand windows and a thousand doors;
Not one of them was ours, my dear, not one of them was ours.

Stood on a great plain in the falling snow;
Ten thousand soldiers marched to and fro:
Looking for you and me, my dear, looking for you and me.

Responding to the Selection

1. Describe the speaker and his situation, giving evidence from the poem to support your opinion.

2. What do you think the phrase "thunder rumbling in the sky" refers to?

3. There are several images and actions in this poem. Find a few examples. How does it affect the poem to have so many verbs of action and be so busy with events and anecdotes?

4. Why do you think the poet has chosen to rhyme the first and second lines of most stanzas but not the third?

---

1 **quay:** a walk or landing structure next to water

The Destructors

Graham Greene

WORLD LENS

•••

ENGLAND

Popular as well as critically acclaimed, the English writer Graham Greene is known for his moral and psychological complexity. Like his fellow Europeans in mid-20th century, he had to contend with the effects of World War II. The *blitzkrieg* (German for "lightning war") took its toll on everyday British citizens—their landscape, health, and psyches. In his fiction, Greene often examined the moral chaos and bewilderment that emanate from war, deprivation, and lost opportunities such as education. Among literary critics, the urban wastelands of stories such as "The Destructors" even have a name: "Greeneland." In such settings, Greene said, "Human nature is not black and white, but black and grey."

It was on the eve of August Bank Holiday that the latest recruit became the leader of the Wormsley Common Gang. No one was surprised except Mike, but Mike at the age of nine was surprised by everything. "If you don't shut your mouth," somebody once said to him, "you'll get a frog down it." After that Mike kept his teeth tightly clamped except when the surprise was too great.

The new recruit had been with the gang since the beginning of the summer holidays, and there were possibilities about his brooding silence that all recognized. He never wasted a word even to tell his name until that was required of him by the rules. When he said "Trevor" it was statement of fact, not as it would have been with the others a statement of shame or defiance. Nor did anyone laugh except Mike, who finding himself without support and meeting the dark gaze of the newcomer opened his mouth and was quiet again. There was every reason why T, as he was afterwards referred to, should have been an object of mockery— there was his name (and they substituted the initial because otherwise they had no excuse not to laugh at it), the fact that his father, a former architect and present clerk, had "come down in the world" and that his mother considered herself better than the neighbours. What but an odd quality of danger, of the unpredictable, established him in the gang without any **ignoble** ceremony of initiation?

The gang met every morning in an **impromptu** car-park, the site of the last bomb of the first blitz.[1] The leader, who was known as Blackie, claimed to have heard it fall, and no one was precise enough in his dates to point out that he would have been one year old and fast asleep on the down platform of Wormsley Common[2] Underground Station.[3] On one side of the car-park leant the first occupied house, No. 3, of the shattered Northwood Terrace—literally leant, for it had suffered from the blast of the bomb and the side walls were supported on wooden struts.[4] A smaller bomb and **incendiaries** had fallen beyond, so that the house stuck up like a jagged tooth and carried on the further wall relics of its neighbour, a dado,[5] the remains of a fireplace. T, whose words were almost confined to voting "Yes" or "No" to the plan of operations proposed each day by Blackie, once startled the whole gang by saying broodingly, "Wren[6] built that house, father says."

"Who's Wren?"

"The man who built St. Paul's."[7]

"Who cares?" Blackie said. "It's only Old Misery's."

Old Misery—whose real name was Thomas—had once been a builder and decorator. He lived alone in the crippled house, doing for himself: once a week you could see him coming back across the common with bread and vegetables, and once as the boys played in the car-park he put his head over the smashed wall

ignoble
dishonorable; degrading

impromptu
improvised; extemporaneous

incendiaries
bombs designed to cause fires

---

1 **first blitz:** the first German air bombardment of London in World War II

2 **common:** a municipal park or square

3 **Underground Station:** London's subway system

4 **struts:** structural supports

5 **dado:** part of a building column

6 **Wren:** Sir Christopher Wren (1632–1723), one of the most famous English architects, particularly known for the churches he designed

7 **St. Paul's:** the London cathedral designed by Wren, which survived the German blitz in World War II

of his garden[8] and looked at them.

"Been to the lav,"[9] one of the boys said, for it was common knowledge that since the bombs fell something had gone wrong with the pipes of the house and Old Misery was too mean to spend money on the property. He could do the redecorating himself at cost price, but he had never learnt plumbing. The lav was a wooden shed at the bottom of the narrow garden with a star-shaped hole in the door: it had escaped the blast which had smashed the house next door and sucked out the window-frames of No. 3.

The next time the gang became aware of Mr. Thomas was more surprising. Blackie, Mike and a thin yellow boy, who for some reason was called by his surname Summers, met him on the common coming back from the market. Mr. Thomas stopped them. He said glumly, "You belong to the lot that play in the car-park?"

Mike was about to answer when Blackie stopped him. As the leader he had responsibilities. "Suppose we are?" he said **ambiguously**.

ambiguously
obscurely; unclearly

"I got some chocolates," Mr. Thomas said. "Don't like 'em myself. Here you are. Not enough to go round, I don't suppose. There never is," he added with sombre conviction. He handed over three packets of Smarties.

The gang was puzzled and perturbed by this action and tried to explain it away. "Bet someone dropped them and he picked 'em up," somebody suggested.

"Pinched[10] 'em and then got in a bleeding funk,"[11] another thought aloud.

"It's a bribe," Summers said. "He wants us to stop bouncing balls on his wall."

"We'll show him we don't take bribes," Blackie said, and they sacrificed the whole morning to the game of bouncing that only Mike was young enough to enjoy. There was no sign from Mr. Thomas.

---

8 **garden:** the British term for "yard"

9 **lav:** short for lavatory, the British term for "bathroom"

10 **pinched:** British slang for "stole"

11 **bleeding funk:** British slang for "worried state"

Next day T astonished them all. He was late at the **rendezvous**, and the voting for that day's exploit took place without him. At Blackie's suggestion the gang was to disperse in pairs, take buses at random and see how many free rides could be snatched from unwary conductors (the operation was to be carried out in pairs to avoid cheating). They were drawing lots for their companions when T arrived.

rendezvous
meeting; appointment

"Where you been, T?" Blackie asked. "You can't vote now. You know the rules."

"I've been *there*," T said. He looked at the ground, as though he had thoughts to hide.

"Where?"

"At Old Misery's." Mike's mouth opened and then hurriedly closed again with a click. He had remembered the frog.

"At Old Misery's?" Blackie said. There was nothing in the rules against it, but he had a sensation that T was treading on dangerous ground. He asked hopefully, "Did you break in?"

"No. I rang the bell."

"And what did you say?"

"I said I wanted to see his house."

"What did he do?"

"He showed it me."

"Pinch anything?"

"No."

"What did you do it for then?"

The gang had gathered round: it was as though an impromptu court were about to form and try some case of **deviation**. T said, "It's a beautiful house," and still watching the ground, meeting no one's eyes, he licked his lips first one way, then the other.

deviation
*nonconformity;
departure from
the norm*

"What do you mean, a beautiful house?" Blackie asked with scorn.

"It's got a staircase two hundred years old like a corkscrew. Nothing holds it up."

"What do you mean, nothing holds it up. Does it float?"

"It's to do with opposite forces, Old Misery said."

"What else?"

"There's panelling."

"Like in the Blue Boar?"

"Two hundred years old."

"Is Old Misery two hundred years old?"

Mike laughed suddenly and then was quiet again. The meeting was in a serious mood. For the first time since T had strolled into the car-park on the first day of the holidays his position was in danger. It only needed a single use of his real name and the gang would be at his heels.

"What did you do it for?" Blackie asked. He was just, he had no jealousy, he was anxious to retain T in the gang if he could. It was the word "beautiful" that worried him—that belonged to a class world[12] that you could still see parodied at the Wormsley Common Empire by a man wearing a top hat and a monocle, with a haw-haw[13] accent. He was tempted to say, "My dear Trevor, old chap," and unleash his hell hounds. "If you'd broken in," he said sadly—that indeed would have been an **exploit** worthy of the gang.

exploit
adventure; feat

"This was better," T said. "I found out things." He continued to stare at his feet, not meeting anybody's eye, as though he were absorbed in some dream he was unwilling—or ashamed—to share.

"What things?"

"Old Misery's going to be away all tomorrow and Bank Holiday."[14]

Blackie said with relief, "You mean we could break in?"

"And pinch things?" somebody asked.

Blackie said, "Nobody's going to pinch things. Breaking in—that's good enough, isn't it? We don't want any court stuff."

"I don't want to pinch anything," T said. "I've got a better idea."

"What is it?"

T raised eyes, as grey and disturbed as the drab August day. "We'll pull it down," he said. "We'll destroy it."

Blackie gave a single hoot of laughter and then, like Mike, fell

---

12 **class world:** an upper-class culture

13 **top hat . . . monocle . . . haw-haw:** symbols of England's old aristocracy; the formal hat, the single eyeglass, and the braying laugh

14 **Bank Holiday:** a public holiday in Great Britain

quiet, daunted by the serious **implacable** gaze. "What'd the police be doing all the time?" he said.

implacable
inflexible; unrelenting

"They'd never know. We'd do it from inside. I've found a way in." He said with a sort of intensity, "We'd be like worms, don't you see, in an apple. When we came out again there'd be nothing there, no staircase, no panels, nothing but just walls, and then we'd make the walls fall down—somehow."

"We'd go to jug,"[15] Blackie said.

"Who's to prove? and anyway we wouldn't have pinched anything." He added without the smallest flicker of glee, "There wouldn't be anything to pinch after we'd finished."

"I've never heard of going to prison for breaking things," Summers said.

"There wouldn't be time," Blackie said. "I've seen housebreakers at work."

"There are twelve of us," T said. "We'd organize."

"None of us know how . . ."

"I know," T said. He looked across at Blackie. "Have you got a better plan?"

"Today," Mike said tactlessly, "we're pinching free rides . . ."

"Free rides," T said. "Kid stuff. You can stand down, Blackie, if you'd rather . . ."

"The gang's got to vote."

"Put it up then."

Blackie said uneasily, "It's proposed that tomorrow and Monday we destroy Old Misery's house."

"Here, here," said a fat boy called Joe.

"Who's in favour?"

T said, "It's carried."

"How do we start?" Summers asked.

"He'll tell you," Blackie said. It was the end of his leadership. He went away to the back of the car-park and began to kick a stone, dribbling it this way and that. There was only one old Morris in the park, for few cars were left there except lorries:[16] without an attendant there was no safety. He took a flying kick at the car and scraped a little paint off the rear mudguard. Beyond,

---

15 **jug:** slang for "prison"

16 **lorries:** British English for "trucks"

fickleness
changeability; inconstancy

paying no more attention to him than to a stranger, the gang had gathered round T; Blackie was dimly aware of the **fickleness** of favour. He thought of going home, of never returning, of letting them all discover the hollowness of T's leadership, but suppose after all what T proposed was possible—nothing like it had ever been done before. The fame of the Wormsley Common car-park gang would surely reach around London. There would be headlines in the papers. Even the grown-up gangs who ran the betting at the all-in wrestling[17] and the barrow-boys[18] would hear with respect of how Old Misery's house

The fame of the Wormsley Common car-park gang would surely reach around London.

altruistic
unselfish; without thought of personal gain

had been destroyed. Driven by the pure, simple and **altruistic** ambition of fame for the gang, Blackie came back to where T stood in the shadow of Old Misery's wall.

T was giving his orders with decision: it was as though this plan had been with him all his life, pondered through the seasons, now in his fifteenth year crystallized with the pain of puberty. "You," he said to Mike, "bring some big nails, the biggest you can find, and a hammer. Anybody who can, better bring a hammer and a screwdriver. We'll need plenty of them. Chisels too. We can't have too many chisels. Can anybody bring a saw?"

"I can," Mike said.

"Not a child's saw," T said. "A real saw."

Blackie realized he had raised his hand like any ordinary member of the gang.

"Right, you bring one, Blackie. But now there's a difficulty. We want a hacksaw."

"What's a hacksaw?" someone asked.

"You can get 'em at Woolworth's," Summers said.

The fat boy called Joe said gloomily, "I knew it would end in a collection."

"I'll get one myself," T said. "I don't want your money. But I

---

17 **all-in wrestling:** submission wrestling, or when opponents wrestle using submission moves such as choke holds, armbars, and leg locks

18 **barrow-boys:** British street hawkers who sold things from wheelbarrows

can't buy a sledge-hammer."

Blackie said, "They are working on No. 15. I know where they'll leave their stuff for Bank Holiday."

"Then that's all," T said. "We meet here at nine sharp."

"I've got to go to church," Mike said.

"Come over the wall and whistle. We'll let you in."

2

On Sunday morning all were punctual except Blackie, even Mike. Mike had a stroke of luck. His mother felt ill, his father was tired after Saturday night, and he was told to go to church alone with many warnings of what would happen if he strayed. Blackie had difficulty in smuggling out the saw, and then in finding the sledge-hammer at the back of No. 15. He approached the house from a lane at the rear of the garden, for fear of the policeman's beat along the main road. The tired evergreens kept off a stormy sun: another wet Bank Holiday was being prepared over the Atlantic, beginning in swirls of dust under the trees. Blackie climbed the wall into Misery's garden.

There was no sign of anybody anywhere. The lav stood like a tomb in a neglected graveyard. The curtains were drawn. The house slept. Blackie lumbered nearer with the saw and the sledge-hammer. Perhaps after all nobody had turned up: the plan had been a wild invention: they had woken wiser. But when he came close to the back door he could hear a confusion of sound hardly louder than a hive in swarm: a clickety-clack, a bang bang, a scraping, a creaking, a sudden painful crack. He thought: it's true, and whistled.

They opened the back door to him and he came in. He had at once the impression of organization, very different from the old happy-go-lucky ways under his leadership. For a while he wandered up and down stairs looking for T. Nobody addressed him: he had a sense of great urgency, and already he could begin to see the plan. The interior of the house was being carefully demolished without touching the walls. Summers with hammer and chisel was ripping out the skirting-boards in the ground-floor dining-room: he had already smashed the panels of the door. In the same room Joe was heaving up the parquet blocks, exposing

La Poitrine, Rene Magritte, 1961

the soft wood floorboards over the cellar. Coils of wire came out of the damaged skirting and Mike sat happily on the floor clipping the wires.

On the curved stairs two of the gang were working hard with an inadequate child's saw on the banisters—when they saw Blackie's big saw they signalled for it wordlessly. When he next saw them a quarter of the banisters had been dropped into the hall. He found T at last in the bathroom—he sat moodily in the least cared-for room in the house, listening to the sounds coming up from below.

"You've really done it," Blackie said with awe. "What's going to happen?"

"We've only just begun," T said. He looked at the sledge-hammer and gave his instructions. "You stay here and break the bath and the wash-basin. Don't bother about the pipes. They come later."

Mike appeared at the door. "I've finished the wires, T," he said.

"Good. You've just got to go wandering round now. The kitchen's in the basement. Smash all the china and glass and bottles you can lay hold of. Don't turn on the taps—we don't want a flood—yet. Then go into all the rooms and turn out the drawers. If they are locked get one of the others to break them open. Tear up any papers you find and smash all the ornaments. Better take a carving knife with you from the kitchen. The bedroom's opposite here. Open the pillows and tear up the sheets. That's enough for the moment. And you Blackie, when you've finished in here crack the plaster in the passage up with your sledge-hammer."

"What are you going to do?" Blackie asked.

"I'm looking for something special," T said.

It was nearly lunch-time before Blackie had finished and went in search of T. Chaos had advanced. The kitchen was a shambles of broken glass and china. The dining-room was stripped of parquet, the skirting was up, the door had been taken off its hinges, and the destroyers had moved up a floor. Streaks of light came in through the closed shutters where they worked with the seriousness of creators—and destruction after all is a form of creation. A kind of imagination had seen this house as it had now become.

Mike said, "I've got to go home for dinner."

"Who else?" T asked, but all the others on one excuse or another had brought provisions with them.

They squatted in the ruins of the room and swapped unwanted sandwiches. Half an hour for lunch and they were at work again. By the time Mike returned they were on the top floor, and by six the superficial damage was completed. The doors were all off, all the skirtings raised, the furniture **pillaged** and ripped and smashed—no one could have slept in the house except on a bed of broken plaster. T gave his orders—eight o'clock next morning, and to escape notice they climbed singly over the

pillaged
destroyed; looted

garden wall, into the car-park. Only Blackie and T were left: the light had nearly gone, and when they touched a switch, nothing worked—Mike had done his job thoroughly.

"Did you find anything special?" Blackie asked.

T nodded. "Come over here," he said, "and look." Out of both pockets he drew bundles of pound notes.[19] "Old Misery's savings," he said. "Mike ripped out the mattress, but he missed them."

"What are you going to do? Share them?"

"We aren't thieves," T said. "Nobody's going to steal anything from this house. I kept these for you and me—a celebration." He knelt down on the floor and counted them out—there were seventy in all. "We'll burn them," he said, "one by one," and taking it in turns they held a note upwards and lit the top corner, so that the flame burnt slowly towards their fingers. The grey ash floated above them and fell on their heads like age. "I'd like to see Old Misery's face when we are through," T said.

"You hate him a lot?" Blackie asked.

"Of course I don't hate him," T said. "There'd be no fun if I hated him." The last burning note illuminated his brooding face. "All this hate and love," he said, "it's soft, it's hooey. There's only things, Blackie," and he looked round the room crowded with the unfamiliar shadows of half things, broken things, former things. "I'll race you home, Blackie," he said.

3

Next morning the serious destruction started. Two were missing—Mike and another boy whose parents were off to Southend and Brighton in spite of the slow warm drops that had begun to fall and the rumble of thunder in the estuary[20] like the first guns of the old blitz. "We've got to hurry," T said.

Summers was restive. "Haven't we done enough?" he asked. "I've been given a bob for slot machines. This is like work."

"We've hardly started," T said. "Why, there's all the floors left, and the stairs. We haven't taken out a single window. You voted like the others. We are going to *destroy* this house. There won't be

---

19 **pound notes:** units of British currency

20 **estuary:** where the sea tide meets the river

anything left when we've finished."

They began again on the first floor picking up the top floorboards next the outer wall, leaving the joists exposed. Then they sawed through the joists and retreated into the hall, as what was left of the floor heeled and sank. They had learnt with practice, and the second floor collapsed more easily. By the evening an odd exhilaration seized them as they looked down the great hollow of the house. They ran risks and made mistakes: when they thought of the windows it was too late to reach them. "Cor," Joe said, and dropped a penny down into the dry rubble-filled well. It cracked and span amongst the broken glass.

"Why did we start this?" Summers asked with astonishment; T was already on the ground, digging at the rubble, clearing a space along the outer wall. "Turn on the taps," he said. "It's too dark for anyone to see now, and in the morning it won't matter." The water overtook them on the stairs and fell through the floorless rooms.

It was then they heard Mike's whistle at the back. "Something's wrong," Blackie said. They could hear his urgent breathing as they unlocked the door.

"The bogies?" Summers asked.

"Old Misery," Mike said. "He's on his way," he said with pride.

"But why?" T said. "He told me . . ." He protested with the fury of the child he had never been, "It isn't fair."

"He was down at Southend," Mike said, "and he was on the train coming back. Said it was too cold and wet." He paused and gazed at the water. "My, you've had a storm here. Is the roof leaking?"

"How long will he be?"

"Five minutes. I gave Ma the slip and ran."

"We better clear," Summers said. "We've done enough, anyway."

"Oh no, we haven't. Anybody could do this—" "this" was the shattered hollowed house with nothing left but the walls. Yet walls could be preserved. Façades[21] were valuable. They could build inside again more beautifully than before. This could again

---

21 **façades:** outer faces of buildings

be a home. He said angrily, "We've got to finish. Don't move. Let me think."

"There's no time," a boy said.

"There's got to be a way," T said. "We couldn't have got this far . . ."

"We've done a lot," Blackie said.

"No. No, we haven't. Somebody watch the front."

"We can't do any more."

"He may come in at the back."

"Watch the back too." T began to plead. "Just give me a minute and I'll fix it. I swear I'll fix it." But his authority had gone with his ambiguity. He was only one of the gang. "Please," he said.

"Please," Summers mimicked him, and then suddenly struck home with the fatal name. "Run along home, Trevor."

T stood with his back to the rubble like a boxer knocked groggy against the ropes. He had no words as his dreams shook and slid. Then Blackie acted before the gang had time to laugh, pushing Summers backward. "I'll watch the front, T," he said, and cautiously he opened the shutters of the hall. The grey wet common stretched ahead, and the lamps gleamed in the puddles. "Someone's coming, T. No, it's not him. What's your plan, T?"

"Tell Mike to go out to the lav and hide close beside it. When he hears me whistle he's got to count ten and start to shout."

"Shout what?"

"Oh, 'Help', anything."

"You hear, Mike," Blackie said. He was the leader again. He took a quick look between the shutters. "He's coming, T."

"Quick, Mike. The lav. Stay here, Blackie, all of you, till I yell."

"Where are you going, T?"

"Don't worry. I'll see to this. I said I would, didn't I?"

Old Misery came limping off the common. He had mud on his shoes and he stopped to scrape them on the pavement's edge. He didn't want to soil his house, which stood jagged and dark between the bomb-sites, saved so narrowly, as he believed, from destruction. Event the fan-light had been left unbroken by the bomb's blast. Somewhere somebody whistled. Old Misery looked sharply round. He didn't trust whistles. A child was shouting: it seemed to come from his own garden. Then a boy ran into the road from the car-park. "Mr. Thomas," he called, "Mr. Thomas."

"What is it?"

"I'm terribly sorry, Mr. Thomas. One of us got taken short, and we thought you wouldn't mind and now he can't get out."

"What do you mean, boy?"

"He's got stuck in your lav."

"He'd no business . . . Haven't I seen you before?"

"You showed me your house."

"So I did. So I did. That doesn't give you the right to . . ."

"Do hurry, Mr. Thomas. He'll suffocate."

"Nonsense. He can't suffocate. Wait till I put my bag in."

"I'll carry your bag."

"Oh no, you don't. I carry my own."

"This way, Mr. Thomas."

"I can't get in the garden that way. I've got to go through the house."

"But you *can* get in the garden this way, Mr. Thomas. We often do."

"You often do?" He followed the boy with a scandalized fascination. "When? What right . . . ?"

"Do you see . . . ? the wall's low."

"I'm not going to climb walls into my own garden. It's absurd."

"This is how we do it. One foot here, one foot there, and over." The boy's face peered down, an arm shot out, and Mr. Thomas found his bag taken and deposited on the other side of the wall.

"Give me back my bag," Mr. Thomas said. From the loo[22] a boy yelled and yelled. "I'll call the police."

"Your bag's all right, Mr. Thomas. Look. One foot there. On your right. Now just above. To your left." Mr. Thomas climbed over his own garden wall. "Here's your bag, Mr. Thomas."

"I'll have the wall built up," Mr. Thomas said, "I'll not have you boys coming over here, using my loo." He stumbled on the path, but the boy caught his elbow and supported him. "Thank you, thank you, my boy," he murmured automatically. Somebody shouted again through the dark. "I'm coming, I'm coming," Mr. Thomas called. He said to the boy bedside him, "I'm not

---

22 **loo:** British slang for "bathroom"

unreasonable. Been a boy myself. As long as things are done regular. I don't mind you playing round the place Saturday mornings. Sometimes I like company. Only it's got to be regular. One of you asks leave and I say Yes. Sometimes I'll say No. Won't feel like it. And you come in at the front door and out at the back. No garden walls."

"Do get him out, Mr. Thomas."

"He won't come to any harm in my loo," Mr. Thomas said, stumbling slowly down the garden. "Oh, my rheumatics," he said. "Always get 'em on Bank Holiday. I've got to be careful. There's loose stones here. Give me your hand. Do you know what my horoscope said yesterday? 'Abstain from any dealings in first half of week. Danger of serious crash.' That might be on this path," Mr. Thomas said. "They speak in parables and double meanings."[23] He paused at the door of the loo. "What's the matter in there?" he called. There was no reply.

"Perhaps he's fainted," the boy said.

"Not in my loo. Here, you, come out," Mr. Thomas said, and giving a great jerk at the door he nearly fell on his back when it swung easily open. A hand first supported him and then pushed him hard. His head hit the opposite wall and he sat heavily down. His bag hit his feet. A hand whipped the key out of the lock and the door slammed. "Let me out," he called, and heard the key turn in the lock. "A serious crash," he thought, and felt dithery and confused and old.

A voice spoke to him softly through the star-shaped hole in the door. "Don't worry, Mr. Thomas," it said, "we won't hurt you, not if you stay quiet."

Mr. Thomas put his head between his hands and pondered. He had noticed that there was only one lorry in the car-park, and he felt certain that the driver would not come for it before the morning. Nobody could hear him from the road in front, and the lane at the back was seldom used. Anyone who passed there would be hurrying home and would not pause for what they would certainly take to be drunken cries. And if he did call "Help", who, on a lonely Bank Holiday evening, would have the

---

23 **parables and double meanings:** short stories containing moral lessons and words that can be interpreted in multiple ways

courage to investigate? Mr. Thomas sat on the loo and pondered with the wisdom of age.

After a while it seemed to him that there were sounds in the silence—they were faint and came from the direction of his house. He stood up and peered through the ventilation-hole—between the cracks in one of the shutters he saw a light, not the light of a lamp, but the wavering light that a candle might give. Then he thought he heard the sound of hammering and scraping and chipping. He thought of burglars—perhaps they had employed the boy as a scout, but why should burglars engage in what sounded more and more like a **stealthy** form of carpentry? Mr. Thomas let out an experimental yell, but nobody answered. The noise could not even have reached his enemies.

stealthy
secret; furtive

4

Mike had gone home to bed, but the rest stayed. The question of leadership no longer concerned the gang. With nails, chisels, screwdrivers, anything that was sharp and penetrating, they moved around the inner walls worrying at the mortar between the bricks. They started too high, and it was Blackie who hit on the damp course and realized the work could be halved if they weakened the joints immediately above. It was a long, tiring, unamusing job, but at last it was finished. The gutted house stood there balanced on a few inches of mortar between the damp course and the bricks.

There remained the most dangerous task of all, out in the open at the edge of the bomb-site. Summers was sent to watch the road for passers-by, and Mr. Thomas, sitting on the loo, heard clearly now the sound of sawing. It no longer came from the house, and that a little reassured him. He felt less concerned. Perhaps the other noises too had no significance.

A voice spoke to him through the hole. "Mr. Thomas."

"Let me out," Mr. Thomas said sternly.

"Here's a blanket," the voice said, and a long grey sausage was worked through the hole and fell in **swathes** over Mr. Thomas's head.

swathes
folds; wraps

"There's nothing personal," the voice said. "We want you to be comfortable tonight."

"Tonight," Mr. Thomas repeated incredulously.

"Catch," the voice said. "Penny buns—we've buttered them, and sausage-rolls. We don't want you to starve, Mr. Thomas."

Mr. Thomas pleaded desperately. "A joke's a joke, boy. Let me out and I won't say a thing. I've got rheumatics. I got to sleep comfortable."

"You wouldn't be comfortable, not in your house, you wouldn't. Not now."

"What do you mean, boy?" But the footsteps receded. There was only the silence of night: no sound of sawing. Mr. Thomas tried one more yell, but he was **daunted** and **rebuked** by the silence—a long way off an owl hooted and made away again on its muffled flight through the soundless world.

At seven next morning the driver came to fetch his lorry. He climbed into the seat and tried to start the engine. He was vaguely aware of a voice shouting, but it didn't concern him. At last the engine responded and he backed the lorry until it touched the great wooden shore that supported Mr. Thomas's house. That way he could drive right out and down the street without reversing. The lorry moved forward, was momentarily checked as though something were pulling it from behind, and then went on to the sound of a long rumbling crash. The driver was astonished to see bricks bouncing ahead of him, while stones hit the roof of his cab. He put on his brakes. When he climbed out the whole landscape had suddenly altered. There was no house beside the car-park, only a hill of rubble. He went round and examined the back of his lorry for damage, and found a rope tied there that was still twisted at the other end round part of a wooden strut.

The driver again became aware of somebody shouting. It came from the wooden erection which was the nearest thing to a house in that desolation of broken brick. The driver climbed the smashed wall and unlocked the door. Mr. Thomas came out of the loo. He was wearing a grey blanket to which flakes of pastry adhered. He gave a sobbing cry. "My house," he said. "Where's my house?"

"Search me," the driver said. His eye lit on the remains of a bath and what had once been a dresser and he began to laugh.

daunted
unnerved; intimidated

rebuked
scolded; reproached

There wasn't anything left anywhere.

"How dare you laugh," Mr. Thomas said. "It was my house. My house."

"I'm sorry," the driver said, making heroic efforts, but when he remembered the sudden check of his lorry, the crash of bricks falling, he became convulsed again. One moment the house had stood there with such dignity between the bomb-sites like a man in a top hat, and then, bang, crash, there wasn't anything left—not anything. He said, "I'm sorry. I can't help it, Mr. Thomas. There's nothing personal, but you got to admit it's funny."

Responding to the Selection

1. Why do you think the young men behave as they do by destroying this old man's house?

2. The atmosphere of a story is its mood, as understood by the reader. How would you characterize the atmosphere of "The Destructors"? Explain what elements contribute to this mood.

3. "Coming down in the world" is a theme in this story. What are some of the things that "come down" in this story in addition to the most obvious one, the house?

4. Why do you think Trevor says "there'd be no fun" in the destruction if he hated Old Misery?

5. What are some ideas the author has about group psychology? Give examples, noting the boys' speech and leadership styles.

The Guitar

Federico García Lorca

WORLD LENS

•••

SPAIN

Federico García Lorca's artistry and intense identification with the landscape, music, and people of Spain make him one of the most important Spanish writers of the 20th century. He was mourned as a victim of Spain's terrible Civil War, which divided the country between 1936 and 1939 and led to much bloodshed and poverty. Lorca's writing often celebrates the gypsy culture of Andalusia in the south of Spain. The mournful guitar music and fiery, stomping flamenco dance are still emblematic of this often romantically depicted region.

Now begins the cry
Of the guitar,
Breaking the vaults
Of dawn.
Now begins the cry
Of the guitar.
Useless
To still it.
It weeps monotonously
As weeps the water,
As weeps the wind
Over snow.
Impossible
To still it.
It weeps
For distant things,
Warm southern sands
Desiring white camellias.[1]

---

1 **camellias:** fragrant, rose-like flowers

It mourns the arrow without a target,
The evening without morning.
And the first bird dead
Upon a branch.
O guitar!
A wounded heart,
Wounded by five swords.

Translated by Elizabeth du Gué Trapier

Responding to the Selection

1. Why do you think the guitar weeps?

2. What are some possible meanings of the lines "Useless to still it. Impossible to still it"?

3. What would you say is the theme of this poem? Cite some examples, such as images, words, or poetic devices, that support your answer.

4. In Spain, the passionate music of the flamenco dancers and gypsies is called *cante jondo*, or deep song. In his verse and plays, García Lorca tries to suggest cante jondo without the benefit of musical notes and rhythm. Do you think this poem conveys emotion convincingly? Explain your answer.

Poor Fish

Alberto Moravia

WORLD LENS

♦♦♦

ITALY

Alberto Moravia endeared himself to Italians with his fiction about the common people. "Poor Fish" comes from *Roman Tales*, a collection of stories depicting "low life" characters in Italy's capital city of Rome.

The story's preoccupation with physical perfection may be its most Italian characteristic. In Italy, beauty is a virtue. Italians are renowned for their contributions to the visual arts—from the imposing Roman architecture of the Ancient period, to the fabulous paintings and sculpture of the Renaissance masters, such as Michaelangelo, Leonardo da Vinci, and Rafael. This visual flair extends even to their most beloved musical form—opera— and the form of entertainment for which they are credited—the circus.

People never know very much about who they are, nor about who is inferior to them and who superior. As for me, I went too far in the direction of thinking myself inferior to everybody. It is true that I was not born with a frame as tough as iron; about as tough as earthenware, let us say. But I looked upon myself as being as fragile as glass, as the thinnest glass, in fact; and that was altogether too much. That was debasing myself too far. I used often to say to myself: now let's run over our own qualities. Physical strength, then—**nil**: I am small, crooked, rickety, my arms and legs are like sticks, I'm like a spider. Intelligence—very little above nil, considering that I've never managed, out of all the jobs there are, to rise above that of dish-washer in an hotel. Looks—less than nil: I have a narrow, yellow face, eyes of an indefinite, dirty colour, and a nose that seems to have been made for a face twice as broad as mine; it is big and long, and looks as if it was going straight down, and then, at the tip, it turns up like a lizard raising its snout. Other qualities, such as courage, quickness, personal charm, likeableness—less

nil
zero; absolutely nothing

Europe

said about them the better. Quite naturally, then, after coming to such conclusions, I was careful not to make advances to women. The only one I ever attempted to approach—a housemaid in the hotel—put me in my place with a very suitable word—"you poor fish," she said. And so I became gradually convinced that I was worth nothing at all and that the best thing for me to do was to keep quiet, in a corner, so as not to get in anybody's way.

Anyone passing along the street at the back of the Rome hotel where I work, during the early hours of the afternoon, can see a row of windows open at ground level, with a strong smell of washing-up coming from them. If his eyes can pierce the gloom, he will also see piles and piles of plates towering up to the ceiling, on tables and on the marble slab of the sink. Well, that was my corner, the corner of the world I had chosen so as not to be conspicuous. But what a queer thing fate is: the last thing I should have expected was that, in that corner, in that very kitchen, I mean, somebody should come and catch me by surprise and pluck me

Ida, among women, was just what I was among men: a poor fish.

like a flower that has been hidden in the grass. Ida, it was, Ida, the new scullery-maid[1] who took Giuditta's place when she was going to have a baby. Ida, among women, was just what I was among men: a poor fish. Like me, she was small and twisted, scraggy, insignificant. But she was passionate, restless, gay, a devil. We quickly became friends, owing to the fact that we stood in front of the same dishes and the same greasy water; and then, one thing leading to another, she prevailed upon me to invite her one Sunday to go to the cinema. I invited her out of politeness; and I was surprised when, in the darkness of the cinema, she took my hand, slipping her five fingers in between mine. I thought there was some mistake and even tried to free myself, but she whispered to me to stay still: what harm could there be in holding hands? Then, as we came out, she explained to me that she had been noticing me for some time, from the very day, it might even be said, that she had been taken on at the hotel. That,

---

1 **scullery-maid:** the maid in charge of kitchen dishes and utensils

ever since then, she had done nothing but think about me. That she hoped, now, that I was a little fond of her, because she, for her part, could not live without me. It was the first time that a woman, even a woman like Ida, had said things like this to me, and I lost my head. I gave her all the answers she wanted, and a great deal more as well.

But I still felt profoundly astonished, and although she went on repeating that she was mad about me, I failed to be convinced. And so, on other occasions, when we went out together, I couldn't keep from harping on the subject, partly for the pleasure of hearing her say it again, and partly because I found it hard to believe. "Now do tell me, I should like to know what it is you see in me? How do you manage to love me?" And would you believe it? Ida used to cling on to my arm with both hands, raise an adoring face towards me, and answer: "I love you because you have all the good qualities . . . for me you're just living perfection." Incredulously I would repeat: "All the good qualities? Well, I never knew that before." "Yes, all . . . . To begin with, you're so good-looking." I couldn't help laughing, I must confess, and I said: "Me good-looking? but have you taken a proper look at me?" "Yes, indeed I have . . . . I'm doing it all the time." "But what about my nose? Have you ever looked at my nose?" "It's just your nose that I like," she answered; and then, taking hold of my nose between two fingers and shaking it like a bell, "Nose, nose," she went on, "for this nose I don't know what I wouldn't do." Then she added: "Besides, you're so intelligent." "Me intelligent? Why, everyone says I'm an idiot." "They say it out of envy," she replied with feminine logic, "but you are intelligent, extremely intelligent . . . . When you talk, I listen to you open-mouthed . . . . You're the most intelligent person I've ever met." "Well, anyhow," I resumed after a moment, "you won't say I'm strong . . . that you can't say." And she answered, with passion: "Yes, you are strong . . . very, very, strong." This took a little swallowing, and for a moment I was left speechless. Then she started off again: "And besides, if you really want to know, you've got something about you that I just love." So I asked her: "But what is this 'something,' I should like to know?" "I don't quite know how to explain," she replied; "it's your voice, your expression, the way you move . . . . Certainly nobody else has got what you have." Naturally for some time I did not believe her; and I used to make her repeat these speeches to me, simply because it amused me to compare them with what I had always thought about myself. But, as the days went by, I began, I must admit, to get ideas into my head. "Suppose it was really true?" I sometimes said to myself. Not that I really believed that I was any different, essentially, from what I had always thought I was. But Ida's remark about the "something" left me in doubt. In that remark, I felt, lay the explanation of the mystery. On account of that "something," I knew, women liked hunchbacks, dwarfs, old men, even monsters. Why shouldn't somebody like me too? I was neither a hunchback, a dwarf, an old man or a monster.

About this time Ida and I decided to go and see a circus which had pitched its tents opposite the Passeggiata Archeologica. We were both of us feeling very cheerful; and, once inside the big tent, we took our places in the cheap seats, cuddling very close together, arm in arm. Beside me was a tall, fair woman, young and handsome, and with her, one seat farther on, a dark young man, big and strong too, a tough, athletic-looking type. I thought of them as what is called "a handsome pair"; and then I thought no more of them and gave all my attention to the circus. The yellow-sanded arena was still empty, but at the far end there was a platform with a band in red uniforms, entirely of brass instruments and flutes, that never stopped playing warlike marches, one after another. At last four clowns came in, two of them dwarfs and two bigger, with whitened faces and large loose trousers, and they cut capers and made jokes, slapping and kicking each other, and Ida laughed so much that she started coughing. Then the band struck up a lively march and it was the turn of the horses—six in all, three dappled grey and three white—which started circling round the ring, as good as could be, while their trainer, all dressed in red and gold, stood in the middle of the arena and cracked his long whip. A woman in a tulle[2] skirt and white tights came dancing in, took hold of the saddle of one of the horses and ran beside it, mounting and dismounting, up and down, while the horses still went round and

---

2 **tulle:** a sheer silk or synthetic material often used for ballet costumes

round, first at a trot and then at a gallop. When the horses had gone, the clowns came back and turned somersaults and kicked each other's behinds, and then came a family of trapezists, father, mother and their little boy, all three wearing blue tights, and all three very muscular, especially the boy. They clapped their hands up and then, houp la! up a knotted rope they climbed, up and up, right to the roof of the tent. There they began to send the trapezes flying backwards and forwards, hanging on now with their hands and now with their feet and throwing the little boy to each other like a ball. Filled with admiration, I said to Ida: "Look at that! How I should like to be a trapezist! I should like to launch myself into the air and then catch hold of the trapeze with my legs!" Ida, in her usual way, nestled up close beside me and answered in a tone of adoration: "It's all a matter of practice . . . . If you practised, you could do it too." The fair woman looked at us and whispered something to her companion, and they both started laughing. After the trapezists came the number one attraction—the lions. A number of young men in red-tail coats came in and rolled up the carpet used by the trapezists. As they carried it away, without noticing they rolled up one of the clowns inside it; and again Ida, seeing his white face poking out of the roll of carpet, almost fell off her chair with laughing. Very nimbly and quickly the young men put up a big nickelled cage in the middle of the arena, and then, to a roll of drums, the great blond head of the first lion appeared through a little door. There entered, in all, five of them, as well as a lioness who looked thoroughly ill-tempered and at once began to roar. Last of all came the lion-tamer, an agreeable, ceremonious little man in a green coat with gold braid on it, who at once started bowing to the public, waving a riding-master's whip in one hand and in the other a stick with a hook on the end, like the ones they use for pulling down the roller-blinds of shops. The lions went circling round him, roaring; he went on bowing, calmly and smilingly; then at last he turned toward them, and, by poking them in the backside with the hook, forced them to climb up, one after another, on to some little stools—really quite small ones—which were arranged in a row at the back of the cage. The lions, **cowering**, poor beasts, on top of these cat-sized seats, roared and

cowering
shrinking from;
showing fear

showed their teeth; two or three of them, as the trainer passed within range, put out a paw in his direction, which he avoided with a pirouette. "What if they eat him?" Ida whispered to me, clinging to my arm. There was a roll of drums; the trainer went up to one of the lions which was older than the rest and which looked three-quarters asleep and was not roaring, opened its mouth and put his head inside, three times in succession. I said to Ida, amid the bursts of applause which followed: "You won't believe me . . . but I should just love to go into that cage and put my head in the lion's mouth too." Filled with admiration, and cuddling up against me, she replied. "I know you'd be quite capable of it." At these words, the fair young woman and the athletic young man burst out laughing, looking significantly at

THE TIGHTROPE
WALKER
Marc Chagall

us. This time we could not ignore the fact that they were laughing at us, and Ida grew angry and muttered to me: "They're laughing at us . . . . Why don't you tell them how rude they are?" But at that moment a bell rang and everyone got up, while the lions went off with their heads down, through the usual little door. The first part of the show was over.

As we left the tent the other two were walking in front of us. Ida went on doggedly whispering to me: "You've got to tell them how rude they are . . . if you don't you're a coward"; and I, **piqued** in my pride, made up my mind to accost them. Outside the big tent, and in the shelter of it, was a shed where you could pay extra to visit the zoo belonging to the circus: it contained a row of cages on one side, with the wild animals, and on the other a space with straw on the floor where the tame ones were kept loose—that is to say, zebras, elephants, horses and dogs. It was almost dark inside the shed, but, as we came in, we could see, in the gloom, the other two standing in front of the bear's cage. The fair woman was leaning forward to look at the bear, which was curled up fast asleep, its furry back against the bars; and the man was pulling her away by the arm. I went straight up to the man and said in a firm voice: "Tell me . . . were you laughing at us?"

He turned slightly and answered without hesitation: "No, we were laughing at a frog pretending to be an ox."

"The frog, I suppose, being me?"

"If the cap fits, wear it."

Ida was pushing me forward with her hand on my arm. Raising my voice, I replied: "You know what you are? You're just an ignorant cad."

He retorted, brutally: "Ah, so the frog's beginning to croak now, is he?"

At this, the woman started to laugh, and Ida, hissing like a viper, broke in: "There's nothing to laugh at . . . instead of laughing, you'd better stop rubbing yourself up against my husband . . . . I suppose you think I didn't see you. . . . You've been rubbing your arm up against him the whole time."

I was astonished, because I hadn't noticed it: at most, since she was sitting beside me, she might have perhaps just touched me with her elbow. Indeed she answered indignantly: "My dear girl,

piqued
irritated; bothered

you're crazy . . . . "

"No, I'm not crazy; I saw you rubbing up against him."

"But why d'you think I should worry about a poor fish like your husband?" she spoke now with the utmost scorn. "If I had to rub up against anyone, I should choose a real man . . . . Here's a real man for you." As she said this she took hold of her boy friend's arm as a pork-butcher might take up a ham to show it off to a customer. "This is the arm I'd rub up against . . . . Look what muscles . . . look how strong he is."

And now in turn, the man came up to me and said threateningly: "That's enough . . . get along with you . . . better for you if you do."

"Who says so?" I cried in exasperation, raising myself on tiptoe to be on a level with him.

The scene that followed I shall remember as long as I live. He made no reply to my remark, but, all of the sudden, took me under the arms and lifted me up in the air like a feather. On the other side from the cages, as I have said, there was a straw-covered space where the tame animals were kept. Just behind us there was a family of elephants—father, mother, and baby, the latter comparatively small but still about the size of a horse. They were standing in a dark corner, poor creatures, with drooping ears and trunks, with their huge dark rumps pressed close together. And so he lifted me up, this great bully, and suddenly dumped me down on the back of the smallest elephant. The animal perhaps thought the moment had come for it to go into the circus-ring, and started trotting, with me on its back, along the gangway beside the cages. People rushed in all directions, Ida was running along behind me, screaming, and I, after sitting astride the little elephant and trying in vain to snatch hold of it by the ears, when we reached the end of the gangway, slipped off and fell to the ground, hitting the back of my head. What happened then, I don't know, because I fainted, and when I came round I found myself at the First Aid post, with Ida sitting beside me holding my hand. Later, as soon as I felt better, we went home without seeing the second part of the show.

Next day I said to Ida: "It was your fault . . . you put such ideas into my head, making me think I was goodness knows what . . . .

But that woman was perfectly right: I'm just a poor fish and nothing more."

But Ida, taking my by the arm and gazing at me, "You were magnificent," she said. "He was frightened, and that was why he put you on to the elephant . . . . And then, riding along on the elephant, you looked really splendid . . . . It was a pity you fell off."

So there was nothing to be done. For her I was one thing, for other people, another. But can you ever tell what women see, when they're in love?

Translated by Angus Davidson

Responding to the Selection

1. The translator of "Poor Fish" claims that other stories in Moravia's collection *Roman Tales* are "so dependent on allusions to places or events of local interest" that they would lose much of their flavor in translation. So, he has chosen not to translate them. What, in your opinion, makes "Poor Fish" understandable to non-Italians?

2. How would it affect this story if the narrator spoke only in the words of a "lowly" dishwasher?

3. Do you think the narrator and his beloved will stay happy together? Explain your opinion.

4. Moravia is especially beloved for writing about the common people of Italy. What is the universal appeal—and risk—of this subject matter for a writer?

The Black Sheep

Italo Calvino

WORLD LENS

◆◆◆

ITALY

As a teenager during World War II, Italo Calvino fought in the Resistance movement that attempted to undermine the fascist Italian dictator, Benito Mussolini, and Hitler's occupying German troops. He credited his fascination with storytelling with his early experiences as a young soldier, swapping stories around the fire at night.

Calvino is as famous for his novels as for his collections of short stories. Though one of his first novels was a realistic depiction of wartime, he later employed a wide variety of styles, switching back and forth between realism and fantasy. Calvino was especially fond of fables—the form of the following story—believing them to be "true."

There was a country where they were all thieves. At night everybody would leave home with skeleton keys and shaded lanterns and go and burgle a neighbor's house. They'd get back at dawn, loaded, to find their own house had been robbed. So everybody lived happily together, nobody lost out, since each stole from the other, and that other from another again, and so on and on until you got to a last person who stole from the first. Trade in the country inevitably involved cheating on the parts both of buyer and seller. The government was a criminal organization that stole from its subjects, and the subjects for their part were only interested in defrauding the government. Thus life went on smoothly, nobody was rich and nobody was poor.

One day, how we don't know, it so happened that an honest man came to live in the place. At night, instead of going out with his sack and his lantern, he stayed home to smoke and read novels.

The thieves came, saw the light on and didn't go in.

BACKYARDS
Hugo Robus

This went on for a while: then they were obliged to explain to him that even if he wanted to live without doing anything, it was no reason to stop others from doing things. Every night he spent at home meant a family would have nothing to eat the following day.

The honest man could hardly object to such reasoning. He took to going out in the evening and coming back the following morning like they did, but he didn't steal. He was honest, there was nothing you could do about it. He went as far as the bridge and watched the water flow by beneath. When he got home he found he had been robbed.

In less than a week the honest man found himself penniless, he had nothing to eat and his house was empty. But this was hardly a problem, since it was his own fault; no, the problem was that his behavior upset everything else. Because he let the others steal everything he had without stealing anything from anybody; so there was always someone who got home at dawn to find their house untouched; the house he should have robbed. In any event after a while the ones who weren't being robbed found themselves richer than the others and didn't want to steal anymore. To make matters worse, the ones who came to steal from the honest man's house found it was always empty; so they became poor.

Meanwhile, the ones who had become rich got into the honest

man's habit of going to the bridge at night to watch the water flow by beneath. This increased the confusion because it meant lots of others became rich and lots of others became poor.

Now, the rich people saw that if they went to the bridge every night they'd soon be poor. And they thought: "Let's pay some of the poor to go and rob for us." They made contracts, fixed salaries, percentages: they were still thieves of course, and they still tried to swindle each other. But, as tends to happen, the rich got richer and richer and the poor got poorer and poorer.

Some of the rich people got so rich that they didn't need to steal or have others steal for them so as to stay rich. But if they stopped stealing they would get poor because the poor stole from them. So they paid the very poorest of the poor to defend their property from the other poor, and that meant setting up a police force and building prisons.

So it was that only a few years after the appearance of the honest man, people no longer spoke of robbing and being robbed, but only of the rich and the poor; but they were still all thieves.

The only honest man had been the one at the beginning, and he died in very short order, of hunger.

Translated by Tim Parks

Responding to the Selection

1. Why does Calvino plant an honest individual among the thieves?

2. What do you think is the meaning of the story's title, "Black Sheep"? Explain why it is ironic.

3. Hyperbole—a literary device using exaggeration for effect—is used often in this story. Find some examples and explain the effect the author may be striving for.

4. Satire is a literary form that ridicules human vices and foibles. What do you think is the point of Calvino's satire?

The Balek Scales

Heinrich Böll

WORLD LENS

•••

GERMANY

Called "the conscience of West Germany," Heinrich Böll received the Nobel Prize for literature in 1972. Like his famous compatriot Günter Grass, his fiction is known for its social criticism and antimilitarism. The latter view came from hard experience: He was conscripted into Hitler's army of the Third Reich and later imprisoned as an American POW in the second world war.

Böll also criticized the corruption in Germany's Catholic church and the worsening values of modern German society. He fervently believed that Germany had a mandate to remember its terrible past. Because his outspokenness made him a controversial figure, he felt it necessary to live abroad for a time.

Where my grandfather came from, most of the people lived by working in the flax[1] sheds. For five generations they had been breathing in the dust which rose from the crushed flax stalks, letting themselves be killed off by slow degrees, a race of long-suffering, cheerful people who ate goat cheese, potatoes, and now and then a rabbit; in the evening they would sit at home spinning and knitting; they sang, drank mint tea and were happy. During the day they would carry the flax stalks to the antiquated machines, with no protection from the dust and at the mercy from the heat which came pouring out of the drying kilns. Each cottage contained only one bed, standing against the wall like a closet and reserved for the parents, while the children slept all round the room on benches. In the morning the room would be filled with the odor of thin soup; on Sundays there was stew, and on feast days the children's faces would light

---

1 **flax:** a crop cultivated mostly for its fiber and seed

up with pleasure as they watched the black acorn coffee turning paler and paler from the milk their smiling mother poured into their coffee mugs.

The parents went off early to the flax sheds; the housework was left to the children: they would sweep the room, tidy up, wash the dishes and peel the potatoes, precious pale-yellow fruit whose thin peel had to be produced afterwards to dispel any suspicion of extravagance or carelessness.

As soon as the children were out of school they had to go off into the woods and, depending on the season, gather mushrooms and herbs: woodruff and thyme, caraway, mint and foxglove, and in summer, when they had brought in the hay from their meager fields, they gathered hayflowers. A kilo[2] of hayflowers was worth one pfennig,[3] and they were sold by the apothecaries[4] in town for twenty pfennigs a kilo to highly strung ladies. The mushrooms were highly prized: they fetched twenty pfennigs a kilo and were sold in the shops in town for one mark[5] twenty. The children would crawl deep into the green darkness of the forest during the autumn when dampness drove the mushrooms out of the soil, and almost every family had its own places where it gathered mushrooms, places which were handed down in whispers from generation to generation.

The woods belonged to the Baleks, as well as the flax sheds, and in my grandfather's village the Baleks had a château,[6] and the wife of the head of the family had a little room next to the dairy where mushrooms, herbs, and hayflowers were weighed and paid for. There on the table stood the great Balek scales, an old-fashioned, ornate bronze-gilt contraption, which my grandfather's grandparents had already faced when they were children, their grubby hands holding their little baskets of mushrooms, their paper bags of hayflowers, breathlessly watching the number of weights Frau Balek had to throw on the scale before the swinging pointer came to rest exactly over the

---

2 **kilo:** a kilogram, a unit for measuring

3 **pfennig:** a German monetary unit comparable to a penny

4 **apothecaries:** pharmacists

5 **mark:** a German monetary unit

6 **château:** French word for a large house in the countryside

The Balek Scales   197

black line, that thin line of justice which had to be redrawn every year. Then Frau Balek would take the big book covered in brown leather, write down the weight, and pay out the money, pfennigs or ten-pfennig pieces and very, very occasionally, a mark. And when my grandfather was a child there was a big glass jar of lemon drops standing there, the kind that cost one mark a kilo, and when Frau Balek—whichever one happened to be presiding over the little room—was in a good mood, she would put her hand into this jar and give each child a lemon drop, and the children's faces would light up with pleasure, the way they used to when on feast days their mother poured milk into their coffee mugs, milk that made the coffee turn paler and paler until it was as pale as the flaxen pigtails of the little girls.

One of the laws imposed by the Baleks on the village was: No one was permitted to have scales in the house. The law was so ancient that nobody gave a thought as to when and how it had arisen, and it had to be obeyed, for anyone who broke it was dismissed from the flax sheds, he could not sell his mushrooms or his thyme or his hayflowers, and the power of the Baleks was so far-reaching that no one in the neighboring villages would give him work either, or buy his forest herbs. But since the days when my grandfather's parents had gone out as small children to gather mushrooms and sell them in order that they might season the meat of the rich people of Prague or be baked into game pies, it had never occurred to anyone to break this law: flour could be measured in cups, eggs could be counted, what they had spun could be measured by the yard, and besides, the old-fashioned bronze-gilt, ornate Balek scales did not look as if there was anything wrong with them, and five generations had entrusted the swinging black pointer with what they had gone out as eager children to gather from the woods.

True, there were some among these quiet people who **flouted** the law, **poachers** bent on making more money in one night than they could earn in a whole month in the flax sheds, but even these people apparently never thought of buying scales or making their own. My grandfather was the first person bold enough to test the justice of the Baleks, the family who lived in the château and drove two carriages, who always maintained one boy from

flouted
disregarded; defied

poachers
trespassers; people who hunt illegally

the village while he studied **theology** at the **seminary** in Prague, the family with whom the priest played taroc[7] every Wednesday, on whom the local reeve,[8] in his carriage emblazoned with the Imperial coat of arms,[9] made an annual New Year's Day call and on whom the Emperor conferred a title on the first day of the year 1900.

My grandfather was hardworking and smart: he crawled further into the woods than the children of his clan had crawled before him, he penetrated as far as the thicket where, according to legend, Bilgan the Giant was supposed to dwell, guarding a treasure. But my grandfather was not afraid of Bilgan: he worked his way deep into the thicket, even when he was quite little, and brought out great quantities of mushrooms; he even found truffles, for which Frau Balek paid thirty pfennigs a pound. Everything my grandfather took to the Baleks he entered on the back of a torn-off calendar page: every pound of mushrooms, every gram of thyme, and on the right-hand side, in his childish handwriting, he entered the amount he received for each item; he scrawled in every pfennig, from the age of seven to the age of twelve, and by the time he was twelve the year 1900 had arrived, and because the Baleks had been raised to the aristocracy by the Emperor, they gave every family in the village a quarter of a pound of real coffee, the Brazilian kind; there was also free beer and tobacco for the men, and at the château there was a great banquet; many carriages stood in the avenue of poplars leading from the entrance gates to the château.

But the day before the banquet the coffee was distributed in the little room which had housed the Balek scales for almost a hundred years, and the Balek family was now called Balek von Bilgan because, according to legend, Bilgan the Giant used to have a great castle on the site of the present Balek estate.

My grandfather often used to tell me how he went there after school to fetch the coffee for four families: the Cechs, the Weidlers, the Vohlas, and his own, the Brüchers. It was the afternoon of New Year's Eve: there were the front rooms to be

---

7 **taroc:** a kind of card game

8 **reeve:** an administrative official

9 **Imperial coat of arms:** the royal symbol or emblem

decorated, the baking to be done, and the families did not want to spare four boys and have each of them go all the way to the château to bring back a quarter of a pound of coffee.

And so my grandfather sat on the narrow wooden bench in the little room while Gertrud the maid counted out the wrapped four-ounce packages of coffee, four of them, and he looked at the scales and saw that the pound weight was still lying on the left-hand scale; Frau Balek von Bilgan was busy with preparations for the banquet. And when Gertrud was about to put her hand into the jar with the lemon drops to give my grandfather one, she discovered it was empty: it was refilled once a year, and held one kilo of the kind that cost a mark.

Gertrud laughed and said: "Wait here while I get the new lot," and my grandfather waited with the four four-ounce packages which had been wrapped and sealed in the factory, facing the scales on which someone had left the pound weight, and my grandfather took the four packages of coffee, put them on the empty scale, and his heart thudded as he watched the black finger of justice come to rest on the left of the black line: the scale with the pound weight stayed down, and the pound of coffee remained up in the air; his heart thudded more than if he had been lying behind a bush in the forest waiting for Bilgan the Giant, and he felt in his pocket for the pebbles he always carried with him so he could use his catapult to shoot the sparrows which pecked away at his mother's cabbage plants—he had to put three, four, five pebbles beside the packages of coffee before the scale with the pound weight rose and the pointer at last came to rest over the black line. My grandfather took the coffee from the scale, wrapped the five pebbles in his kerchief, and when Gertrud came back with the big kilo bag of lemon drops which had to last for another whole year in order to make the children's faces light up with pleasure, when Gertrud let the lemon drops rattle into the glass jar, the pale little fellow was still standing there, and nothing seemed to have changed. My grandfather only took three of the packages, then Gertrud looked in startled surprise at the white-faced child who threw the lemon drop onto the floor, ground it under his heel, and said: "I want to see Frau Balek."

"Balek von Bilgan, if you please," said Gertrud.

"All right, Frau Balek von Bilgan," but Gertrud only laughed at him, and he walked back to the village in the dark, took the Cechs, the Weidlers, and the Vohlas their coffee, and said he had to go and see the priest.

Instead he went out into the dark night with his five pebbles in his kerchief. He had to walk a long way before he found someone who had scales, who was permitted to have them; no one in the villages of Blaugau and Bernau had any, he knew that, and he went straight through them till, after two hours' walking, he reached the little town of Dielheim where Honig the apothecary lived. From Honig's house came the smell of fresh pancakes, and Honig's breath, when he opened the door to the half-frozen boy, already smelled of punch, there was a moist cigar between his narrow lips, and he clasped the boy's cold hands firmly for a moment, saying: "What's the matter, has your father's lung got worse?"

"No, I haven't come for medicine, I wanted . . ." My grandfather undid his kerchief, took out the five pebbles, held them out to Honig and said: "I wanted to have these weighed." He glanced anxiously into Honig's face, but when Honig said nothing and did not get angry, or even ask him anything, my grandfather said: "It is the amount that is short of justice," and

MARKET
George Tooker
1949

201

now, as he went into the warm room, my grandfather realized how wet his feet were. The snow had soaked through his cheap shoes, and in the forest the branches had showered him with snow which was now melting, and he was tired and hungry and suddenly began to cry because he thought of the quantities of mushrooms, the herbs, the flowers, which had been weighed on the scales which were short five pebbles' worth of justice. And when Honig, shaking his head and holding the five pebbles, called his wife, my grandfather thought of the generations of his parents, his grandparents, who had all had to have their mushrooms, their flowers, weighed on the scales, and he was overwhelmed by a great wave of injustice, and began to sob louder than ever, and, without waiting to be asked, he sat down on a chair, ignoring the pancakes, the cup of hot coffee which nice plump Frau Honig put in front of him, and did not stop crying till Honig himself came out from the shop at the back and, rattling the pebbles in his hand, said in a low voice to his wife: "Fifty-five grams, exactly."

My grandfather walked the two hours home through the forest, got a beating at home, said nothing, not a single word, when he was asked about the coffee, spent the whole evening doing sums on the piece of paper on which he had written down everything he had sold to Frau Balek, and when midnight struck, and the cannon could be heard from the château, and the whole village rang with shouting and laughter and the noise of rattles, when the family kissed and embraced all round, he said into the New Year silence: "The Baleks owe me eighteen marks and thirty-two pfennigs." And again he thought of all the children there were in the village, of his brother Fritz who had gathered so many mushrooms, of his sister Ludmilla; he thought of the many hundreds of children who had all gathered mushrooms for the Baleks, and herbs and flowers, and this time he did not cry but told his parents and brothers and sisters of his discovery.

When the Baleks von Bilgan went to High Mass on New Year's Day, their new coat of arms—a giant crouching under a fir tree— already emblazoned in blue and gold on their carriage, they saw the hard, pale faces of the people all staring at them. They had expected garlands in the village, a song in their honor, cheers and hurrahs, but the village was completely deserted as they drove through it, and in church the pale faces of the people were turned toward them, mute and hostile, and when the priest mounted the pulpit to deliver his New Year's sermon he sensed the chill in those otherwise quiet and peaceful faces, and he stumbled painfully through his sermon and went back to the altar drenched in sweat. And as the Baleks von Bilgan left the church after Mass, they walked through a lane of mute, pale faces. But young Frau Balek von Bilgan stopped in front of the children's pews, sought out my grandfather's face, pale little Franz Brücher, and asked him, right there in the church: "Why didn't you take the coffee for your mother?" And my grandfather stood up and said: "Because you owe me as much money as five kilos of coffee would cost." And he pulled the five pebbles from his pocket, held them out to the young woman and said: "This much, fifty-five grams, is short in every pound of your justice"; and before the woman could say anything the men and women in the church lifted up their voices and sang: "The justice of this earth, O Lord, hath put Thee to death . . . ."

While the Baleks were at church, Wilhelm Vohla, the poacher, had broken into the little room, stolen the scales and the big fat leather-bound book in which had been entered every kilo of mushrooms, every kilo of hayflowers, everything bought by the Baleks in the village, and all afternoon of that New Year's Day the men of the village sat in my great-grandparents' front room and calculated, calculated one tenth of everything that had been bought—but when they had calculated many thousands of talers[10] and had still not come to an end, the reeve's gendarmes[11] arrived, made their way into my great-grandfather's front room, shooting and stabbing as they came, and removed the scales and the book by force. My grandfather's little sister Ludmilla lost her life, a few men were wounded, and one of the gendarmes was stabbed to death by Wilhelm Vohla the poacher.

Our village was not the only one to rebel: Blaugau and Bernau did too, and for almost a week no work was done in the flax sheds. But a great many gendarmes appeared, and the men and

---

10 **talers:** silver coins

11 **gendarmes:** law-enforcing soldiers

women were threatened with prison, and the Baleks forced the priest to display the scales publicly in the school and demonstrate that the finger of justice swung to and fro accurately. And the men and women went back to the flax sheds—but no one went to the school to watch the priest: he stood there all alone, helpless and forlorn with his weights, scales, and packages of coffee.

And the children went back to gathering mushrooms, to gathering thyme, flowers, and foxglove, but every Sunday, as soon as the Baleks entered the church, the hymn was struck up: "The justice of this earth, O Lord, hath put Thee to death," until the reeve ordered it proclaimed in every village that the singing of the hymn was forbidden.

My grandfather's parents had to leave the village, and the new grave of their little daughter; they became basket weavers, but did not stay long anywhere because it pained them to see how everywhere the finger of justice swung falsely. They walked along behind their cart, which crept slowly over the country roads, taking their thin goat with them, and passers-by could sometimes hear a voice from the cart singing: "The justice of this earth, O Lord, hath put Thee to death." And those who wanted to listen could hear the tale of the Baleks von Bilgan, whose justice lacked a tenth part. But there were few who listened.

Translated by Leila Vennewitz

Responding to the Selection

1. What do you think is the theme of "The Balek Scales"? Find some elements in the story which point to this idea.

2. When in the story does the author first reveal his sympathies? Find the line(s).

3. Why do you suppose the author chooses to use a first-person narrator to relate this story? Explain what he gains by doing so.

4. What other institutions are bound to the power of the Baleks, according to Böll? Think about whether such relationships continue in any modern societies, especially your own.

The Last Judgment

Karel Čapek

Karel Čapek was one of the most popular and influential writers of the original Czech Republic, esteemed for his democratic ideals and sympathetic explorations of human behavior.

In the 20th century, Czechoslovakia was occupied by successive dictatorships—first the Nazis and then the Soviets. Literature was censored and writers who opposed the official line risked prison, work camps, or death. In this repressive climate, many writers learned to mask their social criticism as fantasy, science fiction, black humor, or allegory. Though Čapek died before the beginning of World War II, his writing fell into many of these categories and so served as a model for other Czech writers.

WORLD LENS
♦♦♦
CZECHOSLOVAKIA

Pursued by several warrants and a whole army of policemen and detectives, the notorious multiple-killer Kugler swore that they'd never take him, and they didn't— at least not alive. The last of his nine murderous deeds was shooting a policeman who was trying to arrest him. The policeman indeed died, but not before putting a total of seven bullets into Kugler, three of which were definitely fatal. To all appearances he had escaped earthly justice.

Kugler's death came so quickly that he had no time to feel any particular pain. When his soul left his body, it might have been surprised at the oddness of the next world, a world beyond space, gray and infinitely **desolate**—but it wasn't. A man who has been jailed on two continents looks upon the next life merely as new surroundings. Kugler expected to charge on through, equipped with a bit of courage, just as he'd done everywhere else.

At length the inevitable Last Judgment got around to Kugler. Heaven being eternally in a state of emergency, he was brought before a special court of three judges and not, as his previous

desolate
deserted; joyless

conduct would ordinarily merit, before a jury. The courtroom was furnished simply, like courtrooms on earth, with one exception: there was no provision for swearing in witnesses. The judges were old and worthy councilors with austere, weary faces. The formalities were somewhat tedious: Kugler, Ferdinand; unemployed; born on such-and-such a date; died . . . At this point it was shown that Kugler did not know the date of his own death. Immediately he realized that his failure to remember was damaging in the eyes of the judges, and his attitude hardened.

"Of what do you consider yourself guilty?" the presiding judge asked.

"Nothing," Kugler replied obstinately.

"Bring in the witness," the judge sighed.

In front of Kugler there appeared an extraordinary gentleman, stately, bearded, and clothed in a blue robe strewn with golden stars; at his entrance the judges rose, and even Kugler stood up, reluctant but fascinated. Only when the old gentleman took a seat did the judges sit down again.

"Witness," began the presiding judge, "Omniscient God, this court has summoned You in order to hear Your testimony in the matter of Kugler, Ferdinand. As You are the Supreme Truth, You need not take the oath. We ask only that, in the interest of the proceedings, You keep to the subject at hand and not branch out into particulars that have no legal bearing on the case. And you, Kugler, don't interrupt the Witness. He knows everything, so there's no use denying anything. And now, Witness, if You would please begin."

That said, the presiding judge took off his spectacles and leaned comfortably on the bench before him, evidently in preparation for a long speech by the witness. The oldest of the three judges nestled down in sleep. The recording angel opened the Book of Life.

The Witness, God, cleared his throat and began:

"Yes, Kugler, Ferdinand. Ferdinand Kugler, son of a factory official, was a bad, unmanageable child from his earliest days. He loved his mother dearly but was ashamed to show it; that's why he was unruly and defiant. Young man, you infuriated everyone! Do you remember how you bit your father on the thumb when he tried to spank you because you'd stolen a rose from the notary's[1] garden?"

"That rose was for Irma, the tax collector's daughter," Kugler recalled.

"I know," said God. "Irma was seven years old then. And do you know what happened to her later?"

"No, I don't."

"She got married; she married Oskar, the son of the factory owner. But she contracted a venereal disease from him and died of a miscarriage. You remember Rudy Zaruba?"

"What happened to him?"

"Why, he joined the navy and died in Bombay. You two were the worst boys in the whole town. Kugler, Ferdinand was a thief before his tenth year and an **inveterate** liar. He kept bad company, the drunken beggar Dlabola, for instance, with whom he shared his food."

inveterate
habitual; confirmed

The presiding judge motioned with his hand, as if perhaps this was unnecessary information; but Kugler himself asked shyly, "And . . . what happened to his daughter?"

"Marka?" said God. "She lowered herself considerably. In her fourteenth year she prostituted herself; in her twentieth year she died, remembering you in the agony of her death. By your fourteenth year you were nearly a drunkard yourself, and you often ran away from home. Your father died from grief and worry, and your mother nearly cried her eyes out. You brought dishonor on your home, and your little sister, your pretty sister Marticka, never married: no young man would come calling at the home of a thief. She's still living alone and in poverty, exhausted from sewing each night and humiliated by her scant earnings from people who take pity on her."

"What's happening right now?"

"This very minute she is at Vlcak's, buying thread. Do you remember that shop? Once, when you were six years old, you bought a colored glass marble there; and that very same day you lost it and never ever found it. Do you remember how sad and angry you were then, and how you blubbered?"

"Where did it roll away to?" Kugler asked eagerly.

---

1 **notary:** the clerk who certifies public mail

"Down the drain and into the gutter. As a matter of fact, it's still there, after thirty years. Right now it's raining on earth, and your marble is shivering in a gush of cold water."

Kugler bent his head, overcome. But the presiding judge fitted his spectacles back on his nose and said mildly, "Witness, we are obliged to get on with the case. Has the accused committed murder?"

The Witness nodded his head. "He murdered nine people. The first one he killed in a brawl, and while in prison for it he was completely corrupted. The second was an unfaithful sweetheart. For that he was sentenced to death, but he escaped. The third was an old man, whom he robbed. The fourth was a night watchman."

"Then he died?" Kugler shouted.

"He died after three days of terrible pain," God said, "and he left six children behind. The fifth and sixth people were an old married couple; he finished them off with an axe and found practically no money, although they had more than twenty thousand hidden away."

Kugler jumped up: "Where? Tell me!"

"In the straw mattress," God said. "In a linen sack inside the mattress. That's where they stored the money they got from **usury** and penny-pinching. The seventh man he killed in America; he was an immigrant, a countryman, helpless as a child."

"So it was in the mattress," Kugler whispered in amazement.

"Yes," the Witness continued. "The eighth man was a passerby who happened to be in the way when Kugler was trying to outrun the police. Kugler had periostitis[2] then and was delirious from the pain. Young man, you were suffering terribly. The last was the policeman who killed Kugler, whom Kugler felled just as he himself was dying."

"And why did the accused commit murder?" queried the presiding judge.

"For the same reasons others do," answered God. "From anger, from greed, deliberately and by chance, sometimes with pleasure and other times from necessity. He was generous and sometimes he helped people. He was kind to women, he loved animals, and

usury
*lending money at a
high rate of interest*

---

2 **periostitis:** an inflammation of the connective tissue of the bone

he kept his word. Should I tell about his good deeds?"

"Thank You," the presiding judge said, "it isn't necessary. Does the accused have anything to say in his defense?"

"No," Kugler replied with honest indifference; it was all the same to him.

"The court will now take this case under advisement," the presiding judge declared, and the councilors withdrew. God and Kugler remained in the courtroom.

"Who are they?" Kugler asked, inclining his head toward the three who were leaving.

"People like you," said God. "They were judges on earth, so they're judges here as well."

Kugler nibbled at his fingertips. "I thought . . . I mean, I didn't worry about it or anything, but . . . I figured that You would judge, since . . . since . . ."

"Since I'm God," finished the **stately** gentleman. "But that's just it, don't you see? Because I know everything, I can't possibly judge. That wouldn't do at all. By the way, do you know who turned you in this time?"

"No, I don't," said Kugler, surprised.

"Lucka, the waitress. She did it out of jealousy."

"Excuse me," Kugler ventured, feeling bolder, "but You forgot to mention that no-good Teddy I shot in Chicago."

"You're wrong there," God objected. "He recovered and is alive this very minute. I know he's an informer, but otherwise he's a good man and truly fond of children. You shouldn't think of anyone as being completely worthless."

"But really, why don't You . . . why don't You Yourself do the judging?" Kugler asked **pensively**.

"Because I know everything. If judges knew everything, absolutely everything, they couldn't judge, either: they would understand everything, and their hearts would ache. How could I possibly judge you? Judges know only about your crimes; but I know everything about you. Everything, Kugler. And that's why I cannot judge you."

"But why are those same people judges . . . even here in heaven?"

"Because people belong to each other. As you see, I'm only a

stately
dignified; majestic

pensively
thoughtfully; musingly

"The only justice people deserve is human justice."

witness; it's people who determine the verdict—even in heaven. Believe me, Kugler, this is the way it should be. The only justice people deserve is human justice."

At that moment, the judges returned from their deliberations. In stern tones the presiding judge announced: "For repeated crimes of first-degree murder, manslaughter, robbery, illegal re-entry, concealment of weapons, and the theft of a rose, Kugler, Ferdinand is sentenced to lifelong punishment in hell. The sentence begins immediately. Next case, please. Is the accused, Machat, Frantisek present in court?"

Translated by Norma Comrada

Responding to the Selection

1. Do you see any purpose to the anecdotes (brief stories) about the people in Kugler's life? Explain.

2. What do you think God means by saying, "Because I know everything, I can't possibly judge"?

3. Some people believe that if an author provides enough information about any character, he or she can make that character sympathetic to a reader no matter how evilly the character behaves. Think about Kugler in "The Last Judgment" as well as characters from other stories you have read, and discuss the wisdom of this belief. Based on what you know, do you agree with this theory?

4. What purpose is served by the story ending with a summons to the next criminal?

A Contribution to Statistics

Wislawa Szymborska

POLAND

Out of a hundred people

those who always know better
—fifty-two,

doubting every step
—nearly all the rest,

glad to lend a hand
if it doesn't take too long
—as high as forty-nine,
always good
because they can't be otherwise
—four, well maybe five,

able to admire without envy,
—eighteen,

suffering illusions
induced by fleeting youth
—sixty, give or take a few,

not to be taken lightly
—forty and four,

living in constant fear
of someone or something
—seventy-seven,

capable of happiness
—twenty-something tops,

harmless singly,
savage in crowds
—half at least,

cruel
when forced by circumstances
—better not to know even ballpark figures,

wise after the fact
—just a couple more
than wise before it,

taking only things from life
—thirty
(I wish I were wrong),
hunched in pain,
no flashlight in the dark
—eighty-three
sooner or later,

righteous
—thirty-five, which is a lot,

righteous
and understanding
—three,

worthy of compassion
—ninety-nine,

mortal
—a hundred out of a hundred.
Thus far this figure still remains unchanged.

Translated by Stanislaw Baranczak and Clare Cavanagh

Responding to the Selection

1. Based on this poem, what would you say is the author's attitude toward the human race?

2. How effective is the poet's use of percentages to define the characteristics of human behavior?

3. Do you agree with any of the speaker's assessments? Say which equations strike you as particularly true or false and give reasons for your answers.

4. The writer, Nobelist Wislawa Szymborska, has lived her whole life in Poland, which suffered both Nazi and Soviet Communist repression in the 20th century. Do you think this poem could have been written by anyone, anywhere, or is there anything about it that seems "foreign"?

And Yet the Books

Czeslaw Milosz

WORLD LENS

•••

POLAND/

UNITED STATES

Though of Lithuanian heritage and U.S. citizenship, the 1980 Nobel laureate Czeslaw Milosz spent his early years in Nazi-occupied Poland, where he was one of the leaders of the avant-garde poetry movement. Like many other writers and intellectuals in the 1930s, Milosz participated in the Resistance movement against the Nazis. In his poem, "Child of Europe," he writes: "Love no country: countries soon disappear, / Love no city: cities are soon rubble." His war experiences have deeply affected his family history and writing, testifying to the traumatic as well as transformative power of war.

And yet the books will be there on the shelves, separate beings,
That appeared once, still wet
As shining chestnuts under a tree in autumn,
And, touched, coddled, began to live
In spite of fires on the horizon, castles blown up,
Tribes on the march, planets in motion.
"We are," they said, even as their pages
Were being torn out, or a buzzing flame
Licked away their letters. So much more durable
Than we are, whose frail warmth
Cools down with memory, disperses, perishes.
I imagine the earth when I am no more:
Nothing happens, no loss, it's still a strange pageant,
Women's dresses, dewy lilacs, a song in the valley.
Yet the books will be there on the shelves, well born,
Derived from people, but also from radiance, heights.

Translated by the author and Robert Hass

Responding to the Selection

1. This poem starts off as if the poet is in mid-conversation. What do you think is the purpose of this device?

2. Some people might disagree with the poet as to the significance of books. Do you? Explain your answer.

3. Where in the poem do you see the books personified? Explain what is gained by the personification in this poem.

4. Explain what you think is meant by the poem's last two lines: "Yet the books will be there on the shelves, well born, / Derived from people, but also from radiance, heights."

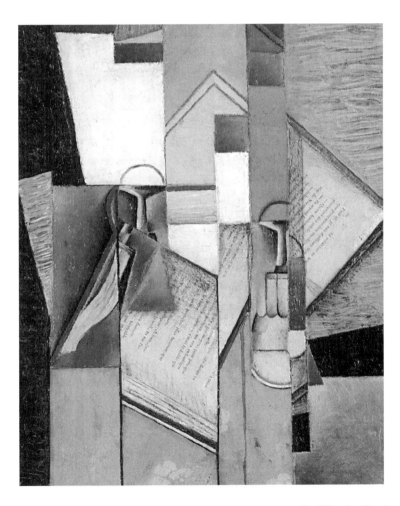

THE BOOK
Juan Gris
1913

And Yet the Books   215

Rhinoceros

Eugene Ionesco

WORLD LENS

◆◆◆

ROMANIA/FRANCE

Eugene Ionesco is usually associated with the theater of the absurd. The Romanian-born French playwright believed that life is a game of chance, and his plays and stories generally demonstrate how unable human beings are to make sense of their universe. "Rhinoceros"—famous foremost as a play—is generally thought to be an allegory about the perils of Nazism. Though his writings employ nightmares, strange metamorphoses, and farce, Ionesco's fundamental sympathy with the human predicament has made him one of the most popular of the absurdist writers.

We were sitting outside the café, my friend Jean and I, peacefully talking about one thing and another, when we caught sight of it on the opposite pavement, huge and powerful, panting noisily, charging straight ahead and brushing against market stalls—a rhinoceros. People in the street stepped hurriedly aside to let it pass. A housewife uttered a cry of terror, her basket dropped from her hands, the wine from a broken bottle spread over the pavement, and some pedestrians, one of them an elderly man, rushed into the shops. It was all over like a flash of lightning. People emerged from their hiding places and gathered in groups which watched the rhinoceros disappear into the distance, made some comments on the incident and then dispersed.

My own reactions are slowish. I absentmindedly took in the image of the rushing beast, without ascribing any very great importance to it. That morning, moreover, I was feeling tired and my mouth was sour, as a result of the previous night's excesses; we had been celebrating a friend's birthday. Jean had not been at the party; and when the first moment of surprise was over, he exclaimed: "A rhinoceros at large in town! Doesn't that surprise you? It ought not to be allowed."

"True," I said, "I hadn't thought of that. It's dangerous."

"We ought to protest to the Town Council."

"Perhaps it's escaped from the zoo," I said.

"You're dreaming," he replied. "There hasn't been a zoo in our town since the animals were decimated by the plague in the seventeenth century."

"Perhaps it belongs to the circus?"

"What circus? The council has forbidden **itinerant** entertainers to stop on municipal territory. None have come here since we were children."

itinerant
traveling; circuit-riding

"Perhaps it has lived here ever since, hidden in the marshy woods round about," I answered with a yawn.

"You're completely lost in a dense alcoholic haze . . . ."

"Which rises from the stomach . . ."

"Yes. And has pervaded your brain. What marshy woods can you think of round about here? Our province is so arid they call it Little Castile.[1]

"Perhaps it sheltered under a pebble? Perhaps it made its nest on a dry branch?"

"How tiresome you are with your **paradoxes**. You're quite incapable of talking seriously."

paradoxes
seeming contradictions; anomalies

"Today, particularly."

"Today and every other day."

"Don't lose your temper, my dear Jean. We're not going to quarrel about that creature . . . ."

We changed the subject of our conversation and began to talk about the weather again, about the rain which fell so rarely in our region, about the need to provide our sky with artificial clouds, and other **banal** and insoluble questions.

banal
trite; overused

We parted. It was Sunday. I went to bed and slept all day: another wasted Sunday. On Monday morning I went to the office, making a solemn promise to myself never to get drunk again, and particularly not on Saturdays, so as not to spoil the following Sundays. For I had one single free day a week and three weeks' holiday in the summer. Instead of drinking and making myself ill, wouldn't it be better to keep fit and healthy, to spend my precious

---

1 **Castile:** central Spain, notable for its sparse rain

moments of freedom in a more intelligent fashion: visiting museums, reading literary magazines and listening to lectures? And instead of spending all my available money on drink, wouldn't it be preferable to buy tickets for interesting plays? I was still unfamiliar with the avant-garde[2] theater, of which I had heard so much talk; I had never seen a play by Ionesco. Now or never was the time to bring myself up-to-date.

The following Sunday I met Jean once again at the same café.

"I've kept my promise," I said, shaking hands with him.

"What promise have you kept?" he asked.

"My promise to myself. I've vowed to give up drinking. Instead of drinking I've decided to cultivate my mind. Today I am clearheaded. This afternoon I'm going to the Municipal Museum, and this evening I've a ticket for the theater. Won't you come with me?"

"Let's hope your good intentions will last," replied Jean. "But I can't go with you. I'm meeting some friends at the brasserie."[3]

"Oh, my dear fellow, now it's you who are setting a bad example. You'll get drunk!"

"Once in a while doesn't imply a habit," replied Jean irritably. "Whereas you . . ."

The discussion was about to take a disagreeable turn, when we heard a mighty trumpeting, the hurried clatter of some perissodactyl's[4] hoofs, cries, a cat's mewing; almost simultaneously we saw a rhinoceros appear, then disappear, on the opposite pavement, panting noisily and charging straight ahead.

. . . we saw a rhinoceros appear, then disappear, on the opposite pavement, panting noisily and charging straight ahead.

Immediately afterwards a woman appeared holding in her arms a shapeless, bloodstained little object:

"It's run over my cat," she wailed, "it's run over

---

2 **avant-garde:** in the arts, especially, refers to the leading edge or the experimental

3 **brasserie:** an informal restaurant serving homecooked, basic fare

4 **perissodactyl:** an order of hoofed mammals that includes rhinoceroses

my cat!"

The poor dishevelled woman, who seemed the very embodiment of grief, was soon surrounded by people offering sympathy.

Jean and I got up. We rushed across the street to the side of the unfortunate woman.

"All cats are mortal," I said stupidly, not knowing how to console her.

"It came past my shop last week!" the grocer recalled.

"It wasn't the same one," Jean declared. "It wasn't the same one: last week's had two horns on its nose—it was an Asian rhinoceros; this one had only one—it's an African rhinoceros."

"You're talking nonsense," I said irritably. "How could you distinguish its horns? The animal rushed past so fast that we could hardly see it; you hadn't time to count them . . . ."

"I don't live in a haze," Jean retorted sharply. "I'm clearheaded, I'm quick at figures."

"He was charging with his head down."

"That made it all the easier to see."

"You're a pretentious fellow, Jean. You're a **pedant**, who isn't even sure of his own knowledge. For in the first place, it's the Asian rhinoceros that has one horn on its nose and the African rhinoceros that has two!"

"You're quite wrong; it's the other way about."

"Would you like to bet on it?"

"I won't bet against you. You're the one who has two horns," he cried, red with fury, "you Asiatic, you!" (He stuck to his guns.)

"I haven't any horns. I shall never wear them. And I'm not an Asiatic, either. In any case, Asiatics are just like other people."

Jean turned his back on me and strode off, cursing.

I felt a fool. I ought to have been more conciliatory and not contradicted him: for I knew he could not bear it. The slightest objection made him foam at the mouth. This was his only fault, for he had a heart of gold and had done me countless good turns. The few people who were there and who had been listening to us had, as a result, quite forgotten about the poor woman's squashed cat. They crowded round me, arguing: some maintained that the Asian rhinoceros was indeed one-horned, and that I was

pedant
person who shows off learning; stickler for details

right; others maintained that on the contrary the African rhinoceros was one-horned, and that therefore the previous speaker had been right.

"That is not the question," interposed a gentleman (straw boater,[5] small moustache, eyeglass, a typical logician's head) who had hitherto stood silent. "The discussion turned on a problem from which you have wandered. You began by asking yourselves whether today's rhinoceros is the same as last Sunday's or whether it is a different one. That is what must be decided. You may have seen one and the same one-horned rhinoceros on two occasions, or you may have seen one and the same two-horned rhinoceros on two occasions. Or again, you may have seen first one one-horned rhinoceros and then a second one-horned rhinoceros. Or else, first one two-horned rhinoceros and then a second two-horned rhinoceros. If on the first occasion you had seen a two-horned rhinoceros and on the second a one-horned rhinoceros, that would not be conclusive either. It might be that since last week the rhinoceros had lost one of his horns and that the one you saw today was the same. Or it might be that two two-horned rhinoceroses had each lost one of their horns. If you could prove that on the first occasion you had seen a one-horned rhinoceros, whether it was Asian or African, and today a two-horned rhinoceros, whether it was African or Asian—that doesn't matter—then we might conclude that two different rhinoceroses were involved, for it is most unlikely that a second horn could grow in a few days, to any visible extent, on a rhinoceros's nose; this would mean that an Asian, or African, rhinoceros had become an African, or Asian, rhinoceros, which is logically impossible, since the same creature cannot be born in two places at once or even successively."

"That seems clear to me," I said. "But it doesn't settle the question."

"Of course," retorted the gentleman, smiling with a knowledgeable air, "only the problem has now been stated correctly."

"That's not the problem either," interrupted the grocer, who being no doubt of an emotional nature cared little about logic.

---

5 **straw boater:** a stiff straw hat

"Can we allow our cats to be run over under our eyes by two-horned or one-horned rhinoceroses, be they Asian or African?"

"He's right, he's right," everybody exclaimed. "We can't allow our cats to be run over, by rhinoceroses or anything else!"

The grocer pointed with a theatrical gesture to the poor weeping woman, who still held and rocked in her arms the shapeless, bleeding remains of what had once been her cat.

◆ ◆ ◆ ◆ ◆

Next day in the paper, under the heading Road Casualties Among Cats, there were two lines describing the death of the poor creature: "crushed underfoot by a pachyderm"[6] it was said, without further details.

On Sunday afternoon I hadn't visited a museum; in the evening I hadn't gone to the theater. I had moped at home by myself, overwhelmed by remorse at having quarrelled with Jean.

"He's so susceptible, I ought to have spared his feelings," I told myself. "It's absurd to lose one's temper about something like that . . . about the horns of a rhinoceros that one had never seen before . . . a native of Africa or of India, such faraway countries, what could it matter to me? Whereas Jean had always been my friend, a friend who . . . to whom I owed so much . . . and who . . ."

In short, while promising myself to go and see Jean as soon as possible and to make it up with him, I had drunk an entire bottle of brandy without noticing. But I did indeed notice it the next day: a sore head, a foul mouth, an uneasy conscience; I was really most uncomfortable. But duty before everything: I got to the office on time, or almost. I was able to sign the register just before it was taken away.

"Well, so you've seen rhinoceroses too?" asked the chief clerk, who, to my great surprise, was already there.

"Sure I've seen him," I said, taking off my town jacket and putting on my old jacket with the frayed sleeves, good enough for work.

"Oh, now you see, I'm not crazy!" exclaimed the typist Daisy

---

6 **pachyderm:** a hoofed, often thick-skinned mammal, such as a rhinoceros or elephant

excitedly. (How pretty she was, with her pink cheeks and fair hair! I found her terribly attractive. If I could fall in love with anybody, it would be with her. . . .) "A one-horned rhinoceros!"

"Two-horned!" corrected my colleague Emile Dudard, Bachelor of Law, eminent jurist, who looked forward to a brilliant future with the firm and, possibly, in Daisy's affections.

"*I've* not seen it! And I don't believe in it!" declared Botard, an ex-schoolmaster who acted as **archivist**. "And nobody's ever seen one in this part of the world, except in the illustrations to school textbooks. These rhinoceroses have blossomed only in the imagination of ignorant women. The thing's a myth, like flying saucers."

I was about to point out to Botard that the expression "blossomed" applied to a rhinoceros, or to a number of them, seemed to me inappropriate, when the jurist exclaimed: "All the same, a cat was crushed, and before witnesses!"

"Collective **psychosis**," retorted Botard, who was a freethinker, "just like religion, the opium of the people!"

"I believe in flying saucers myself," remarked Daisy.

The chief clerk cut short our argument:

"That'll do! Enough chatter! Rhinoceros or no rhinoceros, flying saucers or no flying saucers, work's got to be done."

The typist started typing. I sat down at my desk and became engrossed in my documents. Emile Dudard began correcting the proofs of a commentary on the Law for the Repression of Alcoholism, while the chief clerk, slamming the door, retired into his study.

"It's a hoax!" Botard grumbled once more, aiming his remarks at Dudard. "It's your propaganda that spreads these rumors!"

"It's not propaganda," I interposed.

"I saw it myself . . . ," Daisy confirmed simultaneously.

"You make me laugh," said Dudard to Botard. "Propaganda? For what?"

"You know that better than I do! Don't act the simpleton!"

"In any case, *I'm* not paid by the Pontenegrins!"

"That's an insult!" cried Botard, thumping the table with his fist. The door of the chief clerk's room opened suddenly and his head appeared.

archivist
person who maintains a collection of documents

psychosis
mental derangement; loss of contact with reality

"Monsieur Boeuf hasn't come in today."

"Quite true, he's not here," I said.

"Just when I needed him. Did he tell anyone he was ill? If this goes on I shall give him the sack . . . ."

It was not the first time that the chief clerk had threatened our colleague in this way.

"Has one of you got the key to his desk?" he went on.

Just then Madame Boeuf made her appearance. She seemed terrified.

"I must ask you to excuse my husband. He went to spend the weekend with relations. He's had a slight attack of 'flu. Look, that's what he says in his telegram. He hopes to be back on Wednesday. Give me a glass of water . . . and a chair!" she gasped, collapsing onto the chair we offered her.

"It's very tiresome! But it's no reason to get so alarmed!" remarked the chief clerk.

"I was pursued by a rhinoceros all the way from home," she stammered.

"With one horn or two?" I asked.

"You make me laugh!" exclaimed Botard.

"Why don't you let her speak!" protested Dudard.

Madame Boeuf had to make a great effort to be explicit:

"It's downstairs, in the doorway. It seems to be trying to come upstairs."

At that very moment a tremendous noise was heard: the stairs were undoubtedly giving way under a considerable weight. We rushed out onto the landing. And there, in fact, amidst the debris, was a rhinoceros, its head lowered, trumpeting in an agonized and agonizing voice and turning vainly round and round. I was able to make out two horns.

"It's an African rhinoceros . . . ," I said, "or rather an Asian one."

My mind was so confused that I was no longer sure whether two horns were characteristic of the Asian or of the African rhinoceros, whether a single horn was characteristic of the African or the Asian rhinoceros, or whether on the contrary two horns . . . In short, I was floundering mentally, while Botard glared furiously at Dudard.

"It's an infamous plot!" and, with an orator's gesture, he pointed at the jurist: "It's your fault!"

"It's yours!" the other retorted.

"Keep calm, this is no time to quarrel!" declared Daisy, trying in vain to pacify them.

"For years now I've been asking the board to let us have concrete steps instead of that rickety old staircase," said the chief clerk. "Something like this was bound to happen. It was predictable. I was quite right!"

"As usual," Daisy added ironically. "But how shall we get down?"

"I'll carry you in my arms," the chief clerk joked flirtatiously, stroking the typist's cheek, "and we'll jump together!"

"Don't put your horny hand on my face, you pachydermous creature!"

The chief clerk had not time to react. Madame Boeuf, who had got up and come to join us, and who had for some minutes been staring attentively at the rhinoceros, which was turning round and round below us, suddenly uttered a terrible cry:

"It's my husband! Boeuf, my poor dear Boeuf, what has happened to you?"

The rhinoceros, or rather Boeuf, responded with a violent and yet tender trumpeting, while Madame Boeuf fainted into my arms and Botard, raising his to heaven, stormed: "It's sheer lunacy! What a society!"

◆◆◆◆◆

When we had recovered from our initial astonishment, we telephoned to the fire brigade, who drove up with their ladder and fetched us down. Madame Boeuf, although we advised her against it, rode off on her spouse's back toward their home. She had ample grounds for divorce (but who was the guilty party?), yet she chose rather not to desert her husband in his present state.

At the little bistro[7] where we all went for lunch (all except the Boeufs, of course) we learnt that several rhinoceroses had been seen in various parts of the town: some people said seven, others seventeen, others again said thirty-two. In the face of this

---

7 **bistro:** a small restaurant

accumulated evidence, Botard could no longer deny the rhinoceric facts. But he knew, he declared, what to think about it. He would explain it to us some day. He knew the "why" of things, the "underside" of the story, the names of those responsible, the aim and significance of the outrage. Going back to the office that afternoon, business or no business, was out of the question. We had to wait for the staircase to be repaired.

I took advantage of this to pay a call on Jean, with the intention of making it up with him. He was in bed.

"I don't feel very well!" he said.

"You know, Jean, we were both right. There are two-horned rhinoceroses in the town as well as one-horned ones. It really doesn't matter where either sort comes from. The only significant thing, in my opinion, is the existence of the rhinoceros in itself."

"I don't feel very well," my friend kept on saying without listening to me, "I don't feel very well!"

"What's the matter with you? I'm so sorry!"

"I'm rather feverish, and my head aches."

More precisely, it was his forehead which was aching. He must have had a knock, he said. And in fact a lump was swelling up there, just above his nose. He had gone a greenish color, and his voice was hoarse.

"Have you got a sore throat? It may be tonsillitis."

I took his pulse. It was beating quiet regularly.

"It can't be very serious. A few days' rest and you'll be all right. Have you sent for the doctor?"

As I was about to let go of his wrist, I noticed that his veins were swollen and bulging out. Looking closely, I observed that not only were the veins enlarged but the skin all round them was visibly changing color and growing hard.

"It may be more serious than I imagined," I thought. "We must send for the doctor," I said aloud.

"I felt uncomfortable in my clothes, and now my pajamas are too tight," he said in a hoarse voice.

"What's the matter with your skin? It's like leather . . . ." Then, staring at him: "Do you know what happened to Boeuf? He's turned into a rhinoceros."

"Well, what about it? That's not such a bad thing! After all, rhinoceroses are creatures like ourselves, with just as much right to live . . . ."

"Provided they don't imperil our own lives. Aren't you aware of the difference in mentality?"

"Do you think ours is preferable?"

"All the same, we have our own moral code, which I consider incompatible with that of these animals. We have our philosophy, our irreplaceable system of values . . . ."

"**Humanism** is out of date! You're a ridiculous old sentimentalist. You're talking nonsense."

"I'm surprised to hear you say that, my dear Jean! Have you taken leave of your senses?"

It really looked like it. Blind fury had disfigured his face and altered his voice to such an extent that I could scarcely understand the words that issued from his lips.

"Such assertions, coming from you . . . ," I tried to resume.

He did not give me a chance to do so. He flung back his blankets, tore off his pajamas, and stood up in bed, entirely naked (he who was usually the most modest of men!), green with rage from head to foot.

The lump on his forehead had grown longer; he was staring fixedly at me, apparently without seeing me. Or, rather, he must have seen me quite clearly, for he charged at me with his head lowered. I barely had time to leap to one side; if I hadn't, he would have pinned me to the wall.

"You are a rhinoceros!" I cried.

"I'll trample on you! I'll trample on you!" I made out these words as I dashed toward the door.

I went downstairs four steps at a time, while the walls shook as he butted them with his horn, and I heard him utter fearful angry trumpetings.

"Call the police! Call the police! You've got a rhinoceros in the house!" I called out to the tenants who, in great surprise, looked out of their flats as I passed each landing.

On the ground floor I had great difficulty in dodging the rhinoceros, which emerged from the concierge's[8] lodge and tried to charge me. At last I found myself out in the street, sweating, my

humanism

philosophy that stresses the power of human reason; way of life centered on human interests or values

---

8 **concierge:** the doorkeeper

legs limp, at the end of my tether.

Fortunately there was a bench by the edge of the pavement, and I sat down on it. Scarcely had I more or less got back my breath when I saw a herd of rhinoceroses hurrying down the avenue and nearing, at full speed, the place where I was. If only they had been content to stay in the middle of the street! But they were so many that there was not room for them all there, and they overflowed onto the pavement. I leapt off my bench and flattened myself against the wall: snorting, trumpeting, with a smell of leather and of wild animals in heat, they brushed past me and covered me with a cloud of dust. When they had disappeared, I could not go back to sit on the bench; the animals had demolished it, and it lay in fragments on the pavement.

I did not find it easy to recover from such emotions. I had to stay at home for several days. Daisy came to see me and kept me informed as to the changes that were taking place.

The chief clerk had been the first to turn into a rhinoceros, to the great disgust of Botard, who, nevertheless, became one himself twenty-four hours later.

"One must keep up with one's times!" were his last words as a man.

The case of Botard did not surprise me, in spite of his apparent strength of mind. I found it less easy to understand the chief clerk's transformation. Of course it might have been involuntary, but one would have expected him to put up more resistance.

Daisy recalled that she had commented on the roughness of his palms the very day that Boeuf had appeared in rhinoceros shape. This must have made a deep impression on him; he had not shown it, but he had certainly been cut to the quick.

"If I hadn't been so outspoken, if I had pointed it out to him more tactfully, perhaps this would never have happened."

"I blame myself, too, for not having been gentler with Jean. I ought to have been friendlier, shown more understanding," I said in my turn.

Daisy informed me that Dudard, too, had been transformed, as had also a cousin of hers, whom I did not know. And there were others, mutual friends, strangers.

"There are a great many of them," she said, "about a quarter of the inhabitants of our town."

"They're still in the minority, however."

"The way things are going, that won't last long!" she sighed.

"Alas! And they're so much more efficient."

Herds of rhinoceroses rushing at top speed through the streets became a sight that no longer surprised anybody. People would stand aside to let them pass and then resume their stroll, or attend to their business, as if nothing had happened.

"How can anybody be a rhinoceros! It's unthinkable!" I protested in vain.

More of them kept emerging from courtyards and houses, even from windows, and went to join the rest.

There came a point when the authorities proposed to enclose them in huge parks. For humanitarian reasons, the Society for the Protection of Animals opposed this. Besides, everyone had some close relative or friend among the rhinoceroses, which, for obvious reasons, made the project well-nigh impracticable. It was abandoned.

The situation grew worse, which was only to be expected. One day a whole regiment of rhinoceroses, having knocked down the walls of the barracks, came out with drums at their head and poured onto the boulevards.

At the Ministry of Statistics, statisticians produced their statistics: census of animals, approximate reckoning of their daily increase, percentage of those with one horn, percentage of those with two. . . .What an opportunity for learned controversies! Soon there were defections among the statisticians themselves. The few who remained were paid fantastic sums.

One day from my balcony I caught sight of a rhinoceros charging forward with loud trumpetings, presumably to join his fellows; he wore a straw boater impaled on his horn.

"The logician!" I cried. "He's one too? Is it possible?" Just at that moment Daisy opened the door.

"The logician is a rhinoceros!" I told her.

She knew. She had just seen him in the street. She was bringing me a basket of provisions.

"Shall we have lunch together?" she suggested. "You know, it was difficult to find anything to eat. The shops have been ransacked; they devour everything. A number of shops are closed 'on account of transformations,' the notices say."

"I love you, Daisy, please never leave me."

"Close the window, darling. They make too much noise. And the dust comes in."

"So long as we're together, I'm afraid of nothing, I don't mind about anything." Then, when I had closed the window: "I thought I should never be able to fall in love with a woman again."

I clasped her tightly in my arms. She responded to my embrace.

"How I'd like to make you happy! Could you be happy with me?"

"Why not? You declare you're afraid of nothing and yet you're scared of everything! What can happen to us?"

"My love, my joy!" I stammered, kissing her lips with a passion such as I had forgotten, intense and agonizing.

The ringing of the telephone interrupted us.

She broke from my arms, went to pick up the receiver, then uttered a cry: "Listen. . . ."

I put the receiver to my ear. I heard ferocious trumpetings.

"They're playing tricks on us now!"

"Whatever can be happening?" she inquired in alarm.

We turned on the radio to hear the news; we heard more trumpetings. She was shaking with fear.

"Keep calm," I said, "keep calm!"

She cried out in terror, "They've taken over the broadcasting station!"

"Keep calm, keep calm!" I repeated, increasingly agitated myself.

Next day in the street they were running about in all directions. You could watch for hours without catching sight of a single human being. Our house was shaking under the weight of our perissodactylic neighbors' hoofs.

"What must be must be," said Daisy. "What can we do about it?"

"They've all gone mad. The world is sick."

"It's not you and I who'll cure it."

"We shan't be able to communicate with anybody. Can you understand them?"

"We ought to try to interpret their psychology, to learn their language."

"They have no language."

"What do you know about it?"

"Listen to me, Daisy. We shall have children, and then they will have children. It'll take time, but between us we can regenerate humanity. With a little courage . . ."

"I don't want to have children."

"How do you hope to save the world, then?"

"Perhaps after all it's we who need saving. Perhaps we are the abnormal ones. Do you see anyone else like us?"

"Daisy, I can't have you talking like that!"

I looked at her in despair.

"It's we who are in the right, Daisy, I assure you."

"What arrogance! There's no absolute right. It's the whole world that is right—not you or me."

"Yes, Daisy, I *am* right. The proof is that you understand me and that I love you as much as a man can love a woman."

"I'm rather ashamed of what you call love, that **morbid** thing. . . . It cannot compare with the extraordinary energy displayed by all these beings we see around us."

morbid
unhealthy; gloomy

"Energy? Here's energy for you!" I cried, my powers of argument exhausted, giving her a slap.

Then, as she burst into tears: "I won't give in, no, I won't give in."

She rose, weeping, and flung her sweet-smelling arms round my neck.

"I'll stand fast, with you, to the end."

She was unable to keep her word. She grew melancholy and visibly pined away. One morning when I woke up, I saw that her place in the bed was empty. She had gone away without leaving any message.

The situation became literally unbearable for me. It was my fault if Daisy had gone. Who knows what had become of her? Another burden on my conscience. There was nobody who could help me find her again. I imagined the worst and felt myself responsible.

And on every side there were trumpetings and frenzied chargings and clouds of dust. In vain did I shut myself up in my own room, putting cotton wool in my ears: at night I saw them in my dreams.

"The only way out is to convince them." But of what? Were these **mutations** reversible? And in order to convince them, one would have to talk to them. In order for them to relearn my language (which moreover I was beginning to forget), I should first have to learn theirs. I could not distinguish one trumpeting from another, one rhinoceros from another rhinoceros.

mutations
changes; alterations

One day, looking at myself in the glass, I took a dislike to my long face: I needed a horn, or even two, to give dignity to my flabby features.

And what if, as Daisy had said, it was they who were in the right? I was out of date; I had missed the boat, that was clear.

I discovered that their trumpetings had after all a certain charm, if a somewhat harsh one. I should have noticed that while there was still time. I tried to trumpet: how feeble the sound was, how lacking in vigor! When I made greater efforts, I only succeeded in howling. Howlings are not trumpetings.

It is obvious that one must not always drift blindly behind events and that it's a good thing to maintain one's individuality. However, one must also make allowances for things; asserting one's own difference, to be sure, but yet . . . remaining akin to one's fellows. I no longer bore any likeness to anyone or to anything, except to ancient, old-fashioned photographs which had no connection with living beings.

Each morning I looked at my hands, hoping that the palms would have hardened during my sleep. The skin remained flabby. I gazed at my too-white body, my hairy legs: oh for a hard skin and that magnificent green color, a decent, hairless nudity, like theirs!

My conscience was increasingly uneasy, unhappy. I felt I was a monster. Alas, I would never become a rhinoceros. I could never change.

I dared no longer look at myself. I was ashamed. And yet I couldn't, no, I couldn't.

Responding to the Selection

1. What is the theme of this play-turned-story? Explain what details and events lead you to this conclusion.

2. In a short story, space is compressed, and so things that are brought up more than once usually have more significance than they might in real life. Can you think of any reason that drinking is mentioned several times in this story?

3. What is a "collective psychosis"? Explain how the phrase fits in with the themes of this story.

4. There are many absurd transformations in this story. Name some of them and find, if you can, any similarities between these changes and the changes that would have been taking place in Nazi Germany during Ionesco's life.

Alone

Tomas Tranströmer

SWEDEN

I
One evening in February I came near to dying here.
The car skidded sideways on the ice, out
on the wrong side of the road. The approaching cars—
their lights—closed in.

My name, my girls, my job
broke free and were left silently behind
further and further away. I was anonymous
like a boy in a playground surrounded by enemies.

The approaching traffic had huge lights.
They shone on me while I pulled at the wheel
in a transparent terror that floated like egg white.
The seconds grew—there was space in them—
they grew big as hospital buildings.

You could almost pause
and breathe out for a while
before being crushed.

Then something caught: a helping grain of sand
or a wonderful gust of wind. The car broke free
and scuttled smartly right over the road.
A post shot up and cracked—a sharp clang—it
flew away in the darkness.

Then—stillness. I sat back in my seat-belt
and saw someone coming through the whirling snow
to see what had become of me.

II
I have been walking for a long time
on the frozen Östergötland fields.
I have not seen a single person.

In other parts of the world
there are people who are born, live and die
in a perpetual crowd.

To be always visible—to live
in a swarm of eyes—
a special expression must develop.
Face coated with clay.

The murmuring rises and falls
while they divide up among themselves
the sky, the shadows, the sand grains.

I must be alone
ten minutes in the morning
and ten minutes in the evening.
—Without a program.

Everyone is queuing at everyone's door.

Many.

One.

Translated by Robin Fulton

Responding to the Selection

1. This poem is divided into two parts. How would you characterize the two sections, and how does the first part of the poem relate to the second part?

2. In the second part of the poem, the speaker says "I must be alone." Which kind of world would you prefer to live in—the isolated Swedish fields of the poem, or where people "live and die / in a perpetual crowd"? Explain your answer.

The Nobel Prize

Boris Pasternak

WORLD LENS

◆◆◆

RUSSIA

In 1958, Boris Pasternak was pressured by the Communist Russian government to turn down one of the most distinguished prizes in world literature, the Nobel Prize. It was the height of the Cold War, the post-World War II tensions between the capitalistic Western powers and the Communist Soviet bloc countries. Soviet writers such as Pasternak were prohibited to speak or travel freely and were discouraged from communicating with literary and cultural outposts in the west, such as universities, conferences, and periodicals.

In his writing, Pasternak returns to themes of war, self-identity, and a poet's quest for independence.

I've fallen beast-like in a snare:
Light, people, freedom, somewhere bide:
But at my back I hear the chase
And there is no escape outside.

Darkest wood and lakeside shore,
Gaunt trunk of a levelled tree,
My way is cut off on all sides:
Let what may, come; all's one to me.

Is there some ill I have committed?
Am I a murderer, miscreant?
For I have made the whole world weep
Over the beauty of my land.

But even at the very grave
I trust the time shall come to be
When over malice, over wrong,
The good will win its victory.

Translated by Henry Kamen

Responding to the Selection

1. Pasternak had to decline the world's most famous literary award, the Nobel Prize, as a result of the Soviet censorship of his novel, *Doctor Zhivago*. What is the poet's attitude toward this disappointment?

2. Think about one of your proudest accomplishments. Now think about how you would feel if your government and fellow Americans denied its importance and worse, called on you to denounce your own work. How would that make you feel? Decide whether Pasternak's poem adequately conveys his anguish.

3. Why do you think the speaker compares himself to a beast in the first line of the poem?

4. Lyrical poetry, such as this poem by Pasternak, expresses almost musically the emotions of the poet or speaker of the poem. What are some of the emotions revealed in the poem?

In the Outskirts of Moscow in 1941, Alexander Deineka

First Frost

Andrei Voznesensky

RUSSIA

A girl is freezing in a telephone booth,
huddled in her flimsy coat,
her face stained by tears
and smeared with lipstick.

She breathes on her thin little fingers.
Fingers like ice. Glass beads in her ears.

She has to beat her way back alone
down the icy street.

First frost. A beginning of losses.
The first frost of telephone phrases.

It is the start of winter glittering on her cheek,
the first frost of having been hurt.

Responding to the Selection

1. What do you think the girl has just experienced? Find clues in the poem that point out the source of her disappointment.

2. Is there anything in the poem "First Frost" that reveals the poet's nationality or could it have been written by a poet from almost any culture?

3. Alliteration is a literary device wherein successive words begin with the same sound or sounds, usually beginning consonants. The alliterative phrase "first frost" is repeated in this short poem. What effect do you think this has?

Forbidden Fruit

Fazil Iskander

WORLD LENS

• • •

REPUBLIC OF
ABKHAZIA/

RUSSIA

Born on the Black Sea, in Soviet Abkhazia, Fazil Iskander is a writer of both prose and poetry. He speaks Abkhazian as well as Russian, but mindful of the widest possible audience for his writing, composes in Russian. His satires and parodies are often directed squarely at the government. As a result, he has run up against the Soviet censorship bureaucracy. Twice he has been nominated for the prestigious Lenin Prize only to have his nomination turned down by authorities. Iskander's playful style and depiction of the Abkhazian culture have made him a unique voice in contemporary Russian prose.

latitude
freedom; leeway

abstinence
*avoidance; voluntary
giving up*

Neither children nor grownups in our family ever ate pork. Though another of Mohammed's[1] commandments—the one on alcoholic drinks—was broken (and without constraint, as I know now), no **latitude** was allowed with respect to pork.

The ban provoked hot dreams and icy **abstinence**. I dreamt interminably of eating pork. The smell of fried pork made me faint. I would loiter for hours in front of foodstore showcases and contemplate sausages beaded with fat and dappled with pork. I imagined myself skinning these sausages and letting my teeth sink into the juicy, luxuriant meat. I imagined the taste of sausage so accurately that, when I tasted it later, I was surprised at how truly my imagination had anticipated reality.

Of course, in childhood there were occasions when I could have tasted pork in kindergarten or ate at the home of a friend, but I never broke the commandment.

When we had rice and pork in kindergarten, I fished out all the

---

1 **Mohammed:** (also Muhammad), the prophet who founded the Islamic faith

pieces of pork and gave them to my friends. I conquered the agony of yearning by the sweetness of self-denial. I enjoyed my **ideological** superiority. It was pleasant to be an **enigma**, to behave in a way baffling to everyone around. And yet, all the more intensely did I dream of a transgression.

One of our neighbors was a nurse called Auntie Sonya. For some reason or other, we believed Auntie Sonya was a doctor. In general, I notice that as one grows older, the status of people seems to drop.

Auntie Sonya was an elderly woman with bobbed hair and a sorrowing expression never absent from her face. She always spoke in a low voice as though she had long ago realized that there was nothing in life worth speaking up about.

When she quarreled with her neighbors, she rarely raised her voice. That created problems for her adversaries because they could not grasp her last words, lost the thread, and the quarrel flagged disastrously.

Auntie Sonya and our family were friends, and Mother used to say that Auntie Sonya had saved me. I had been very sick, and she and my mother had taken turns looking after me for a whole month. To tell the truth, I did not feel properly grateful for my saved life, but, out of politeness, whenever the incident came up, I wore the expression of a person happy to have been saved.

Auntie Sonya spent evenings with our family and often told us the story of her life, and the principal hero was her first husband, who had been killed in the Civil War.[2] I had heard the story many times, but my heart always dropped when she reached the point where she found her husband among the corpses. Here she would begin to cry, and my mother and older sister would weep too. Then they would comfort her, beg her to have some tea, or bring her a glass of water. I was always astonished at how quickly the women composed themselves and chattered with fresh, and even cheery, animation about all sorts of trifles. Then Auntie Sonya would leave because it was time for her husband, Uncle Shura, to come home.

ideological
based on beliefs

enigma
puzzle; mystery

---

2 **Civil War:** also known as the October Revolution, the years following the 1917 revolution in Russia that had toppled the Czar. The revolutionary Bolsheviks, led by Vladimir Lenin, fought the old Russian aristocracy for complete power. The war ended in 1920 with Lenin heading the new Communist state.

I liked Uncle Shura. I liked his black hair and that unruly lock over his forehead, his neatly rolled-up sleeves and strong arms. I even liked his stoop. His was not a clerk's stoop but a pleasant old worker's stoop, though Uncle Shura was neither an old man nor a worker.

After hours he would always tinker with something: a desk lamp, or an electric iron, or a radio set, or even a watch which his neighbors brought and which he repaired, charging them nothing.

prodigiously
enormously; excessively

Auntie Sonya sat across the table, smoked **prodigiously**, and poked fun at him, telling him that he was a jack of all trades, that he would never fix what he was trying to fix, and so on and so forth.

"We'll see if I won't fix it," Uncle Shura muttered through his teeth because he had a cigarette in his mouth. He would handle the thing a neighbor had brought with graceful confidence, dust it off, and then suddenly look at it from some unexpected angle.

"I can see them laughing at you," Auntie Sonya would counter with an arrogant puff of smoke, wrapping her robe tighter around her.

Finally, he would wind the watch, or the radio set would crackle snatches of music.

"I like to see them laughing at me. I don't mind a bit," he would say with a wink at me.

I wanted my smile to show that I had nothing to

do with his triumph but that I appreciated his trust.

"You brag too much," Auntie Sonya would say. "Lay the table for tea."

In her voice I detected hidden pride, and I wondered if Uncle Shura was of a less heroic mold than that hero of the Civil War whom Auntie Sonya could not forget.

✦✦✦✦✦

Once, when I was spending an evening with them, my sister dropped in, and they invited her to tea. Auntie Sonya sliced some pork fat of an unbelievably delicate pink and put a cruet[3] of mustard on the table. They had often eaten pork before and asked me to have some, but I invariably and firmly refused, which always moved Uncle Shura to mirth for some reason or other. This time they also asked me to have some, but they did not insist. Uncle Shura put several slices of pork fat on a chunk of bread and gave it to my sister. After the few no's required by decency, she accepted the horrible sandwich and began to eat it. Indignation stiffened my throat, and I had difficulty getting my tea down.

"That's what it is," said Uncle Shura. "You're a monk, that's what you are!"

I could say nothing. She ate the sandwich with shameless neatness, a vacant look in her eyes. That vacancy was meant to show that she was eating officially, purely out of respect for her hosts. It was meant to suggest that the sacrilege was not to be taken seriously and did not count at all.

"It does count!" I thought maliciously, watching the sandwich becoming smaller at an agonizingly slow rate.

I felt she was enjoying it. It was evident from the way she licked the crumbs, from the way she swallowed each bite—slowed her chewing in the silliest way as though listening to the sound the food made going down her gullet. The slices of fat were thinner at the edge she nibbled, the surest sign that she was enjoying it because all normal children leave the tidbit for last. In other words, all the evidence was there.

---

3 **cruet:** a glass condiment bottle

Now she was coming to the edge of the sandwich where the piece of pork was thickest. She kept her enjoyment in crescendo. Meanwhile, she was serenely (woman's infinite ability to pretend) telling how my brother jumped out of a window when the teacher called on our parents. The story had a dual purpose: first, to divert attention from what she was doing, and second, to flatter me in a very subtle way since everyone knew that the teacher had no reason to complain of me, and still less had I any reason to flee from her through a window.

As she was telling all this, she would look at me from time to time to see whether I was still watching her or, carried away by her story, was forgetting about her sin. But my expression was not to be doubted: my vigilance never flagged. In self-defense she goggled her eyes like one surprised that so much attention was being paid to a trifling matter. I only smirked, a hint of the retribution to come.

For a moment I thought that it had come already because she began to cough. I watched **transfixed**. Uncle Shura slapped her on the back, and she stopped coughing to indicate that his cure had helped and that her discomfort was insignificant. But I felt that the piece was still stuck in her throat. She pretended she was all right now and took another bite.

"Chew away!" I thought. "Let's see you swallow it."

But evidently, somewhere on high the retribution was rescheduled. My sister swallowed this bite without difficulty, and perhaps it even helped her swallow down its predecessor because she gave a sigh of relief and looked around cheerfully. Now she chewed and licked her lips after each bite with special care, or maybe she was simply sticking out her tongue at me.

She was at the edge of the sandwich with the thickest piece of fat. Before committing it to her mouth, she bit off the last edge of the bread uncovered by fat. That climaxed that last tidbit even more. Then she swallowed it down, too, and licked her lips as though trying to prolong the pleasure and show that there were no traces of the sin left.

All this did not take much time, of course, and was almost imperceptible to an outsider. At any rate, Uncle Shura and Auntie Sonya did not seem to notice anything. Her sandwich finished,

transfixed
held motionless; spellbound

my sister proceeded to her tea, still pretending that nothing had happened. As soon as she touched her cup, I gulped mine down. I did not want to share anything with her. A few minutes before, I had refused to eat some cookies so I could run the whole **gamut** of suffering and have no earthly joys in her presence. Besides, I resented Uncle Shura, who had not urged me nearly as much as he had my sister. I would not have accepted the cookies anyway, but his urging would have made my refusal a better lesson in principles for my sister.

> **gamut**
> *range; spectrum*

In short, I was terribly let down and went home as soon as I finished my tea. They begged me to stay, but I was adamant.

"I have to do my lessons!" I said piously.

My sister asked me to stay with special insistence. She was sure that I would tell on her at home, and, besides, she was afraid to cross the yard alone.

At home, I slipped out of my clothes and into my bed to luxuriate in the contemplation of my sister's apostasy.[4] All kinds of visions rushed through my mind. Here I was, a Red partisan captured by the Whites,[5] who are forcing me to eat pork. They torture me, but I will not touch it. Surprised, the officers shake their heads: What sort of boy is this? As a matter of fact, I'm surprised myself. I just won't eat pork. Kill me, but eat pork I will not.

The door creaked and my sister came in. She immediately asked about me.

"He's gone to bed," I heard my mother reply. "He came home in the dumps. Anything happen?"

"Why, nothing," my sister answered and went over to my bed. I was afraid she would begin coaxing me and all that. Pardon was out of the question, anyway, and besides I did not want her to change the state of mind I was in. I, therefore, pretended to be asleep. She stood for a while and stroked my hair, but I turned over to show that I knew her treacherous hand even in my sleep. She stood there for a while longer and then went away. I thought she was feeling guilty and did not know how to redeem herself.

---

4 **apostasy:** an abandonment of principle

5 **Red partisan . . . Whites:** the Reds were the bolsheviks, or followers of Lenin, and the Whites represented the old guard of power in Russia.

Forbidden Fruit   243

I was sorry for her, but, as it turned out, she was not worth it. A minute later she was saying something to mother in a loud whisper; they began to giggle and then stopped, afraid to wake me up. Gradually they settled to a mood fit for going to bed.

Next day we sat at the table waiting dinner for father. He was late and angry at being waited for. Something was wrong on the job, and he was often gloomy and absentminded.

◆ ◆ ◆ ◆ ◆

I was all prepared to divulge my sister's crime, but I realized that this was not a proper time for my exposure. Nevertheless, I looked at my sister from time to time and pretended I was going to tell. I even opened my mouth but said something else instead. As soon as I opened my mouth, she dropped her eyes and bent her head as though expecting a blow. I discovered that keeping her on the verge of exposure was even more fun than exposing her right away could possibly be.

She would turn pale and then blush. From time to time she would toss her head contemptuously, and then her eyes would beg me to forgive her this gesture of wild defiance. She barely touched her soup, but mother insisted that she eat it.

"Of course," I said, "yesterday she ate so much at Uncle Shura's that—"

"What did you eat there?" my brother asked—as always, he understood nothing.

Mother looked at me anxiously and shook her head imperceptibly for father. My sister pulled up the plate and continued eating. I was getting a full taste of it. I fished a boiled onion out of my soup and spooned it into hers; we all hated boiled onions. Mother looked at me severely.

"She likes onions," I said. "You like onions, don't you?" I asked my sister with velvety softness.

She said nothing but her head went down still lower.

"If you like onions, take mine too!" My brother said, and started to transfer his. However, my father looked at him in a way to make his spoon freeze in midair and beat a hasty retreat.

Between the first and second course I invented another diversion. I put some slices of cucumber from the salad on a slice of bread and began to eat it, pausing from time to time as though the sandwich was too delicious to proceed. That was a witty little skit recreating her fall. She looked at me in pretended puzzlement, refusing to recognize the picture or to admit that it was so shameful. That was the limit to which her protest rose.

In short, the dinner was magnificent. Virtue blackmailed, and vice lowered its head in disgrace. Dinner was followed by tea. Father cheered up, and we shared his mood, especially my sister. Her cheeks reddened and her eyes shone. She started telling some school story, calling on me to testify as though nothing had happened. Her familiarity shocked me. It seemed to me that a person with such a record ought to be more **diffident**, more **self-effacing**, ought to wait for worthier people to tell the story. I was on the point of calling her to order, but father produced a package and unwrapped it. It turned out to be a batch of brand-new notebooks.

In those years before the war, it was difficult to get notebooks, just as it was some other things. The notebooks father had brought were of the best kind, made of wonderful paper, cool, heavy, bluish white like skimmed milk, with clear red lines for the margins.

There were nine notebooks in all, and father divided them, three notebooks apiece. My elation went. This **egalitarian** approach seemed to me simply unjust.

The fact was that I did well in school and sometimes even got high marks. The family would tell relatives and friends that all my marks were very high, but probably that was done to balance my brother's academic **notoriety**.

At school he was considered one of the laziest and most unruly boys. As his teacher put it, his ability to evaluate his behavior lagged far behind his temperament. I imagined my brother's temperament as a little ruffian running helter-skelter far ahead of him, my brother unable to catch up. It was perhaps to overtake him that my brother had wanted to become a car driver ever since the fourth grade. On every scrap of paper he would write the same text:

Virtue blackmailed, and vice lowered its head in disgrace.

diffident
hesitant; unassuming

self-effacing
modest; not seeking attention

egalitarian
equal; fair-minded

notoriety
disrepute; poor reputation

"To: Transport Office
Chief Manager
"I hereby request that you employ me at your agency since I am a third-class driver."

Later he realized his childhood dream, but it turned out that he had to exceed speed limits to overtake his temperament and finally had to change his trade.

And here I, with my almost invariably high marks, was equalized with my brother, who would, of course, use those beautiful notebooks to pen his idiotic car-driving applications. And my sister, who gobbled up pork fat yesterday, would receive an underserved gift today.

I put my notebooks aside. I felt hard and humiliating tears scalding my eyes and a big lump in my throat. Father coaxed and soothed me and promised to take me to a mountain river for fishing. But the more he consoled me, the more acutely I felt the injustice of it all.

"I have two blotters!" my sister suddenly yelled as she opened one of her notebooks. That was the last straw. Everything might have been different if it hadn't been for those two blotters.

I stood up and said in a trembling voice, addressing myself to father, "She ate pork yesterday."

There was a horrible silence. I realized that something was wrong. Perhaps I hadn't expressed myself properly, or maybe Mohammed's great **tenets** and a little urge to capture someone else's notebooks didn't go together.

tenets
principles; teachings

Father looked at me, his glance growing heavy with wrath. I made the last pathetic attempt to redeem the situation and direct his wrath into the proper channel.

"She ate pork at Uncle Shura's," I said in despair, and felt that everything was lost.

Father grabbed me by my ears, shook my head as though to make sure that it would not come off, and then flung me to the floor. For a fleeting instant I felt a flash of pain and the crunch of pulled ears.

"You little louse!" he yelled. "All I need now is a stool pigeon at home!"

Grabbing his leather coat, he left the room, slamming the door so hard that plaster crumbled off the wall. I was not crushed by the pain or his words but by that expression of hatred and disgust on his face, as though I were a dangerous snake.

I lay on the floor. Mother tried to pick me up while my brother pranced around me in frantic ecstasy.

"He always gets high marks!" he screamed, pointing to my ears.

I liked my father, and this was the first time he had treated me so.

Many years have passed since. I have long been eating pork like everyone else, though perhaps this does not make me any happier. Still, at that time I realized that no principle justifies treachery, and besides, that treachery is always a hairy caterpillar bred of a small butterfly called envy, no matter how lofty the principles involved.

Responding to the Selection

1. Do you find this story funny? If so, name a line or incident in the story that amuses you.

2. Hyperbole is a form of comic exaggeration. Find some places in the story where the narrator uses hyperbole to create humor as well as sympathy for his predicament.

3. Despite being a humorous family story, "Forbidden Fruit" has an essentially serious message for the boy about how to act in the world. What would you say that message is?

4. Not eating pork is a practice known to Muslims. Name some rules of other religions that might, at least to outsiders, seem to be a hardship or inconvenience. Why do you think religions have such taboos?

Europe

Discussing

1. Both "First Confession" and "Forbidden Fruit" have reminiscient narrators: narrators telling the story from the viewpoint of their younger selves. Talk about the advantages and disadvantages of this point of view.

2. Compare the poems by Thomas, Smith, Auden, Szymborska, and Milosz. All are important 20th century writers treating a similar theme: death. Which poets address it in terms of the times they live in (and its threat of fascism) and which address it in a more personal way? Characterize each poet's treatment of this theme.

3. World War II and Nazism influenced many of these European writers. Look at the selections by Auden, Greene, Milosz, and Ionesco for evidence of such influences. Why is war such a rich theme for writers? Compare the very different tones and perspectives these writers bring to bear on this subject.

4. Irony and black humor are often seen in Western European writing. Which selections in this unit display this sort of humor? Discuss why European writers, in particular, might favor this form of expression.

5. Some of the writers here, such as Eliot, Auden, Calvino, and Ionesco, are modernists. This 20th century school of writing breaks from formal traditions of the past, its writers choosing free verse, internal monologues, and stream of consciousness over more traditional forms of expression. Their writing often explores the psychology of the individual and tends toward a dark tone, particularly writing after World War I. After making sure of the definitions of these literary terms, find examples of one or more of them in the selections by these writers.

Writing

6. After reading the Seamus Heaney poem, "*from* Clearances," write about a ritual you have participated in with a loved one. Try to pick something simple that you both appreciated. Write down every sensory detail that will help you to remember this activity later.

7. Try to write a poem based on the general format of "A Contribution to Statistics," using your own formulas and assessments of human behavior.

Speaking/Listening

8. Conduct a mock jury trial of Kugler from "The Last Judgment." Have one class member preside as judge and others perform the tasks of defense and prosecution lawyers, witnesses, and jury members. Add to the details of the crimes mentioned in the stories and conclude with a verdict based on the evidence presented at trial.

9. Give an oral report on some aspect of World War II that moves, fascinates, or horrifies you, or that gives you some critical insight. Refer to Researching the World and the Research Handbook for ideas about what to research and how to narrow the focus of your presentation.

Hands-on Project

Many Americans have European ancestors or are familiar with European culture because of its widespread influence. Choose a European cuisine that you are familiar with or that you would like to learn more about—for example, Italian, German, Spanish, or Portuguese—and demonstrate how to make a certain dish or holiday repast for your classmates. Try to choose something tasty that is typical of the region.

Personal Connections

After reading the selections in this unit, choose one of the following questions to write about in your journal.

1. Which characters or selections helped open your eyes to a new way of seeing the world?

2. What new understanding do you have about American culture, your family, or yourself?

3. Which differences among cultures do you think really matter? Explain.

RESEARCHING THE WORLD

General Research Subjects

The following general subjects are merely starting points for research. After choosing one that interests you, you will have to narrow your topic considerably.

Belief Systems
Celebrations and
   Ceremonies
Children and Family
Coming of Age
Courtship and Marriage
Crime and Justice
The Economy
Education

The Environment
Famous Figures
Food
Geography
Globalism
Important Events
Language
Literature and the Arts
The Media

Oppression and Exile
Popular Culture
Rural and Urban Life
Sports
Technology
Travel
Work and Leisure

Specific Research Topics

Pick from the following topics or use them as starting points for your research. Some topics can be applied to more than one country in this region; others pertain to a single country or group of people. Note that in order to be a manageable size, many of these topics will require further narrowing.

Arts/Leisure

- Beatlemania and the British Invasion in popular music
- *Samizdat* (censored) writing in the former Soviet Union
- 20th-century abstract painting

- Traditional dances (Spanish flamenco, Irish step-dancing)
- Modern European playrights (Ibsen, Brecht, Beckett)
- Mediterranean tourism

Culture/Geography

- Minority cultures (Basque, Catalan, Romany)
- *Panegirias* celebrations in Greece
- The canals and *polders* of the Netherlands

- Scandinavia's seafaring traditions
- Multilingual countries (Belgium, Switzerland, Luxemburg)

History/Politics

- Diaries and letters of war refugees
- The euphemisms of war ("ethnic cleansing")

- Dictators (Hitler, Mussolini, Franco, Stalin)
- Underground war resistance movements
- Immigration politics

AUTHOR BIOGRAPHIES

W. H. Auden (1907–1973) Wysten Hugh Auden was born in England, became an American citizen, and died in Austria. In addition to his poetry, he wrote plays, opera librettos, and criticism. His most important works include *The Age of Anxiety* and *Selected Poems*. An active leftist during his middle years, he advocated socialism and fought in the Spanish Civil War. Though openly gay, he married Erika Mann, the daughter of the German novelist Thomas Mann, to help her escape Nazi Germany in 1935. He later became disillusioned with leftism and became devoutly religious. But through his many personal changes, Auden always maintained his compassion for human suffering in a troubled century. "We are here on Earth to do good to others," he once observed. "What the others are here for, I don't know."

Heinrich Böll (1917–1985) As a young man, Heinrich Böll reluctantly served as a German soldier during World War II. Horrified both by war and Nazism, Böll faced the "frightful fate of being a soldier and having to wish that the war might be lost." He described his wartime experience in his first novel, *The Train Was on Time*. After this he began to explore the spiritual and moral emptiness of postwar Germany in works like *Billiards at Half-Past Nine* and *The Clown*. Committedly pacifist and anti-authoritarian, Böll believed that literature plays a critical role in shaping human society. As he wrote upon winning the Nobel Prize for literature in 1972, "Art is always a good hiding place, not for dynamite, but for intellectual explosives and social time bombs."

Italo Calvino (1923–1985) Born in Cuba, fiction writer Italo Calvino moved to Italy as a youth and lived there for the rest of his life. His early works, based on his experiences fighting for the Italian Resistance during World War II, were realistic. Later he developed a flair for fantasy for which he is most famous. In *Cosmicomics*, a character named Qfwfq relates the history of the universe. *The Castle of Crossed Destinies* is a collection of tales based on tarot cards. *If on a Winter's Night a Traveller* treats the reader as the central character. Calvino traveled through Italy collecting stories for his *Italian Fables*. He was deeply preoccupied with myth, which he described as "the hidden part of every story, the buried part, the region that is still unexplored because there are as yet no words to enable us to get there."

Karel Čapek (1890–1938) The Czechoslovakian author Karel Čapek often wrote in collaboration with his brother, Josef. In addition to numerous novels, stories, and essays, Čapek is especially famous for two science fiction plays— *The Life of Insects* and *R.U.R.: Rossum's Universal Robots*. The latter work is the frightening story of a future in which robots take over the world. For this play, Čapek actually invented the word "robot," basing it on the Czech word for forced labor. Devoted to democracy and deeply fearful of totalitarianism, some of Čapek's final writings warned against the impending threat of Nazi Germany. In frail health throughout his life, Čapek died of pneumonia just before the Nazis decided to arrest him.

T. S. Eliot (1888–1965) Thomas Stearns Eliot was born in St. Louis, Missouri, but moved permanently to England in 1914. There he thoroughly transformed himself into an Englishman. He was working as a bank clerk in 1917 when his first book of poems, *Prufrock and Other Observations*, established him as one of the most important poets writing in English. His later poems include *The Waste Land* and *Four Quartets*. A critic, playwright, and editor as well as poet, he won the Nobel Prize for literature in 1948. Some years after his death, his *Old Possum's Book of Practical Cats* became the basis for the Broadway musical *Cats*. Eliot's verse is marked by the conversational language of an educated person. It is also packed with references to other works. As Eliot himself put it, "Immature poets imitate; mature poets steal . . . "

Federico García Lorca (1898–1936) Possibly the greatest Spanish-language poet and playwright of his century, Federico García Lorca was also a musician and painter. Because he read his works in public, many of his poems became famous before they were even published. He felt that this was appropriate. "Verse is made to be recited," he once observed, "in a book it is dead." His most famous works for the stage include a trilogy of "folk plays" about Spanish life: *Blood Wedding, Yerma,* and *The House of Bernarda Alba*. Many of his writings show a deep preoccupation with death, as if he had some premonition that his own life would be cut short. During the early days of the Spanish Civil War, he was executed by right-wing Nationalists, perhaps less for his leftist sympathies than for his homosexuality.

Graham Greene (1904–1991) Henry Graham Greene was a versatile writer whose work ranged from film criticism to fiction. He specialized in stories that he called "entertainments"—thrillers and mysteries of greater than usual depth and literary quality. One of his best-known novels is *The Third Man*, which was made into an even more famous film in 1949. He traveled widely to research his books—to Mexico for *The Power and the Glory*, to the Congo for *A Burnt-Out Case*, and to Cuba for *Our Man in Havana*. Greene's fictional world is full of emotionally wounded characters making difficult moral choices—a world in which innocence is in scant supply. "Innocence," he wrote, "is like a dumb leper who has lost his bell, wandering the world, meaning no harm."

Seamus Heaney (1939–) Poet, translator, and essayist Seamus Heaney was born and raised an Irish Catholic in predominantly Protestant Northern Ireland. He is widely regarded as the greatest poet writing today in English. He is also sometimes called the "laureate of violence" because much of his poetry deals with the cycle of religious and political bloodshed in his native country. Nevertheless, as he said upon winning the 1995 Nobel Prize for literature, he has tried "to make space in my reckoning and imagining for the marvelous as well as for the murderous." His books of poetry include *Death of a Naturalist, Field Work,* and *The Spirit Level.* In 2000, his acclaimed translation of the Anglo-Saxon epic *Beowulf* surprised the literary world by appearing on the *New York Times* fiction bestseller list.

Eugene Ionesco (1909–1994) Born in Romania, Ionesco lived most of his life in France and wrote in French. In plays like *The Lesson, The Chairs,* and *Rhinoceros,* he helped create the theater of the absurd, a movement which emphasized the meaninglessness of existence. Ionesco became especially concerned about the absurdity of human communication while trying to learn English from a badly written textbook. This experience inspired his first play, "The Bald Soprano." In it, a man and a woman—apparently strangers—exchange meaningless small talk until they realize they're actually married. Such comical moments thinly disguise Ionesco's tragic viewpoint. "It's not a certain society that seems ridiculous to me," he once said, "it's mankind."

Fazil Iskander (1929–) Born in the Georgian Republic of Abkhazia, Fazil Iskander has lived most of his life in Russia. He has published more than 200 works of poetry and prose in Russian, many of which have been translated into other languages. In his fiction, such as the novel *Sandro from Chegem,* Iskander is known for his use of humor and irony to satirize people and society. He has said, "If you want to make subtle humor your tool, you've got to go to the extreme of pessimism, glimpse the dark abyss to make sure there is nothing in it and then slowly come back."

Czeslaw Milosz (1911–) Although Czeslaw Milosz was born in Lithuania, his family moved to Poland after World War I. As a young man, he also lived in Paris, where he became serious about writing poetry. Milosz returned to Poland just before World War II and wrote for anti-Nazi publications during the German occupation. After the war, political turmoil continued in Poland, and Milosz moved to the United States. Milosz's poems and his memoir, *The Worlds Within,* have been published in English. In 1980, he won the Nobel Prize for literature. Milosz told an interviewer, "It's like suddenly feeling you're an alligator. You never wanted to be an alligator, and then suddenly one day you wake up and you're an alligator, or a famous, celebrated poet."

Alberto Moravia (1907–1990) Italian author Alberto Pincherle used the pen name Alberto Moravia. He began writing as a teenager while cooped up at home due to illness. His first novel, *Gli Indifferenti*, or *Time of Indifference*, was an immediate sensation. However, Moravia's attacks on fascism led Mussolini, Italy's fascist dictator, to ban his work. After World War II, when Moravia could again publish his short stories and novels, many were adapted for films. "When I sit at my table to write," Moravia said, "I never know what it's going to be till I'm under way. I trust in inspiration, which sometimes comes and sometimes doesn't. But I don't sit back waiting for it. I work every day."

Frank O'Connor (1903–1966) Irish author Michael O'Donovan wrote fiction, poetry, criticism, and drama and translated works of Gaelic literature. He used the name Frank O'Connor, probably to avoid identification with his alcoholic father. He is best known for his realistic and often humorous short stories, including "My Oedipus Complex" and the more serious "Guests of the Nation." O'Connor said that in his stories he wanted to "lay bare a person's fundamental character in one moment of crisis."

Boris Pasternak (1890–1960) Boris Pasternak began publishing poetry in his native Russia, but the Bolshevik regime disapproved of his work. Authorities felt that he didn't fully support the Communist revolution. Unable to publish, Pasternak made his living doing translations. After World War II, he wrote *Doctor Zhivago*, a novel about lovers who try to live apart from the political turmoil of their time. It was banned in the Soviet Union, but a copy was smuggled out and published in the West. Pasternak was awarded the Nobel Prize in literature in 1958. This embarrassed the Soviets, and Pasternak was pressured to turn down the award. In 1965, *Doctor Zhivago* was made into a film by British director David Lean. In 1988, the novel was finally published in Russia, and the next year Pasternak's son accepted his father's Nobel Prize medal.

Stevie Smith (1902–1971) English poet and novelist Florence Margaret Smith is known for her eccentric and sometimes bitter humor. She published three novels, but it was her poetry that eventually gained attention and won literary awards. Beneath the apparent lightheartedness of her work, there often hides a darker, more serious comment. For example, she might use humor to make a point about loneliness, love, death, or religion. Smith wrote in a variety of poetic styles. She sometimes used well-known songs, nursery rhymes, and hymns—but always gave them a new twist. Many of her poems were illustrated with her own drawings.

Wislawa Szymborska (1923–) Polish poet Wislawa Szymborska's first published work—"Szukam Slowa" (I am looking for a word)—appeared in a newspaper in 1945. Since then, her poems have won many international awards. Collections have been published in more than a dozen languages, including English. In 1996, Szymborska won the Nobel Prize for literature. In her Nobel acceptance speech, Szymborska said that "inspiration is not the exclusive privilege of poets or artists generally." Inspired people include any "who've consciously chosen their calling and do their job with love and imagination." For such people, "work becomes one continuous adventure as long as they manage to keep discovering new challenges in it . . . ."

Dylan Thomas (1914–1953) Born in Wales, Dylan Thomas was a sickly child who preferred reading on his own to school. His first book of poetry, published after he moved to London in 1934, was highly praised. Thomas went on to write short stories, film scripts, and radio plays—including the well-known *Under Milkwood*—in addition to poetry. He expressed himself with emotional intensity, and lived his life in the tradition of the Romantic poets—drinking, brawling, and captivating audiences with public readings of his work. As he put it, "I hold a beast, an angel, and a madman in me." After a bout of heavy drinking in New York City, Thomas collapsed and died from alcoholism at the age of 39.

Tomas Tranströmer (1931–) Swedish poet Tomas Tranströmer studied both psychology and poetry at the University of Stockholm. As a psychologist, he has worked with young offenders in prison as well as with the disabled, convicts, and drug addicts. He is one of Sweden's most respected poets, known for his experimental verse forms and unusual use of imagery. His collections of poems, such as *The Half-Finished Heaven, Baltics,* and *The Truth Barrier* have been translated into 30 languages and won international literary awards. He has discussed his own creative process in terms of "interior interest" and "outward perception," saying that inspiration is like "the feeling of being in two places at the same time."

Andrei Voznesensky (1933–) A friend and protégé of fellow Russian Boris Pasternak, Andrei Voznesensky began publishing poetry in 1958. His work quickly became very popular, and audiences of 50,000 Russian people packed soccer stadiums to hear him read. However, in the 1960s and 1970s, the Communist government censored Voznesensky's writing. He was put under surveillance and even work that was not political was withdrawn from publication. However, Voznesensky has observed, "The art of creation is older than the art of killing." Since the fall of communism, he has been free to write again. His work published in English includes *An Arrow in the Wall: Selected Poetry and Prose by Andrei Voznesensky.*

The Literature of Africa

Robert M. Baum

Professor of Religious Studies, Iowa State University, Ames, Iowa

African literature of the 20th century is a unique blend of oral and written forms. It draws on European influences, but is rooted in the rich diversity of African cultures. As far back as we know anything about Africa, oral traditions have been handed down from generation to generation. African cultures have always honored literature, giving professional poets the task of composing lengthy epic poems to be sung in honor of kings and other leaders. These traditions continue to be important in Africa today.

From the tenth to the 19th centuries, the literature of this vast continent was written in African languages using Arabic script. That changed, however, with the influence of Europeans who first enslaved African people, and then conquered and colonized African societies. In the 19th century, Europeans in Africa established schools in which European languages were taught. There was a practical reason for this: British, French, Portuguese, Belgian, and German administrators wanted to train local people to assist them in running government and businesses. Missionaries also established schools in order to convert Africans to Christianity. By the early 20th century, an influential group of Western-educated Africans began writing in European languages about the tensions of their role as intermediaries between Europeans and their fellow Africans. They used the literary forms of the novel, short story, play, and essay to examine their lives. Increasingly, they returned to the storytelling tradition of their elders, incorporating its style and power into their writing.

In the late 1920s, a group of students and young professionals from throughout the French-speaking black world began to write about being uprooted. They no longer belonged fully to their home societies in Africa, but they were also not accepted by Europeans in the colonies or France. They began to publish essays, short stories, and plays about their predicament. This early form of black consciousness was dubbed Negritude. Celebrating the contributions of black cultures to world civilization, it had a strong influence on both African and African American writers. Rather than accepting negative European stereotypes about Africa, Negritude writers insisted that the increasingly complex, industrial societies of Europe and America had much to learn from the rich and vibrant culture of Africa.

Since the 1950s and 1960s, a time when many African states achieved political independence, African writers began to rediscover their own history and culture. They searched through oral traditions and written archives to understand their past and build their national futures. They spoke of the obligations of African writers to serve their new nations and help to develop African unity. As the great expectations of political independence and economic development were not met, however, post-colonial writers began to examine the difficulties standing in the way of true political and economic freedom. Nadine Gordimer, Bessie Head, and others have explored the deep-rooted system of racial separation in South Africa known as apartheid. Although apartheid was officially dismantled in 1994, its pervasive effects linger on.

During the last century, Africa's writers have struggled to understand the role of African customs and values within a society that is largely liberated, but still not free from European dominance. Living in such a place, African writers have had a unique perspective on the collision of cultures. Some wondered, as Chinua Achebe did, whether things would fall apart. Others hoped new forms of culture would develop out of the long process of national liberation sweeping Africa in the last half of the 20th century. Together African writers have created a deeply critical, self-reflective, and politically committed literature, one that plays an important role in illuminating what it means to be African at the dawn of the 21st century.

The Literature of Africa

Literary Map of Africa

Léopold Sédar Senghor   Senegal

Sembene Ousmane   Senegal

David Diop   Senegal

Ben Okri   Nigeria

Chinua Achebe   Nigeria

Adewale Maja-Pearce   Nigeria

Wole Soyinka   Nigeria

Bessie Head   South Africa

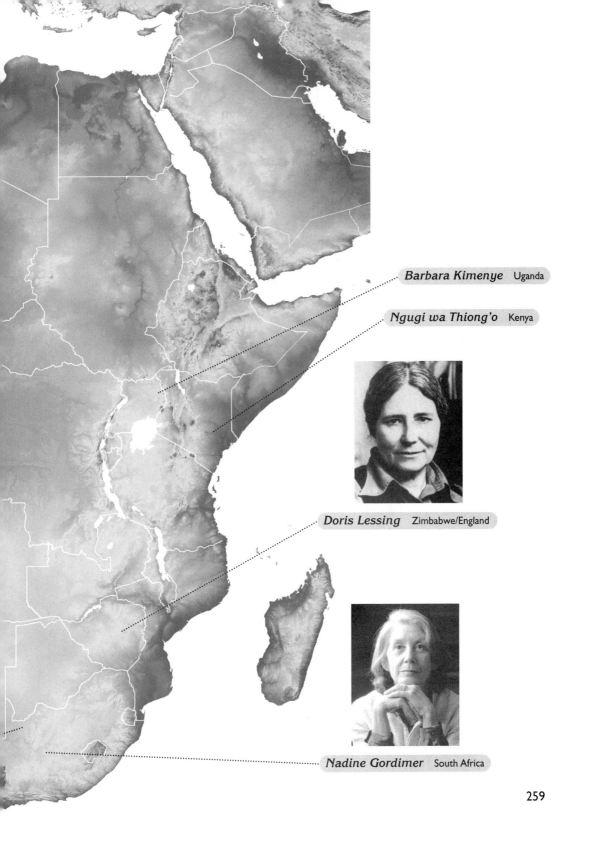

Barbara Kimenye Uganda

Ngugi wa Thiong'o Kenya

Doris Lessing Zimbabwe/England

Nadine Gordimer South Africa

259

Africa

David Diop

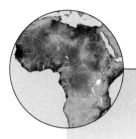

WORLD LENS

◆◆◆

SENEGAL

Senegalese writer David Diop was influential in the Negritude (French for "blackness") movement, a literary movement arising in the 1930s that celebrated the contributions of African cultures to world civilization. Diop and other Negritude writers wanted Africans to reclaim their values and pride after years of destructive European colonization.

Africa my Africa
Africa of proud warriors in ancestral savannahs[1]
Africa of whom my grandmother sings
On the banks of the distant river
I have never known you
But your blood flows in my veins
Your beautiful black blood that irrigates the fields
The blood of your sweat
The sweat of your work
The work of your slavery
The slavery of your children
Africa tell me Africa
Is this you this back that is bent
This back that breaks under the weight of humiliation
This back trembling with red scars
And saying yes to the whip under the midday sun
But a grave voice answers me
Impetuous son that tree young and strong
That tree there
In splendid loveliness amidst white and faded flowers

---

1 **savannahs:** (also savannas) a common type of grasslands in parts of Africa where it is rainy in summer, dry in winter

That is Africa your Africa
That grows again patiently obstinately
And its fruit gradually acquires
The bitter taste of liberty.

Responding to the Selection

1. You have read about the "black pride" movement known as Negritude, something this poet played a part in. How is this poem a good example of the tenets of Negritude?

2. How does the tree serve as a metaphor for Africa?

3. What do you think is the meaning of the lines at the end: "And its fruit gradually acquires / The bitter taste of liberty"? Consider how anything free can be bitter.

4. Read this poem aloud and pay special attention to the uses of repetition. How do you think they add to the power of this poem?

5. Personification means the comparison of a non-human object to a person. What role does personification play in this poem?

MOTHER OF AFRICA
Mmakgabo Mmapula Helen Sebidi

Black Girl

Sembene Ousmane

WORLD LENS

♦♦♦

SENEGAL

Aware that his readership in Africa was limited by widespread illiteracy, Senegalese Sembene Ousmane decided to rely on film to reach a larger audience. Soon after "Black Girl" was published in the early 1960s, he turned the story into his first narrative film. Now he is widely considered to be one of Africa's most important filmmakers. Critics call him the "voice of the voiceless" for his attempts to revive a sense of worth and pride in the exploited people of Africa.

It was the morning of the 23rd of June in the year of Our Lord nineteen hundred fifty-eight. At Antibes, along the Riviera, neither the fate of the French Republic nor the future of Algeria nor the state of the colonial territories preoccupied those who swarmed across the beaches below La Croisette.

Above, on the road leading to the Hermitage, two old-style Citroens,[1] one behind the other, were moving up the mountain. They stopped and several men quickly got out, rushing down the gravel walk toward a house on which a worn sign spelled out Villa of Green Happiness. The men were the police chief of the town of Grasse, a medical officer, and two police inspectors from Antibes, flanked by officers in uniform.

There was nothing green about the Villa of Green Happiness except its name. The garden was kept in the French manner, the walks covered with gravel, set off by a couple of palm trees with dropping fronds. The chief looked closely at the house, his eyes stopping at the third window, the broken glass, the ladder.

Inside were other inspectors and a photographer. Three people who seemed to be reporters were looking with rather

---

1 **Citroen:** a kind of European car

absentminded interest at the African statues, masks, animal skins, and ostrich eggs set here and there. Entering the living room was like violating the privacy of a hunter's lair.

Two women were hunched together, sobbing. They looked very much alike, the same straight forehead, the same curved nose, the same dark circles about eyes reddened from crying. The one in the pale dress was speaking: "After my nap, I felt like taking a bath. The door was locked from the inside"—blowing her nose—"and I thought to myself, it's the maid taking her bath. I say 'the maid,'" she corrected, "but we never called her anything else but her name, Diouana. I waited for more than an hour, but didn't see her come out. I went back and called, knocking on the door. There was no answer. Then I phoned our neighbor, the Commodore . . ."

She stopped, wiped her nose, and began to cry again. Her sister, the younger of the two, hair cut in a boyish style, sat hanging her head.

"You're the one who discovered the body?" the chief asked the Commodore.

"Yes . . . that is, when Madame Pouchet called and told me that the black girl had locked herself in the bathroom, I thought it was a joke. I spent thirty-five years at sea, you know. I've roamed the seven seas. I'm retired from the Navy."

"Yes, yes, we know."

"Yes, well, when Madame Pouchet called I brought my ladder."

"You brought the ladder?"

"No. It was Mademoiselle Dubois, Madame's sister, who suggested the idea. And when I got to the window, I saw the black girl swimming in blood."

"Where is the key to the door?"

"Here it is, your honor," said the inspector.

"Just wanted to see it."

"I've checked the window," said the other inspector.

"I'm the one who opened it, after breaking the pane," said the retired Navy man.

"Which pane did you break?"

"Which pane?" he repeated. He was wearing white linen

trousers and a blue jacket.

"Yes, I saw it, but I'd like to ask precisely."

"The second from the top," answered the sister.

At this, two stretcher-bearers came down, carrying a body wrapped in a blanket. Blood dripped on the steps. The magistrate lifted a corner of the blanket and frowned. A black girl lay dead on the stretcher, her throat cut from one ear to the other.

"It was with this knife. A kitchen knife," said another man, from the top of the stairs.

"Did you bring her from Africa, or did you hire her here?"

"We brought her back from Africa, in April. She came by boat. My husband is with aerial navigation in Dakar, but the company only pays air passage for the family. She worked for us in Dakar. For two and a half or three years."

"How old is she?"

"I don't know exactly."

"According to her passport, she was born in 1927."

"Oh! The natives don't know when they are born," offered the naval officer, plunging his hands into his pockets.

"I don't know why she killed herself. She was well treated here, she ate the same food, shared the same rooms as my children."

"And your husband, where is he?"

"He left for Paris the day before yesterday."

"Ah!" said the inspector, still looking at the knickknacks. "Why do you think it was suicide?"

"Why?" said the retired officer . . . "Oh! Who do you think would make an attempt on the life of a Negro girl? She never went out. She didn't know anyone, except for Madame's children."

The reporters were getting impatient. The suicide of a maid— even if she was black—didn't amount to a hill of beans. There was nothing newsworthy in it.

"It must have been homesickness. Because lately she'd been behaving very strangely. She wasn't the same."

The police magistrate went upstairs, accompanied by one of the inspectors. They examined the bathroom, the window.

"Some boomerang, this story," said the inspector.

The others waited in the living room.

"We'll let you know when the **coroner** is finished," said the inspector, on his way out with the police magistrate an hour after their arrival.

coroner
official who investigates deaths not due to natural causes

The cars and the reporters left. In the Villa of Green Happiness the two women and the retired naval officer remained silent.

Bit by bit, Madame Pouchet searched her memory. She thought back to Africa and her elegant villa on the road to Hann. She remembered Diouana pushing open the iron gate and signaling to the German shepherd to stop barking.

It was there, in Africa, that everything had started. Diouana had made the six-kilometer round trip on foot three times a week. For the last month she had made it gaily—enraptured, her heart beating as if she were in love for the first time. Beginning at the outskirts of Dakar, brand-new houses were scattered like jewels in a landscape of cactus, bougainvillea, and jasmine. The asphalt of the Avenue Gambetta stretched out like a long black ribbon. Joyous and happy as usual, the little maid had no complaints about the road or her employers. Though it was a long way, it had no longer seemed so far the past month, ever since Madame had announced she would take her to France. France! Diouana shouted the word in her head. Everything around her had become ugly, the magnificent villas she had so often admired seemed shabby.

In order to be able to travel, in order to go to France, since she was originally from the Casamance, she had needed an identity card. All her paltry savings went to get one. "So what?" she thought. "I'm on my way to France!"

"Is that you, Diouana?"

"*Viye*, Madame," came her answer in the Senegalese accent. She spoke from the vestibule, nicely dressed in her light-colored cotton, her hair neatly combed.

"Good! Monsieur is in town. Will you look after the children?"

"*Viye*, Madame," she agreed in her childish voice.

Though her identity card read "Born in 1927," Diouana was not yet thirty. But she must have been over twenty-one. She went to find the children. Every room was in the same condition. Parcels packed and tied with string, boxes piled here and there.

After ten whole days of washing and ironing, there wasn't much left for Diouana to do. In the proper sense of her duties, she was a laundress. There was a cook, a houseboy, and herself. Three people. The servants.

"Diouana . . . Diouana," Madame called.

"Madame?" she answered, emerging from the children's room.

Madame was standing with a notebook in her hands, making an inventory of the baggage. The movers would be coming at any moment.

"Have you been to see your parents? Do you think they will be happy?"

"*Viye*, Madame. The whole family is agreed. I tell Mama for myself. Also tell Papa Boutoupa," she said.

Her face, which had been radiant with happiness, fixed on the empty walls, and began to fade. Her heartbeat slowed. She would be ill if Madame changed her mind. Diouana's ebony-black face grew gloomy; she lowered her eyes, ready to plead her case.

"You're not going to tell me at the last moment, on this very day, that you're leaving us in the lurch?"

"No, Madame, me go."

They were not speaking the same language. Diouana wanted to see France, this country whose beauty, richness, and joy of living everyone praised. She wanted to see it and make a triumphal return. This was where people got rich. Already, without having left African soil, she could see herself on the dock, returning from France, wealthy to the millions, with gifts of clothes for everyone. She dreamed of the freedom to go where she wished without having to work like a beast of burden. If Madame should change her mind, refuse to take her, it would truly make her ill.

As for Madame, she was remembering the last few holidays she had spent in France. Three of them. And then she had had only two children. In Africa, Madame had acquired bad habits when it came to servants. In France when she hired a maid not only was the salary higher but the maid demanded a day off to boot. Madame had had to let her go and hired another. The next one was no different from the first, if not worse. She answered Madame tit for tat. "Anyone who is capable of having children should take a turn with them herself. I can't live in. I have my own children to take care of and a husband, too," she declared.

Used to being waited on hand and foot, Madame had yielded to her wifely duties, and clumsily fulfilled the role of mother. As for a real vacation, she had hardly had any. She soon persuaded her husband to return to Africa.

On her return, grown thin and thoroughly exasperated, she had conceived a plan for her next vacation. She put want ads in all the newspapers. A hundred young girls answered. Her choice fell on Diouana, newly arrived from her native bush.[2] Producing two more children during the three years that Diouana worked for her, between the last holiday and the one to come, Madame sang the praises of France. For three thousand francs a month, any young African girl would have followed her to the end of the earth. And to top it off, from time to time, especially lately, Madame would give Diouana little gifts of this and that, old clothes, shoes that could be mended.

This was the insurmountable moat that separated the maid and her employer.

"Did you give Monsieur your identity card?"

"*Viye*, Madame."

"You may go back to your work. Tell the cook to give the three of you a good meal."

"*Merci*,[3] Madame," she answered, and went off to the kitchen.

Madame continued her inventory.

Monsieur returned on the stroke of noon, his arrival announced by the barking of the dog. Getting out of his Peugeot 403, he found his wife, **indefatigable**, pencil in hand.

indefatigable
untiring; inexhaustible

"Haven't the baggage men come yet?" she said nervously.

"They'll be here at a quarter to two. Our bags will be on top. That way they'll be out first when we land in Marseilles. And what about Diouana? Diouana!"

The eldest of the children ran to fetch her. She was under the trees with the littlest one.

"*Viye*, Madame."

---

2 **bush:** undeveloped land, often dense with jungle vegetation and other bushy growth

3 *Merci:* French for "thank you"

"It's Monsieur who was calling you."

"That's fine. Here are your ticket and your identity card."

Diouana held out a hand to take them.

"You keep the identity card, I'll take care of the ticket. The Duponts are returning on the same ship, they'll look after you. Are you glad to be going to France?"

"*Viye*, Monsieur."

"Good. Where are your bags?"

"At Rue Escarfait, Monsieur."

"After I've had lunch, we'll go fetch them in the car."

"Bring the children in, Diouana, it's time for their nap."

"*Viye*, Madame."

Diouana wasn't hungry. The cook's helper, two years younger than she, brought the plates and took the empty ones away noiselessly. The cook was sweating heavily. He wasn't happy. He was going to be out of work. This was how the departure affected him. And for this reason he was a bit resentful of the maid. Leaning out the wide window overlooking the sea, transported, Diouana watched the birds flying high above in the immense expanse of blue. In the distance she could barely make out the Island of Gorée. She was holding her identity card, turning it over and over, examining it and smiling quietly to herself. The picture was a gloomy one. She wasn't pleased with the pose or with the exposure. "What does it matter? I'm leaving!" she thought.

"Samba," said Monsieur, who had come to the kitchen, "the meal was excellent today. You outdid yourself. Madame is very pleased with you."

The cook's helper stood at attention. Samba, the cook, adjusted his tall white hat and made an effort to smile.

"Thank you very much, Monsieur," he said. "I too am happy, very happy, because Monsieur and Madame are happy. Monsieur very nice. My family big, unhappy. Monsieur leave, me no more work."

"We'll be back, my good man. And then, with your talent you'll soon find another job!"

Samba, the cook, wasn't so sure. The whites were stingy. And in a Dakar filled with country people each claiming to be a master cook, it wouldn't be easy to find a job.

"We'll be back, Samba. Maybe sooner than you think. The last time we stayed only two and a half months."

To these consoling words from Madame, who had joined her husband in the kitchen, Samba could only answer: "*Merci*, Madame. Madame very nice lady."

Madame was glad. She knew from experience what it meant to have a good reputation with the servants.

"You can go home this afternoon at four with Monsieur. I'll pack up the rest. When we come back I promise to hire you again. Are you pleased?"

"*Merci*, Madame."

Madame and Monsieur were gone. Samba gave Diouana a slap. She hit him back angrily.

"Hey! Careful. Careful. You're going away today. So we shouldn't fight."

"That hurt!" she said.

"And Monsieur, does he hurt you too?"

Samba suspected a secret **liaison** between the maid and her employer.

liaison
affair; intrigue

"They're calling for you, Diouana. I hear the car starting."

She left without even saying goodbye.

The car moved along the highway. Diouana didn't often have the privilege of being driven by Monsieur. Her very look invited the pedestrians' admiration, though she dared not wave a hand or shout while going past, "I'm on my way to France!" Yes, France! She was sure her happiness was plain to see. The subterranean sources of this **tumultuous** joy made her a bit shaky. When the car stopped in front of the house at Rue Escarfait, she was surprised. "Already?" she thought. Next door to her humble house, at the Gay Navigator Café, a few customers were seated at the tables and several were talking quietly on the sidewalk.

tumultuous
uproarious; wild

"Is it today you're leaving, little one?" asked Tive Correa. Already tipsy, he steadied himself, legs apart, holding his bottle by the neck. His clothes were rumpled.

Diouana would have nothing to do with the drunkard. She didn't listen to Tive Correa's advice. An old sailor, Tive Correa had come home from Europe after twenty years' absence. He had left, rich with youth, full of ambition, and come home a wreck. From

PWO MASK
SHOWING
SCARIFICATION
INDICATING TEARS
from the Chokwe
Culture, Angola

having wanted everything, he had returned with nothing but an excessive love for the bottle. For Diouana he predicted nothing but misfortune. Once, when she had asked his advice, his opinion had been that she shouldn't go. In spite of his serious state of **inebriety**, he made a few steps toward Monsieur, bottle still in hand.

inebriety
drunkenness;
intoxication

"Is it true that Diouana's leaving with you, Monsieur?"

Monsieur did not answer. He took out a cigarette and lit it, blew the smoke through the car door, and looked Tive Correa over from head to toe. What a bum he was, greasy clothes,

Africa

stinking of palm wine.

Correa leaned over, putting a hand on the car door. "I was there. I lived in France for twenty years," he began, with a note of pride in his voice. "I, whom you see this way, ruin though I am today, I know France better than you do. During the war I lived in Toulon, and the Germans sent us with the other Africans to Aix-en-Provence, to the mines at Gardanne. I've been against her going."

"We haven't forced her to go! She wants to," Monsieur answered dryly.

"Certainly. What young African doesn't dream of going to France? Unfortunately, they confuse living in France with being a servant in France. I come from the village next to Diouana's, in Casamance. There, we don't say the way you do that it is the light that attracts the moth, but the other way round. In my country, Casamance, we say that the darkness pursues the moth."

In the meantime, Diouana returned, escorted by several women. They were chatting along, each begging for a little souvenir. Diouana promised happily; she was smiling, her white teeth gleaming.

"The others are at the dock," said one. "Don't forget my dress."

"For me, some shoes for the children. You've got the size in your suitcase. And remember the sewing machine."

"The petticoats, too."

"Write and tell me how much the hair-straightening irons cost and also the price of a red jacket with big buttons, size 44."

"Don't forget to send a little money to your mother in Boutoupa . . ."

Each one had something to tell her, some request to make of her; Diouana promised. Her face was radiant. Tive Correa took the suitcase, pushing it drunkenly but not roughly into the car.

"Let her go, girls. Do you think money grows on trees in France? She'll have something to say about that when she gets back."

Loud protests from the women.

"Goodbye, little cousin. Take care of yourself. You have the address of the cousin in Toulon. Write to him as soon as you get there, he will help you. Come, give me a kiss."

They all kissed each other goodbye. Monsieur was getting impatient. He started up the motor to indicate politely that he wished they'd be done with it.

The Peugeot was moving. Everyone waved.

At the dock it was the same—relatives, friends, little commissions. Everyone pressed around her. Always under the watchful eye of Monsieur. She embarked.

A week at sea. "No news," she would have written if she'd been keeping a diary, in which case she'd also have had to know how to read and write. Water in front, behind, to port, to starboard.[4] Nothing but a sheet of liquid, and above it, the sky.

When the boat landed, Monsieur was there. After the formalities, they quickly made their way to the Côte d'Azur. She devoured everything with her eyes, marveling, astonished. She packed every detail into her head. It was beautiful. Africa seemed a **sordid** slum by comparison. Towns, buses, trains, trucks went by along the coastal highway. The heaviness of the traffic surprised her.

"Did you have a good crossing?"

"*Viye*, Monsieur," she would have answered, if Monsieur had asked the question.

After a two-hour drive, they were in Antibes.

Days, weeks, and the first month went by. The third month began. Diouana was no longer the joyous young girl with the ready laugh, full of life. Her eyes were beginning to look hollow, her glance was less alert, she no longer noticed details. She had a lot more work to do here than in Africa. At first her fretting was hardly noticeable. Of France, la Belle France, she had only a vague idea, a fleeting vision. French gardens, the hedges of the other villas, the crests of roofs appearing above the green trees, the palms. Everyone lived his own life, isolated, shut up in his own house. Monsieur and Madame went out a good deal, leaving her with the four children. The children quickly organized a mafia and persecuted her. "You've got to keep them happy," Madame would say. The oldest, a real scamp, recruited others of like inclination and they played explorer. Diouana was the "savage." The children pestered her. Once in a while the eldest got a good

sordid
dirty; wretched

---

4 **to port, to starboard:** from left to right

spanking. Having picked up phrases from the conversations of Mama, Papa, or the neighbors back in Africa—phrases in which notions of racial prejudice played a part—he made exaggerated remarks to his pals. Without the knowledge of his parents, they would turn up, chanting, "Black Girl, Black Girl. She's as black as midnight."

Perpetually harassed, Diouana began to waste away. In Dakar she had never had to think about the color of her skin. With the youngsters teasing, she began to question it. She understood that here she was alone. There was nothing that connected her with the others. And it aggravated her, poisoned her life, the very air she breathed.

Everything grew blunt—her old dreams, her contentment eroded. She did a lot of hard work. It was she who did all the cooking, laundry, baby-sitting, ironing. Madame's sister came to stay at the villa, making seven people to look after. At night, as soon as she went up to bed, Diouana slept like a log.

The venom was poisoning her heart. She had never hated anything. Everything became monotonous. Where was France? The beautiful cities she had seen at the movies in Dakar, the rare foods, the interesting crowds? The population of France reduced itself to these spiteful monsters, Monsieur, Madame, and Mademoiselle, who had become strangers to her. The country seemed limited to the immediate surroundings of the villa. Little by little she was drowning. The wide horizons of a short while ago stopped now at the color of her skin, which suddenly filled her with an **invincible** terror. Her skin. Her blackness. Timidly, she retreated into herself.

With no one from her universe to exchange ideas with, she held long moments of palaver[5] with herself. A week ago, Monsieur and Madame had cleverly taken her along to visit their relatives in Cannes.

> # Where was France? The beautiful cities she had seen at the movies in Dakar, the rare foods, the interesting crowds?

invincible
*unconquerable;
unbeatable*

---

5 **palaver:** idle speech

"Tomorrow we'll go to Cannes. My parents have never tasted African food. You'll do us African honor with your cooking," Madame had said. She was nearly bare, and getting bronzed from the sun.

"*Viye*, Madame."

"I've ordered some rice and two chickens . . . You'll be careful not to spice it too much?"

"*Viye*, Madame."

Answering this way, she felt her heart harden. It seemed the hundredth time that she'd been trailed from villa to villa. To this one's house and then to that one's. It was at the Commodore's— everyone called him the Commodore—that she had rebelled the first time. Some silly people, who followed her about, hanging on her heels in the kitchen, had been there for dinner. Their presence was an **oppressive** shadow on her slightest movement. She had the feeling of not knowing how to do anything. These strange, self-centered, sophisticated beings never stopped asking her idiotic questions about how African women do their cooking. She kept herself under control.

The three women were still chirping when she waited on them at the table, testing the first spoonful on the tip of their tongues, then gluttonously devouring the rest.

"This time, at my parents', you must outdo yourself."

"*Viye*, Madame."

Restored to her kitchen, she thought of Madame's former kindness. She detested it. Madame had been good to her, but in a self-seeking way. The only reason for her attentiveness had been to wind the strings around Diouana, the better to make her sweat. She loathed everything. Back in Dakar, Diouana used to gather Monsieur and Madame's leftovers to take home to Rue Escarfait. She had taken pride then in working for "important white people." Now she was so alone their meals made her sick to her stomach. The resentment spoiled her relations with her employers. She stood her ground, they stood theirs. They no longer exchanged any remarks but those of a business nature.

"Diouana, will you do the washing today?"

"*Viye*, Madame."

"Last time you didn't do a good job on my slips. The iron was too hot. And the collars of Monsieur's shirts were scorched. Do pay attention to what you're doing, will you?"

"*Viye*, Madame."

"Oh. I forgot. There are some buttons missing on Monsieur's shirts and his shorts."

Every little job was Diouana's. And then Madame started speaking to her in pidgin[6] French, even in front of guests. And this was the only thing she did with honesty. In the end, no one in the house ever spoke to the maid anymore except in terms of "Missie," Senegalese pidgin talk. Bewildered by her inadequacies in French, Diouana closed herself into a sort of solitary confinement. After long, lonely meditation she came to the conclusion first of all that she was nothing but a useful object, and furthermore that she was being put on exhibit like a trophy. At parties, when Monsieur or Madame made remarks about "native" psychology, Diouana was taken as an illustration. The neighbors would say: "It's the Pouchets' black girl . . ." She wasn't "the African girl" in her own right, but theirs. And that hurt.

The fourth month began. Things got worse. Her thoughts grew more **lucid** every day. She had work and work to spare. All week long. Sunday was Mademoiselle's favorite day for asking friends over. There were lots of them. The weeks began and ended with them.

Everything became clear. Why had Madame wanted her to come? Her generosities had been premeditated. Madame no longer took care of her children. She kissed them every morning, that was all. And where was la Belle France? These questions kept repeating themselves. "I am cook, nursemaid, chambermaid; I do all the washing and ironing and for a mere three thousand francs a month. I do housework for six people. What am I doing here?"

Diouana gave way to her memories. She compared her "native bush" to these dead shrubs. How different from the forest of her home in Casamance. The memory of her village, of the community life, cut her off from the others even more. She bit her lip, sorry to have come. And on this film of the past, a thousand other details were projected.

As she returned to these surroundings, where she was doubly

lucid
clear; unambiguous

---

6 **pidgin:** a simplified form of the language

an outsider, her feelings hardened. She thought often of Tive Correa. His predictions had come cruelly true. She would have liked to write to him, but couldn't. Since arriving in France, she had had only two letters from her mother. She didn't have the time to answer, even though Madame had promised to write for her. Was it possible to tell Madame what she was thinking? She was angry with herself. Her ignorance made her mute. It was infuriating. And besides, Mademoiselle had made off with her stamps.

A pleasant idea crossed her mind, though, and raised a smile. This evening only Monsieur was at home, watching television. She decided to take advantage of the opportunity. Then, unexpectedly finding Madame there too, Diouana stopped abruptly and left the room.

"Sold, sold. Bought, bought," she repeated to herself. "They've bought me. For three thousand francs I do all this work. They lured me, tied me to them, and I'm stuck here like a slave." She was determined now. That night she opened her suitcase, looked at the objects in it, and wept. No one cared.

Yet she went through the same motions and remained as sealed off from the others as an oyster at low tide on the beach of her native Casamance.

"Douna"—it was Mademoiselle calling her. Why was it impossible for her to say Di-ou-a-na?

Her anger redoubled. Mademoiselle was even lazier than Madame: "Come take this away"—"There is such-and-such to be done, Douna"—"Why don't you do this, Douna?"—"Douna, now and then please rake the garden." For an answer Mademoiselle would receive an **incendiary** glance. Madame complained about her to Monsieur.

"What is the matter with you, Diouana? Are you ill or something?" he asked.

She no longer opened her mouth.

"You can tell me what's the matter. Perhaps you'd like to go to Toulon. I haven't had the time to go, but tomorrow I'll take you with me."

"Anyone would think we disgust her," said Madame.

Three days later Diouana took her bath.

incendiary
rebellious;
inflammatory

Returning home after a morning of shopping, Madame Pouchet went in the bathroom and quickly emerged.

"Diouana! Diouana!" she called. "You are dirty, in spite of everything. You might have left the bathroom clean."

"No me, Madame. It was the children, *viye*."

"The children! The children are tidy. It may be that you're fed up with them. But to find you telling lies, like a native, that I don't like. I don't like liars and you are a liar!"

Diouana kept silent, though her lips were trembling. She went upstairs to the bathroom and took her clothes off. It was there they found her, dead.

"Suicide," the investigators concluded. The case was closed.

The next day, in the newspaper, on page 4, column 6, hardly noticeable, was a small headline:

"Homesick African Girl Cuts Throat in Antibes."

Translated by Ellen Conroy Kennedy

Responding to the Selection

1. Look for examples of irony in this story, taking into account the dialogue, the details of the setting, and the names of things.

2. What is the theme of "Black Girl"? Find details in the text that support your answer.

3. Think about what Diouana wants and what her French family, particularly the mother, wants. How do these different desires create conflict?

4. Why does Diouana kill herself? Discuss what other options she had.

5. What are some of the attitudes toward black Africans that are revealed in the police investigation of Diouana's death? Look to both the opening and the ending of the story for a complete answer.

I Will Pronounce Your Name (for Tama)

Léopold Sédar Senghor

WORLD LENS

•••

SENEGAL

Senegalese poet Léopold Sédar Senghor was a leader of the Negritude movement of the 1930s, declaring, *"Je suis le Dyali"*: I am the griot. In parts of Africa, *griots* are the praise-speakers—poets, historians, and musicians who travel and carry on the native oral tradition. Senghor used poetry to commemorate African philosophy, African self-definition, and most importantly, the power and role of the African poet.

I will pronounce your name, Naëtt, I will declaim you, Naëtt!
Naëtt, your name is mild like cinnamon, it is the fragrance in which
    the lemon grove sleeps,
Naëtt, your name is the sugared clarity of blooming coffee trees
And it resembles the savannah, that blossoms forth under the
    masculine ardour of the midday sun.
Name of dew, fresher than shadows of tamarind,[1]
Fresher even than the short dusk, when the heat of the day is
    silenced.
Naëtt, that is the dry tornado, the hard clasp of lightning
Naëtt, coin of gold, shining coal, you my night, my sun! . . .
I am your hero, and now I have become your sorcerer, in order to
    pronounce your names.
Princess of Elissa, banished from Futa[2] on the fateful day.

Translated by Gerald Moore and Ulli Beier

---

1 **tamarind:** a large tropical tree

2 **Princess of Elissa . . . Futa:** the Princess of Elissa, also known as Dido, is a
mythical figure from the epic Roman poem *The Aeneid*; she is said to have founded
Carthage (now Tunisia). Futa refers to Futa Jallon, a mountainous region in Africa.

Responding to the Selection

1. An ode can be a tribute or song of praise in lyric poetry. In what ways is the Senghor poem an ode?

2. Metaphors are comparisons of unlike things. Explain how the metaphors in this poem add to its power and beauty.

3. Write down all of the things, in order, that the name Naëtt is compared to. Do you notice any kind of order, or progression, to these images over the course of the poem?

4. Senghor is one of the pioneers of the Negritude movement. What elements of the poem may be inspired by this literary philosophy?

Telephone Conversation

Wole Soyinka

WORLD LENS

♦♦♦

NIGERIA

The first African to win the Nobel Prize in literature, in 1986, Nigerian Wole Soyinka has established himself as one of the most compelling literary forces on the continent. His multiple talents qualify him as a "renaissance man": a novelist, playwright, critic, teacher, poet, actor, translator, and politician. According to one critic, Soyinka's writing "blends African with European cultural traditions, the high seriousness of modernist elite literature, and the topicality of African popular theater."

The price seemed reasonable, location
Indifferent. The landlady swore she lived
Off premises. Nothing remained
But self-confession. "Madam," I warned,
"I hate a wasted journey—I am African."
Silence. Silenced transmission of
Pressurized good breeding. Voice, when it came,
Lipstick-coated, long-gold rolled
Cigarette-holder pipped. Caught I was, foully.
"HOW DARK?" . . . I had not misheard . . . "ARE YOU LIGHT
OR VERY DARK?" Button B. Button A. Stench
Of rancid breath of public hide-and-speak.
Red booth. Red pillar-box. Red double-tiered
Omnibus squelching tar. It *was* real! Shamed
By ill-mannered silence, surrender
Pushed dumbfounded to beg simplification.
Considerate she was, varying the emphasis—
"ARE YOU DARK? OR VERY LIGHT?" Revelation came.
"You mean—like plain or milk chocolate?"
Her assent was very clinical, crushing in its light
Impersonality. Rapidly, wave-length adjusted,

I chose. "West African sepia"—and as afterthought,
"Down in my passport." Silence for spectroscopic
Flight of fancy, till truthfulness clanged her accent
Hard on the mouthpiece. "WHAT'S THAT?" conceding
"DON'T KNOW WHAT THAT IS." "Like brunette."
"THAT'S DARK, ISN'T IT?" "Not altogether.
Facially, I am brunette, but madam, you should see
The rest of me. Palm of my hand, soles of my feet
Are peroxide blonde. Friction, caused—
Foolishly madam—by sitting down, has turned
My bottom raven black—One moment madam!"—sensing
Her receiver rearing on the thunderclap
About my ears—"Madam," I pleaded, "wouldn't you rather
See for youself?"

Responding to the Selection

1. Why does the landlady want to know about the speaker's skin color?

2. Describe the writer's attitude after he figures out the landlady's "game" and decide whether you think his feelings and reactions are justified.

3. How is silence used to communicate in this poem?

4. What does the speaker mean by the line: "It *was* real!"?

Marriage Is a Private Affair

Chinua Achebe

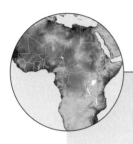

Chinua Achebe is one of the most widely read African writers of the 20th century. A native of Nigeria and member of the dominant Ibo ethnic group, Achebe is both a defender and a critic of his people. He decries the disintegration of the Ibo culture due to colonial and missionary influences, but acknowledges the problems inherent to some Ibo customs. In the following story, Achebe addresses themes common to his writing and important to life in modern-day Nigeria: the fragmentation of families and the gap between generations, as well as the conflicts between Christians and non-Christians, urban and rural dwellers.

Have you written to your dad yet?" asked Nene one afternoon as she sat with Nnaemeka in her room at 16 Kasanga Street, Lagos.[1]

"No. I've been thinking about it. I think it's better to tell him when I get home on leave!"

"But why? Your leave is such a long way off yet—six whole weeks. He should be let into our happiness now."

Nnaemeka was silent for a while, and then began very slowly as if he groped for his words: "I wish I were sure it would be happiness to him."

"Of course it must," replied Nene, a little surprised. "Why shouldn't it?"

"You have lived in Lagos all your life, and you know very little about people in remote parts of the country."

"That's what you always say. But I don't believe anybody will

---

1 **Lagos:** the capital of Nigeria

be so unlike other people that they will be unhappy when their sons are engaged to marry."

"Yes. They are most unhappy if the engagement is not arranged by them. In our case it's worse—you are not even an Ibo."

This was said so seriously and so bluntly that Nene could not find speech immediately. In the **cosmopolitan** atmosphere of the city it had always seemed to her something of a joke that a person's tribe could determine whom he married.

cosmopolitan
sophisticated; worldly

As last she said, "You don't really mean that he will object to your marrying me simply on that account? I had always thought you Ibos were kindly disposed to other people."

"So we are. But when it comes to marriage, well, it's not quite so simple. And this," he added, "is not peculiar to the Ibos. If your father were alive and lived in the heart of Ibibio-land he would be exactly like my father."

"I don't know. But anyway, as your father is so fond of you, I'm sure he will forgive you soon enough. Come on then, be a good boy and send him a nice lovely letter . . ."

"It would not be wise to break the news to him by writing. A letter will bring it upon him with a shock. I'm quite sure about that."

"All right, honey, suit yourself. You know your father."

As Nnaemeka walked home that evening he turned over in his mind different ways of overcoming his father's opposition, especially now that he had gone and found a girl for him. He had thought of showing his letter to Nene but decided on second thoughts not to, at least for the moment. He read it again when he got home and couldn't help smiling to himself. He remembered Ugoye quite well, an Amazon[2] of a girl who used to beat up all the boys, himself included, on the way to the stream, a complete dunce at school.

I have found a girl who will suit you admirably—Ugoye Nweke, the eldest daughter of our neighbour, Jacob Newke. She has a proper Christian upbringing. When she stopped schooling some years ago her father (a man of sound judgement) sent her to live

---

2 **Amazon:** a large, powerful woman, alluding to the myth of a race of female warriors

in the house of a pastor where she has received all the training a wife could need. Her Sunday School teacher has told me that she reads her Bible very fluently. I hope we shall begin negotiations when you come home in December.

On the second evening of his return from Lagos Nnaemeka sat with his father under a cassia tree. This was the old man's retreat where he went to read his Bible when the parching December sun had set and a fresh, reviving wind blew on the leaves.

"Father," began Nnaemeka suddenly, "I have come to ask for forgiveness."

"Forgiveness? For what, my son?" he asked in amazement.

"It's about this marriage question."

"Which marriage question?"

"I can't—we must—I mean it is impossible for me to marry Nweke's daughter."

"Impossible? Why?" asked his father.

"I don't love her."

"Nobody said you did. Why should you?" he asked.

"Marriage today is different . . ."

"Look here, my son," interrupted his father, "nothing is different. What one looks for in a wife are a good character and a Christian background."

Nnaemeka saw there was no hope along the present line of argument.

"Moreover," he said, "I am engaged to marry another girl who has all of Ugoye's good qualities, and who . . ."

His father did not believe his ears. "What did you say?" he asked slowly and **disconcertingly**.

disconcertingly
disturbingly; upsettingly

"She is a good Christian," his son went on, "and a teacher in a Girls' School in Lagos."

"Teacher, did you say? If you consider that a qualification for a good wife I should like to point out to you, Emeka, that no Christian woman should teach. St. Paul in his letter to the Corinthians says that women should keep silence." He rose slowly from his seat and paced forwards and backwards. This was his pet subject, and he condemned vehemently those church leaders who encouraged women to teach in their schools. After he had spent his emotion on a long homily[3] he at last came back to his son's engagement, in a seemingly milder tone.

"Whose daughter is she, anyway?"

"She is Nene Atang."

"What!" All the mildness was gone again. "Did you say Neneataga, what does that mean?"

"Nene Atang from Calabar. She is the only girl I can marry." This was a very rash reply and Nnaemeka expected the storm to burst. But it did not. His father merely walked away into his room. This was most unexpected and perplexed Nnaemeka. His father's silence was infinitely more menacing than a flood of threatening speech. That night the old man did not eat.

When he sent for Nnaemeka a day later he applied all possible ways of dissuasion. But the young man's heart was hardened, and his father eventually gave him up as lost.

"I owe it to you, my son, as a duty to show you what is right and what is wrong. Whoever put this idea into your head might as well have cut your throat. It is Satan's work." He waved his son away.

> **"Whoever put this idea into your head might as well have cut your throat."**

"You will change your mind, Father, when you know Nene."

"I shall never see her," was the reply. From that night the father scarcely spoke to his son. He did not, however, cease hoping that he would realize how serious was the danger he was heading for. Day and night he put him in his prayers.

Nnaemeka, for his own part, was very deeply affected by his father's grief. But he kept hoping that it would pass away. If it had occurred to him that never in the history of his people had a man married a woman who spoke a different tongue, he might have been less optimistic. "It has never been heard," was the verdict of an old man speaking a few weeks later. In that short sentence he spoke for all of his people. This man had come with others to commiserate with Okeke when news went round about his son's behaviour. By that time the son had gone back to Lagos.

"It has never been heard," said the old man again with a sad shake of his head.

---

3 **homily:** a short lecture or moralizing speech

"What did Our Lord say?" asked another gentleman. "Sons shall rise against their Fathers; it is there in the Holy Book."

"It is the beginning of the end," said another.

The discussion thus tending to become theological, Madubogwu, a highly practical man, brought it down once more to the ordinary level.

"Have you thought of consulting a native doctor about your son?" he asked Nnaemeka's father.

"He isn't sick," was the reply.

"What is he then? The boy's mind is diseased and only a good herbalist can bring him back to his right senses. The medicine he requires is *Amalile*, the same that women apply with success to recapture their husbands' straying affection."

"Madubogwu is right," said another gentleman. "This thing calls for medicine."

"I shall not call in a native doctor." Nnaemeka's father was known to be obstinately ahead of his more superstitious neighbours in these matters. "I will not be another Mrs. Ochuba. If my son wants to kill himself let him do it with his own hands. It is not for me to help him."

"But it was her fault," said Madubogwu. "She ought to have gone to an honest herbalist. She was a clever woman, nevertheless."

"She was a wicked murderess," said Jonathan who rarely argued with his neighbours because, he often said, they were incapable of reasoning. "The medicine was prepared for her husband, it was his name they called in its preparation and I am sure it would have been perfectly beneficial to him. It was wicked to put it into the herbalist's food, and say you were only trying it out."

♦ ♦ ♦ ♦ ♦

Six months later, Nnaemeka was showing his young wife a short letter from his father:

It amazes me that you could be so unfeeling as to send me your wedding picture. I would have sent it back. But on further thought I decided just to cut off your wife and send it back to you because I have nothing to do with her. How I wish that I had nothing to do with you either.

When Nene read through this letter and looked at the mutilated picture her eyes filled with tears, and she began to sob.

"Don't cry, my darling," said her husband. "He is essentially good-natured and will one day look more kindly on our marriage." But years passed and that one day did not come.

For eight years, Okeke would have nothing to do with his son, Nnaemeka. Only three times (when Nnaemeka asked to come home and spend his leave) did he write to him.

"I can't have you in my house," he replied on one occasion. "It can be of no interest to me where or how you spend your leave— or your life, for that matter."

The prejudice against Nnaemeka's marriage was not confined to his little village. In Lagos, especially among his people who worked there, it showed itself in a different way. Their women, when they met at their village meeting, were not hostile to Nene. Rather, they paid her such excessive deference as to make her feel she was not one of them. But as time went on, Nene gradually broke through some of this prejudice and even began to make friends among them. Slowly and grudgingly they began to admit that she kept her home much better than most of them.

The story eventually got to the little village in the heart of the Ibo country that Nnaemeka and his young wife were a most happy couple. But his father was one of the few people in the village who knew nothing about this. He always displayed so much temper whenever his son's name was mentioned that everyone avoided it in his presence. By a tremendous effort of will he had succeeded in pushing his son to the back of his mind. The strain had nearly killed him but he had persevered, and won.

Then one day he received a letter from Nene, and in spite of himself he began to glance through it perfunctorily until all of a sudden the expression on his face changed and he began to read more carefully.

. . . *Our two sons, from the day they learnt that they have a grandfather, have insisted on being taken to him. I find it impossible to tell them that you will not see them. I implore you to allow Nnaemeka to bring them home for a short time during his leave next month. I shall remain here in Lagos . . .*

The old man at once felt the resolution he had built up over so many years falling in. He was telling himself that he must not give in. He tried to steel his heart against all emotional appeals. It was a re-enactment of that other struggle. He leaned against a window and looked out. The sky was overcast with heavy black clouds and a high wind began to blow filling the air with dust and dry leaves. It was one of those rare occasions when even Nature takes a hand in a human fight. Very soon it began to rain, the first rain in the year. It came down in large sharp drops and was accompanied by the lightning and thunder which mark a change of season. Okeke was trying hard not think of his two grandsons. But he knew he was now fighting a losing battle. He tried to hum a favourite hymn but the pattering of large rain drops on the roof broke up the tune. His mind immediately returned to the children. How could he shut his door against them? By a curious mental process he imagined them standing, sad and forsaken, under the harsh angry weather—shut out from his house.

That night he hardly slept, from remorse—and a vague fear that he might die without making it up to them.

Responding to the Selection

1. Examine the collision of modern and traditional ways in this story. Is there any way for progress to take place without some sort of conflict?

2. What does the rain symbolize in this story?

3. Despite the strong conflict, Nnaemeka and Nene don't appear to harbor resentment against Okeke. Explain what you think this reveals and how it adds to the overall tone of the story.

4. What is universal about this African story?

5. Why do you think the writer has chosen "Marriage Is a Private Affair" for the story's title?

In the Shadow of War

Ben Okri

WORLD LENS

◆◆◆

NIGERIA

Ben Okri's literary career began when he was only 19 years old. His award-winning novels, short stories, and poems often focus on the fast-paced, sometimes chaotic cities of his homeland, Nigeria. Known to mix fantastic events with a realistic writing style, Okri's short stories often describe events so extraordinary that they are difficult to identify as real. "In the Shadow of War" tells of a series of mysterious events experienced by a young boy, Omovo, amid the tense atmosphere of civil war.

That afternoon three soldiers came to the village. They scattered the goats and chickens. They went to the palm-frond bar and ordered a calabash[1] of palm wine. They drank amidst the flies.

Omovo watched them from the window as he waited for his father to go out. They both listened to the radio. His father had bought the old Grundig[2] cheaply from a family that had to escape the city when the war broke out. He had covered the radio with a white cloth and made it look like a household fetish.[3] They listened to the news of bombings and air raids in the interior of the country. His father combed his hair, parted it carefully, and slapped some after-shave on his unshaven face. Then he struggled into the shabby coat that he had long outgrown.

Omovo stared out of the window, irritated with his father. At that hour, for the past seven days, a strange woman with a black veil over her head had been going past the house. She went up the village paths, crossed the Express road, and disappeared into the forest. Omovo waited for her to appear.

---

1 **calabash:** a container made out of a gourd
2 **Grundig:** the brand name of a German radio
3 **fetish:** an object thought to have supernatural powers

The main news was over. The radio announcer said an eclipse of the moon was expected that night. Omovo's father wiped the sweat off his face with his palm and said, with some bitterness:

"As if an eclipse will stop this war."

"What is an eclipse?" Omovo asked.

"That's when the world goes dark and strange things happen."

"Like what?"

His father lit a cigarette.

"The dead start to walk about and sing. So don't stay out late, eh."

Omovo nodded.

"Heclipses hate children. They eat them."

Omovo didn't believe him. His father smiled, gave Omovo his ten kobo[4] allowance, and said:

"Turn off the radio. It's bad for a child to listen to news of war."

Omovo turned it off. His father poured a libation[5] at the doorway and then prayed to his ancestors. When he had finished he picked up his briefcase and strutted out briskly. Omovo watched him as he threaded his way up the path to the bus stop at the main road. When a danfo bus[6] came, and his father went with it, Omovo turned the radio back on. He sat on the windowsill and waited for the woman. The last time he saw her she had glided past with agitated flutters of her yellow smock. The children stopped what they were doing and stared at her. They had said that she had no shadow. They had said that her feet never touched the ground. As she went past, the children began to throw things at her. She didn't flinch, didn't quicken her pace, and didn't look back.

The heat was **stupefying**. Noises dimmed and lost their edges. The villagers stumbled about their various tasks as if they were sleepwalking. The three soldiers drank palm wine and played draughts[7] beneath the sun's oppressive glare. Omovo noticed that whenever children went past the bar the soldiers called them,

---

4 **kobo:** a unit of money in Nigeria

5 **libation:** a liquid poured on the ground to appease the gods

6 **danfo bus:** in this part of Nigeria, a small, dilapidated bus

7 **draughts:** the British term for "checkers"

talked to them, and gave them some money. Omovo ran down the stairs and slowly walked past the bar. The soldiers stared at him. On his way back one of them called him.

"What's your name?" he asked.

Omovo hesitated, smiled mischievously, and said:

"Heclipse."

The soldier laughed, spraying Omovo's face with spit. He had a face crowded with veins. His companions seemed uninterested. They swiped flies and concentrated on their game. Their guns were on the table. Omovo noticed that they had numbers on them. The man said:

"Did your father give you that name because you have big lips?"

His companions looked at Omovo and laughed. Omovo nodded.

"You are a good boy," the man said. He paused. Then he asked, in a different voice:

"Have you seen that woman who covers her face with a black cloth?"

"No."

The man gave Omovo ten kobo and said:

"She is a spy. She helps our enemies. If you see her, come and tell us at once, you hear?"

Omovo refused the money and went back upstairs. He repositioned himself on the windowsill. The soldiers occasionally looked at him. The heat got to him and soon he fell asleep in a sitting position.

The cocks, crowing dispiritedly, woke him up. He could feel the afternoon softening into evening. The soldiers dozed in the bar. The hourly news came on. Omovo listened without comprehension to the day's casualties. The announcer **succumbed** to the stupor, yawned, apologized, and gave further details of the fighting.

succumbed
yielded; gave in

Omovo looked up and saw that the woman had already gone past. The men had left the bar. He saw them weaving between the eaves of the thatch houses, stumbling through the heat-mists. The woman was further up the path. Omovo ran downstairs and followed the men. One of them had taken off his uniform top. The soldier behind had buttocks so big they had begun to split his pants. Omovo followed them across the Express road. When they got into the forest the men stopped following the woman, and took a different route. They seemed to know what they were doing. Omovo hurried to keep the woman in view.

He followed her through the dense vegetation. She wore faded wrappers and a gray shawl, with the black veil covering her face. She had a red basket on her head. He completely forgot to determine if she had a shadow, or whether her feet touched the ground.

ostentatious
showy; flamboyant

He passed unfinished estates, with their flaking, **ostentatious** signboards and their collapsing fences. He passed an empty cement factory: Blocks lay crumbled in heaps and the workers' sheds were deserted. He passed a baobab[8] tree, under which was the intact skeleton of a large animal. A snake dropped from a branch and slithered through the undergrowth. In the distance, over the cliff edge, he heard loud music and people singing war slogans above the noise.

He followed the woman till they came to a rough camp on the plain below. Shadowy figures moved about in the half-light of the cave. The woman went to them. The figures surrounded her and touched her and led her into the cave. He heard their weary voices thanking her. When the woman reappeared she was without the basket. Children with kwashiorkor[9] stomachs and women wearing rags led her halfway up the hill. Then, reluctantly,

---

8 **baobab:** a short, broad-trunked tropical tree

9 **kwashiorkor:** a disease of malnutrition that results from protein deficiency and causes childrens' stomachs to bloat

Africa

touching her as if they might not see her again, they went back.

He followed her till they came to a muddied river. She moved as if an invisible force were trying to blow her away. Omovo saw capsized canoes and trailing, waterlogged clothes on the dark water. He saw floating items of sacrifice: loaves of bread in polythene[10] wrappings, gourds of food, Coca-Cola cans. When he looked at the canoes again they had changed into the shapes of swollen dead animals. He saw outdated currencies on the riverbank. He noticed the terrible smell in the air. Then he heard the sound of heavy breathing from behind him, then someone coughing and spitting. He recognized the voice of one of the soldiers urging the others to move faster. Omovo crouched in the shadow of a tree. The soldiers strode past. Not long afterward he heard a scream. The men had caught up with the woman. They crowded round her.

She moved as if an invisible force were trying to blow her away.

"Where are the others?" shouted one of them.

The woman was silent.

"You dis witch! You want to die, eh? Where are they?"

She stayed silent. Her head was bowed. One of the soldiers coughed and spat toward the river.

"Talk! Talk!" he said, slapping her.

The fat soldier tore off her veil and threw it to the ground. She bent down to pick it up and stopped in the attitude of kneeling, her head still bowed. Her head was bald, and disfigured with a deep **corrugation**. There was a **livid** gash along the side of her face. The bare-chested soldier pushed her. She fell on her face and lay still. The lights changed over the forest and for the first time Omovo saw that the dead animals on the river were in fact the corpses of grown men. Their bodies were tangled with riverweed and their eyes were bloated. Before he could react, he heard another scream. The woman was getting up, with the veil in her hand. She turned to the fat soldier, drew herself to her fullest height, and spat in his face. Waving the veil in the air, she began to howl **dementedly**. The two other soldiers backed away. The fat

corrugation
wrinkle; furrow

livid
bruised; discolored

dementedly
hysterically; madly

---

10 **polythene:** a synthetic substance like plastic wrap

soldier wiped his face and lifted the gun to the level of her stomach. A moment before Omovo heard the shot a violent beating of wings just above him scared him from his hiding place. He ran through the forest screaming. The soldiers tramped after him. He ran through a mist which seemed to have risen from the rocks. As he ran he saw an owl staring at him from a canopy of leaves. He tripped over the roots of a tree and blacked out when his head hit the ground.

When he woke up it was very dark. He waved his fingers in front of his face and saw nothing. Mistaking the darkness for blindness he screamed, thrashed around, and ran into a door. When he recovered from his shock he heard voices outside and the radio crackling on about the war. He found his way to the balcony, full of wonder that his sight had returned. But when he got there he was surprised to find his father sitting on the sunken cane chair, drinking palm wine with the three soldiers. Omovo rushed to his father and pointed frantically at the three men.

"You must thank them," his father said. "They brought you back from the forest."

Omovo, overcome with delirium, began to tell his father what he had seen. But his father, smiling apologetically at the soldiers, picked up his son and carried him off to bed.

Responding to the Selection

1. Look at the first two paragraphs, noting how setting details establish that this is a foreign place, in tense times. Cite details that give the writing the feel of reality.

2. Notice the many references—both literal and suggestive—to shadows, including the eclipse. Who are the shadows the author is probably calling to mind?

3. What part does the woman with the black veil play in this story?

4. What kind of men are these soldiers? Name some of the details that prepare you for the way they behave in the ending.

Loyalties

Adewale Maja-Pearce

From 1967 to 1970, Ibo tribespeople in Nigeria fought to form a nation of their own, Biafra. This genocidal border conflict moved Nigerian authors such as Chinua Achebe and Wole Soyinka to make war, with all its painful reality, one of their main subjects. But Adewale Maja-Pearce was still a child in London during the war years. Later, he was drawn to write the following humorous parable about the time that Biafra seceded from Nigeria.

WORLD LENS
♦♦♦
NIGERIA

I was twelve years old at the time. One afternoon my father came rushing home earlier than usual.

"Wife," he shouted to my mother who was out the back preparing food; "wife, have you not heard the news?" He was so excited he went rushing through the house. I followed him.

"Aren't you ashamed of yourself, a grown man like you rushing around like a small boy? What is it?" my mother said.

"Ojukwu has announced the new state of Biafra. We are no longer Nigerians, you hear? We are now Biafrans," he said and smiled.

"And what then?" my mother asked.

"Woman, don't you know what you are saying? Don't you realize this is an important day, an historic occasion?"

My mother stood up and put her hands on her hips. Her face was streaming from the heat of the fire.

"Whether we are in Nigeria or whether we are in Biafra we are almost out of firewood," she said.

My father raised his hands to the sky.

"Events of world importance are taking place and you are telling me about firewood. Trust a woman," he said and

> **"We are no longer Nigerians, you hear? We are now Biafrans . . ."**

walked away.

That evening the schoolmaster and the barber and the man who owned the Post Office came to our house.

"Boy, come here," the schoolmaster called.

"Come and hear what teacher has to say," my father ordered.

"Seven nines are?"

"Sixty-three," I answered.

"Good. Now, if twenty Nigerian soldiers march into our village and five Biafran women attack them with saucepans who will win?" he asked, and the barber collapsed on the floor. My mother took me by the arm and we left the room. But I crept back and stood by the door.

"What was I telling you the other day? That Ojukwu is a real man, just the sort of leader we need to get things moving. Those dirty Nigerians will taste pepper if they try to attack us, let me tell you," my father was saying.

"That's the way to talk," the schoolmaster said. "Just let them try. Biafra stands supreme."

"They were saying on the news that five countries have already recognized us," the postmaster said.

My mother called me. "Where were you? Must you always be sneaking about listening to what foolish men are saying? Biafra, Nigeria, what difference? Have we suddenly acquired two heads? Go and collect the goat and tie him up for the night," she said, and added: "After all, he is now a Biafran goat so we must take better care of it."

During the next few weeks everybody was talking about it. But as my mother kept saying, the only difference it made was the increased cost of food.

And then there was a rumour that Federal troops were marching towards us. Biafran soldiers appeared overnight. In their new uniforms and polished guns they looked smart. They drove up and down in their jeeps and raised dust everywhere. All my friends worshipped them.

One morning I woke up and heard gunfire in the distance. A plane flew overhead.

"Hurry, hurry, we are under attack," my father shouted.

"Where are we going?" my mother asked.

"Are you blind, woman, can't you see the others heading for the forest?" my father said.

"But what about our troops?" I asked.

"What troops? They ran away last night."

My mother rushed into the bedroom and started dragging clothes onto the bed.

"We have no time for that," my father said.

When we got outside I saw that it was true. The entire village was heading for the forest, the schoolmaster in the lead.

We spent two days and nights in the bush.

"So this is your great Biafra," my mother said. "Where is Ojukwu, I didn't see him?"

"Shut up, woman," my father said.

On the third day my father said to me: "Go and see if the soldiers are still there."

"You want to get the boy killed?" my mother said, reaching for me.

"Leave him, they won't harm a child," my father said; and to me: "I don't ask you to show yourself, you hear?"

I crept to the edge of the forest. The village was completely deserted, except for a few hens. And then I saw our goat. He was eating the food in front of the Post Office. I knew the owner would be angry. I forgot my father's warning and started running. Three armed Nigerian soldiers stepped out of the barber's shop, their rifles in their hands, and waited for me.

"Where are your people?" one of them asked. I pointed in the direction.

"Are they afraid of us?"

I nodded.

"Go and tell them we mean no harm."

As soon as I got back to the clearing everyone began talking at once. I told them what had happened. An argument began. Some wanted to stay and others wanted to go, but we were all hungry and there was no food left. Because of the mosquitoes no one had slept well. So we went.

The soldiers kept to their word. By the next day everything had returned to normal. At the end of the week the soldiers pulled out.

One evening the barber, the schoolmaster and the man who owned the Post Office came to our house. My father sent me out to buy bottles of beer. When I returned my father was saying:

"Those dirty Biafrans, what did I tell you? As usual it was all talk. When it comes to talk there is nothing they cannot do."

The schoolmaster called me. "Boy, if the Biafran soldiers cover twenty miles a day how long will it take them to reach the Cameroons?"

The barber held his sides and groaned.

"Don't mind them," my father said. My mother called me from the back.

"Go and collect our Nigerian goat," she said.

Responding to the Selection

1. Why do you think the writer gives the last word to the boy's mother?

2. Genocide is the deliberate destruction of an entire racial, political, or cultural group. The Nigerian war with Biafra has been described as being genocidal in its proportions. What do you think of using humor to tell a story set amid such violence?

3. What do you think the author is suggesting about national loyalties?

4. What do you consider a "normal" or typical citizen response to border aggression by another nation? Think about why the characters in this story do not appear to have any heartfelt national loyalty.

A Meeting in the Dark

Ngugi wa Thiong'o

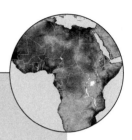

Ngugi wa Thiong'o is East Africa's most significant and popular literary figure, an eloquent voice against the continued legacy of colonialism in Africa. Controversially, Ngugi wa Thiong'o believes that African writers should write only in their native language. Since about 1978, he has written in Gikuyu, the oral language of his native Kenya.

"A Meeting in the Dark" shows the emotional turmoil and confusion of a young man living in post-colonial Africa. It typifies a theme often found in 20th-century African writing: the clash of modern and traditional values. One tradition mentioned in the story is the custom of female circumcision, a practice widespread in Nigeria as well as the rest of Africa. Those defending circumcision claim it is part of African culture and an important rite of passage for girls.

WORLD LENS

♦♦♦

KENYA

His mother used to tell him stories. "Once upon a time there was a young girl who lived with her father and mother in a lonely house that was hidden by a hill. The house was old but strong. When the rains came and the winds blew, the house remained firm. Her father and mother liked her, but they quarreled sometimes and she would cry. Otherwise, she was happy. Nobody knew of the house. So nobody came to see them. Then one day a stranger came. He was tall and handsome. He had milk-white teeth. Her mother gave him food. Then he told them of a beautiful country beyond the hill. The girl wanted to go there. Secretly, she followed the man. They had not gone very far when the stranger turned into an Irimu.[1] He became ugly and he had another mouth at the back which was hidden by his long hair. Occasionally, the hair was blown by the wind. Flies

1 **Irimu:** a lion-demon of African myth

were taken in and the mouth would be shut. The girl ran back. The bad Irimu followed her. She ran hard, hard, and the Irimu could not catch her. But he was getting nearer her all the time. When she came close to her home, she found the Irimu had stopped running. But the house was no longer there. She had no home to go to and she could not go forward to the beautiful land, to see all the good things, because the Irimu was in the way."

How did the story end? John wondered. He thought: "I wish I were young again in our old home, then I would ask my mother about it." But now he was not young; not young anymore. And he was not a man yet!

He stood at the door of the hut and saw his old, frail, but energetic father coming along the village street, with a rather dirty bag made out of strong calico swinging by his side. His father always carried this bag. John knew what it contained: a Bible, a hymn book, and probably a notebook and a pen. His father was a preacher. It must have been he who had stopped his mother from telling him stories. His mother had stopped telling him stories long ago. She would say, "Now, don't ask for any more stories. Your father may come." So he feared his father. John went in and warned his mother of his father's coming. Then his father came in. John stood aside, then walked toward the door. He lingered there doubtfully; then he went out.

"John, hei, John!"

"Baba!"

"Come back."

He stood doubtfully in front of his father. His heart beat faster and an agitated voice within him seemed to ask: Does he know?

"Sit down. Where are you going?"

"For a walk, Father," he answered evasively.

"To the village?"

"Well—yes—no. I mean, nowhere in particular." John saw his father look at him hard, seeming to read his face. John sighed a very slow sigh. He did not like the way his father eyed him. He always looked at him as though John was a sinner, one who had to be watched all the time. "I am," his heart told him. John guiltily refused to meet the old man's gaze and looked past him and appealingly to his mother, who was quietly peeling potatoes.

But she seemed to be **oblivious** of everything around her.

"Why do you look away? What have you done?"

John shrank within himself with fear. But his face remained expressionless. However, he could hear the loud beats of his heart. It was like an engine pumping water. He felt no doubt his father knew all about it. He thought: "Why does he torture me? Why does he not at once say he knows?" Then another voice told him: "No, he doesn't know, otherwise he would already have jumped at you." A **consolation**. He faced his thoughtful father with courage.

"When is the journey?"

Again John thought—why does he ask? I have told him many times.

Aloud, he said, "Next week, Tuesday."

"Right. Tomorrow we go to the shops, hear?"

"Yes, Father."

"Then be prepared."

"Yes, Father."

"You can go."

"Thank you, Father." He began to move.

"John!"

"Yes?" John's heart almost stopped beating. That second, before his father's next words, was an age.

"You seem to be in a hurry. I don't want to hear of you loitering in the village. I know you young men, going to show off just because you are going away! I don't want to hear of trouble in the village."

Much relieved, John went out. He could guess what his father meant by not wanting trouble in the village. How did the story end? Funny, but he could not remember how his mother had ended it. It had been so long ago. Her home was not there. Where did she go? What did she do?

"Why do you persecute the boy so much?" Susan spoke for the first time. Apparently she had carefully listened to the whole drama without a word. Now was her time to speak. She looked at her tough old preacher who had been a companion for life. She had married him a long time ago. She could not tell the number of years. They had been happy. Then the man became a convert.

oblivious
unaware; inattentive

consolation
comfort; relief

And everything in the home put on a religious tone. He even made her stop telling stories to the child. "Tell him of Jesus. Jesus died for you. Jesus died for the child. He must know the Lord." She too had been converted. But she was never blind to the moral torture he inflicted on the boy (that's what she always called John), so that the boy had grown up mortally afraid of him. She always wondered if it was love for the son. Or could it be a resentment because, well, they two had "sinned" before marriage? John had been the result of that sin. But that had not been John's fault. It was the boy who ought to complain. She often wondered if the boy had . . . but no. The boy had been very small when they left Fort Hall. She looked at her husband. He remained mute, though his left hand did, rather irritably, feel about his face.

"It is as if he was not your son. Or do you . . ."

"Hm, sister." The voice was pleading. She was seeking a quarrel but he did not feel equal to one. Really, women could never understand. Women were women, whether saved or not.

Their son had to be protected against all evil influences.

Their son had to be protected against all evil influences. He must be made to grow in the footsteps of the Lord. He looked at her, frowning a little. She had made him sin but that had been a long time ago. And he had been saved. John must not follow the same road.

"You ought to tell us to leave. You know I can go away. Go back to Fort Hall. And then everybody . . ."

"Look, sister." He hastily interrupted. He always called her sister. Sister-in-the-Lord, in full. But he sometimes wondered if she had been truly saved. In his heart, he prayed: Lord, be with our sister Susan. Aloud, he continued, "You know I want the boy to grow in the Lord."

"But you torture him so! You make him fear you!"

"Why! He should not fear me. I have really nothing against him."

"It is you. You. You have always been cruel to him . . ." She stood up. The peelings dropped from her dress and fell in a heap on the floor.

"Stanley!"

"Sister." He was startled by the **vehemence** in her voice. He had never seen her like this. Lord, take the devil out of her. Save her this minute. She did not say what she wanted to say. Stanley looked away from her. It was a surprise, but it seemed he feared his wife. If you had told people in the village about this, they would not have believed you. He took his Bible and began to read. On Sunday he would preach to a congregation of brethren and sisters.

vehemence
intensity; force

Susan, a rather tall, thin woman who had once been beautiful, sat down again and went on with her work. She did not know what was troubling her son. Was it the coming journey?

Outside, John strolled aimlessly along the path that led from his home. He stood near the wattle tree which was a little way from his father's hose, and surveyed the whole village. They lay before his eyes—crammed—rows and rows of mud and grass huts, ending in sharp sticks that pointed to heaven. Smoke was coming out of various huts, an indication that many women had already come from the *shambas*.[2] Night would soon fall. To the west, the sun was hurrying home behind the misty hills. Again, John looked at the crammed rows and rows of huts that formed Makeno Village, one of the new mushroom "towns" that grew up all over the country during the Mau Mau War.[3] It looked so ugly. A pang of pain rose in his heart and he felt like crying—I hate you, I hate you. You trapped me alive. Away from you, it would never have happened. He did not shout. He just watched.

A woman was coming toward where he stood. A path into the village was just near there. She was carrying a big load of *kuni*,[4] which bent her into an Akamba[5]-bow shape. She greeted him.

"Is it well with you, Njooni?"

"It is well with me, mother." There was no trace of bitterness in his voice. John was by nature polite. Everyone knew this. He was quite unlike the other proud, educated sons of the tribe—

---

2 ***shambas:*** residential gardens

3 **Mau Mau War:** (1952–1956), the conflict between natives and white Europeans for control of Kenya. The British forces prevailed, sending the revolutionaries back to the hills in 1956 and eventually relocating many of them.

4 ***kuni:*** Swahili for "wood"

5 **Akamba:** a group of Kenyan people known for their agricultural skills

A Meeting in the Dark

sons who came back from the other side of the waters with white or Negro wives who spoke English. And they behaved just like Europeans! John was a favorite, a model of humility and moral perfection. Everyone knew that, though a clergyman's son, John would never betray the tribe.

"When are you going to—to—"

"Makerere?"

"Makelele." She laughed. The way she pronounced the name was funny. And the way she laughed, too. She enjoyed it. But John felt hurt. So everyone knew of this.

"Next week."

"I wish you well."

"Thank you, mother."

She said quietly—as if trying to pronounce it better—

"Makelele." She laughed at herself again but she was tired. The load was heavy.

"Stay well, son."

"Go well and in peace, mother."

And the woman, who all the time had stood, moved on, panting like a donkey, but obviously pleased with John's kindness.

John remained long looking at her. What made such a woman live on day to day, working hard, yet happy? Had she much faith in life? Or was her faith in the tribe? She and her kind, who had never been touched by the ways of the white man, looked as though they had something to cling to. As he watched her disappear, he felt proud that he had a place in their esteem. And then came the pang. *Father will know. They will know.* He did not know what he feared most: the action his father would take when he knew, or the loss of the little faith the simple villagers had placed in him, when they knew.

He went down to the small local tea shop. He met many people who wished him well at college. All of them knew that the Pastor's son had finished all the white man's learning in Kenya. He would now go to Uganda; they had read this in the *Baraza*, a Swahili[6] weekly paper. John did not stay long at the shop. The sun had already gone to rest and now darkness was coming. The evening meal was ready. His tough father was still at the table reading his Bible. He did not look up when John entered. Strange silence settled in the hut.

"You look unhappy." His mother broke the silence first. John laughed. It was a nervous little laugh.

"No, Mother," he hastily replied, nervously looking at his father. He secretly hoped that Wamuhu had not blabbed.

"Then I am glad."

She did not know. He ate his dinner and went out to his hut. A man's hut. Every young man had his own hut. John was never allowed to bring any girl visitor in there. He did not want trouble. Even to be seen standing with one was a crime. His father could easily thrash him. He wished he had rebelled earlier, like all the

---

6 **Swahili:** the language of Swahili; the official language of Kenya and Tanzania and spoken throughout East Africa and parts of the Congo

other young educated men. He lit the lantern. He took it in his hand. The yellow light flickered dangerously and then went out. He knew his hands were shaking. He lit it again and hurriedly took his big coat and a huge Kofia,[7] which were lying on the unmade bed. He left the lantern burning, so that his father would see it and think him in. John bit his lower lip spitefully. He hated himself for being so girlish. It was unnatural for a boy of his age.

Like a shadow, he stealthily crossed the courtyard and went on to the village street.

He met young men and women lining the streets. They were laughing, talking, whispering. They were obviously enjoying themselves. John thought, They are more free than I am. He envied their exuberance. They clearly stood outside or above the strict morality that the educated ones had to be judged by. Would he have gladly changed places with them? He wondered. At last, he came to the hut. It stood at the very heart of the village. How well he knew it—to his sorrow. He wondered what he would do! Wait for her outside? What if her mother came out instead? He decided to enter.

"*Hodi!*"[8]

"Enter. We are in."

John pulled down his hat before he entered. Indeed, they were all there—all except she whom he wanted. The fire in the hearth was dying. Only a small flame from a lighted lantern vaguely illuminated the whole hut. The flame and the giant shadow created on the wall seemed to be mocking him. He prayed that Wamuhu's parents would not recognize him. He tried to be "thin," and to disguise his voice as he greeted them. They recognized him and made themselves busy on his account. To be visited by such an educated one who knew all about the white man's world and knowledge, and who would now go to another land beyond, was not such a frequent occurrence that it could be taken lightly. Who knew but he might be interested in their daughter? Stranger things had happened. After all, learning was not the only thing. Though Wamuhu had no learning, yet charms

---

7 **Kofia:** a brimless hat worn by Muslim men

8 **"*Hodi!*":** a customary Swahili greeting used when entering a home; the host will reply in kind, which means "Be welcome."

she had and she could be trusted to captivate any young man's heart with her looks and smiles.

"You will sit down. Take that stool."

"No!" He noticed with bitterness that he did not call her "mother."

"Where is Wamuhu?" The mother threw a triumphant glance at her husband. They exchanged a knowing look. John bit his lip again and felt like bolting. He controlled himself with difficulty.

"She has gone out to get some tea leaves. Please sit down. She will cook you some tea when she comes."

"I am afraid . . ." He muttered some inaudible words and went out. He almost collided with Wamuhu.

In the hut:

"Didn't I tell you? Trust a woman's eye!"

"You don't know these young men."

"But you see, John is different. Everyone speaks well of him and he is a clergyman's son."

"Y-e-e-s! A clergyman's son? You forgot your daughter is circumcised."[9] The old man was remembering his own day. He had found for himself a good, virtuous woman, initiated in all the tribe's ways. And she had known no other man. He had married her. They were happy. Other men of his *Rika*[10] had done the same. All their girls had been virgins, it being a taboo to touch a girl in that way, even if you slept in the same bed, as indeed so many young men and girls did. Then the white men had come, preaching a strange religion, strange ways, which all men followed. The tribe's code of behavior was broken. The new faith could not keep the tribe together. How could it? The men who followed the new faith would not let the girls be circumcised. And they would not let their sons marry circumcised girls. Puu! Look at what was happening. Their young men went away to the land of the white men. What did they bring? White women. Black women who spoke English. Aaa—bad. And the young men who were left just did not mind. They made unmarried girls their wives and then left them with fatherless children.

---

9 **circumcised:** had parts of the sexual organs removed, a cultural rite that can have initiation and/or purification significance

10 ***Rika:*** age group; members pass through initiation rituals at puberty together and remain like brothers and sisters for the rest of their lives

"What does it matter?" his wife was replying. "Is Wamuhu not as good as the best of them? Anyway, John is different."

"Different! different! Puu! They are all alike. Those coated with the white clay of the white man's ways are the worst. They have nothing inside. Nothing—nothing here." He took a piece of wood and nervously poked the dying fire. A strange numbness came over him. He trembled. And he feared; he feared for the tribe. For now he said it was not only the educated men who were coated with strange ways, but the whole tribe. The tribe had followed a false Irimu like the girl in the story. For the old man trembled and cried inside, mourning for a tribe that had crumbled. The tribe had nowhere to go to. And it could not be what it was before. He stopped poking and looked hard at the ground.

"I wonder why he came. I wonder." Then he looked at his wife and said, "Have you seen strange behavior with your daughter?"

His wife did not answer. She was preoccupied with her own great hopes . . .

John and Wamuhu walked on in silence. The intricate streets and turns were well known to them both. Wamuhu walked with quick light steps; John knew she was in a happy mood. His steps were heavy and he avoided people even though it was dark. But why should he feel ashamed? The girl was beautiful, probably the most beautiful girl in the whole of Limuru. Yet he feared being seen with her. It was all wrong. He knew that he could have loved her, even then he wondered if he did not love her. Perhaps it was hard to tell but had he been one of the young men he had met, he would not have hesitated in his answer.

Outside the village he stopped. She, too, stopped. Neither had spoken a word all through. Perhaps the silence spoke louder than words. Each was only too conscious of the other.

"Do they know?" Silence. Wamuhu was probably considering the question. "Don't keep me waiting. Please answer me," he implored. He felt weary, very weary, like an old man who had suddenly reached his journey's end.

"No. You told me to give you one more week. A week is over today."

"Yes. That's why I came!" John whispered hoarsely.

Wamuhu did not speak. John looked at her. Darkness was now between them. He was not really seeing her; before him was the image of his father—haughtily religious and dominating. Again he thought: I John, a priest's son, respected by all and going to college, will fall, fall to the ground. He did not want to contemplate the fall.

"It was your fault." He found himself accusing her. In his heart he knew he was lying.

"Why do you keep on telling me that? Don't you want to marry me?"

John sighed. He did not know what to do.

Once upon a time there was a young girl . . . She had no home to go to . . . She could not go forward to the beautiful land and see all the good things because the Irimu was in the way . . .

"When will you tell them?"

"Tonight." He felt desperate. Next week he would go to the college. If he could persuade her to wait, he might be able to get away and come back when the storm and consternation had **abated**. But then the government might withdraw his bursary.[11]

> **abated**
> *lessened; subsided*

He was frightened and there was a sad note of appeal as he turned to her and said: "Look, Wamuhu, how long have you been pre—I mean like this?"

"I have told you over and over again. I have been pregnant for three months and Mother is being suspicious. Only yesterday she said I breathed like a woman with child."

"Do you think you could wait for three weeks more?" She laughed. Ah! the little witch! She knew his trick. Her laughter always aroused many emotions in him.

"All right. Give me just tomorrow. I'll think up something. Tomorrow I'll let you know all."

"I agree. Tomorrow. I cannot wait anymore unless you mean to marry me."

Why not marry her? She is beautiful! Why not marry her? And do I or don't I love her?

She left. John felt as if she was deliberately blackmailing him. His knees were weak and lost strength. He could not move but sank on the ground in a heap. Sweat poured profusely down his

---

11 **bursary:** a scholarship given for higher education

cheeks, as if he had been running hard under a strong sun. But this was cold sweat. He lay on the grass; he did not want to think. Oh! No! He could not possibly face his father. Or his mother. Or Reverend Thomas Carstone, who had had such faith in him. John realized that he was not more secure than anybody else, in spite of his education. He was no better than Wamuhu. *Then why don't you marry her?* He did not know. John had grown up under a Calvinistic[12] father and learned under a Calvinistic headmaster— a missionary! John tried to pray. But to whom was he praying? To Carstone's God? It sounded false. It was as if he was blaspheming.[13] Could he pray to the God of the tribe? His sense of guilt crushed him.

He woke up. Where was he? Then he understood. Wamuhu had left him. She had given him one day. He stood up; he felt good. Weakly, he began to walk back home. It was lucky that darkness blanketed the whole earth, and him in it. From the various huts, he could hear laughter, heated talks, or quarrels. Little fires could be seen flickering red through the open doors. Village stars, John thought. He raised up his eyes. The heavenly stars, cold and distant, looked down on him impersonally. Here and there, groups of boys and girls could be heard laughing and shouting. For them life seemed to go on as usual. John consoled himself by thinking that they, too, would come to face their day of trial.

John was shaky. Why! Why! Why could he not defy all expectations, all prospects of a future, and marry the girl? No. No. It was impossible. She was circumcised, and he knew that his father and the Church would never consent to such a marriage. She had no learning, or rather she had not gone beyond Standard 4. Marrying her would probably ruin his chances of ever going to a university . . .

He tried to move briskly. His strength had returned. His imagination and thought took flight. He was trying to explain his action before an accusing world—he had done so many times before, ever since he knew of this. He still wondered what he

---

12 **Calvinistic:** like the Calvinists, a religious group regarded as being strict

13 **blaspheming:** using God's name disrespectfully

could have done. The girl had attracted him. She was graceful and her smile had been very bewitching. There was none who could equal her and no girl in the village had any pretense to any higher standard of education. Women's education was very low. Perhaps that was why so many Africans went "away" and came back married. He, too, wished he had gone with the others, especially in the last giant student airlift to America. If only Wamuhu had learning . . . and she was uncircumcised . . . then he might probably rebel . . .

The light still shone in his mother's hut. John wondered if he should go in for the night prayers. But he thought against it; he might not be strong enough to face his parents. In his hut, the light had gone out. He hoped his father had not noticed it . . .

John woke up early. He was frightened. He was normally not superstitious but still he did not like the dreams of the night. He dreamed of circumcision; he had just been initiated in the tribal manner. Somebody—he could not tell his face—came and led him because he took pity on him. They went, went into a strange land. Somehow, he found himself alone. The somebody had vanished. A ghost came. He recognized it as the ghost of the home he had left. It pulled him back; then another ghost came. It was the ghost of the land he had come to. It pulled him from the front. The two contested. Then came other ghosts from all sides and pulled him from all sides so that his body began to fall into pieces. And the ghosts were unsubstantial. He could not cling to any. Only they were pulling him, and he was becoming nothing, nothing . . . he was now standing a distance away. It had not been him. But he was looking at the girl, the girl in the story. She had nowhere to go. He thought he would go to help her; he would show her the way. But as he went to her, he lost his way . . . He was all alone . . . Something destructive was coming toward him, coming, coming . . . He woke up. He was sweating all over—

Dreams about circumcision were no good. They **portended** death. He dismissed the dream with a laugh. He opened the window only to find the whole country clouded in mist. It was perfect July weather in Limuru. The hills, ridges, valleys, and plains that surrounded the village were lost in the mist. It looked such a strange place. But there was almost a magic fascination in

portended
foreshadowed; predicted

A Meeting in the Dark   311

it. Limuru was a land of contrasts and evoked differing emotions at different times. Once, John would be fascinated and would yearn to touch the land, embrace it or just be on the grass. At another time he would feel repelled by the dust, the strong sun, and the potholed roads. If only his struggle were just against the dust, the mist, the sun and the rain, he might feel content. Content to live here. At least he thought he would never like to die and be buried anywhere else but at Limuru. But there was the human element whose vices and betrayal of other men were embodied as the new ugly villages. The last night's incident rushed into his mind like a flood, making him weak again. He came out of his blankets and went out. Today he would go to the shops. He was uneasy. An odd feeling was coming to him, in fact had been coming, that his relationship with his father was perhaps unnatural. But he dismissed the thought. Tonight would be the "day of reckoning." He shuddered to think of it. It was unfortunate that this scar had come into his life at this time when he was going to Makerere and it would have brought him closer to his father.

They went to the shops. All day long, John remained quiet as they moved from shop to shop, buying things from the lanky but wistful Indian traders. And all day long, John wondered why he feared his father so much. He had grown up fearing him, trembling whenever he spoke or gave commands. John was not alone in this.

Stanley was feared by all.

He preached with great vigor, defying the very gates of hell. Even during the Emergency,[14] he had gone on preaching, scolding, judging, and condemning. All those who were not saved were destined for hell. Above all, Stanley was known for his great moral observances—a bit too strict, rather pharisaical[15] in nature. None noticed this; certainly not the sheep he shepherded. If an elder broke any of the rules, he was liable to be expelled, or excommunicated. Young men and women, seen standing together "in a manner prejudicial to church and God's morality" (they were one anyway), were liable to be excommunicated. And

---

14 **the Emergency:** (1952–1956), the Mau Mau rebellion against Britain

15 **pharisaical:** like the Pharisees, known for their rigid religious conduct

so, many young men tried to serve two masters, by seeing their girls at night and going to church by day. The alternative was to give up churchgoing altogether . . .

Stanley took a fatherly attitude toward all the people in the village. You must be strict with what is yours. And because of all this, he wanted his house to be a good example. That is why he wanted his son to grow up right. But motives behind many human actions may be mixed. He could never forget that he had also fallen before his marriage. Stanley was also a product of the disintegration of the tribe due to the new influences.

The shopping took a long time. His father strictly observed the silences between them and neither by word nor by hint did he refer to last night. They reached home and John was thinking that all was well when his father called him.

"John."

"Yes, Father."

"Why did you not come for prayers last night?"

"I forgot—"

"Where were you?"

Why do you ask me? What right have you to know where I was? One day I am going to revolt against you. But immediately, John knew that this act of rebellion was something beyond him—not unless something happened to push him into it. It needed someone with something he lacked.

"I—I—I mean, I was—"

"You should not sleep so early before prayers. Remember to be there tonight."

"I will."

Something in the boy's voice made the father look up. John went away relieved. All was still well.

Evening came. John dressed like the night before and walked with faltering steps toward the fatal place. The night of reckoning had come. And he had not thought of anything. After this night, all would know. Even Reverend Thomas Carstone would hear of it. He remembered Mr. Carstone and the last words of blessing he had spoken to him. No! he did not want to remember. It was no good remembering these things; and yet the words came. They were clearly written in the air, or in the darkness of his mind.

"You are going into the world. The world is waiting even like a hungry lion, to swallow you, to devour you. Therefore, beware of the world. Jesus said, Hold fast unto . . ." John felt a pain—a pain that wriggled through his flesh as he remembered these words. He contemplated the coming fall. Yes! He, John, would fall from the Gates of Heaven down through the open waiting gates of Hell. Ah! He could see it all, and what people would say. Everybody would shun his company, would give him oblique looks that told so much. The trouble with John was that his imagination magnified the fall from the heights of "goodness" out of proportion. And fear of people and consequences ranked high in the things that made him contemplate the fall with so much horror.

> **"The world is waiting even like a hungry lion, to swallow you, to devour you."**

John devised all sorts of punishment for himself. And when it came to thinking of a way out, only fantastic and impossible ways of escape came into his head. He simply could not make up his mind. And because he could not and he feared father and people, and he did not know his true attitude toward the girl, he came to the agreed spot having nothing to tell the girl. Whatever he did looked fatal to him.

Then suddenly he said: "Look, Wamuhu. Let me give you money. You might then say that someone else was responsible. Lots of girls have done this. Then that man may marry you. For me, it is impossible. You know that."

"No. I cannot do that. How can you, you—"

"I will give you two hundred shillings."

"No!"

"Three hundred!"

"No!" She was almost crying. It pained her to see him so.

"Four hundred, five hundred, six hundred!" John had begun calmly but now his voice was running high. He was excited. He was becoming more desperate. Did he know what he was talking about? He spoke quickly, breathlessly, as if he was in a hurry. The figure was rapidly rising—nine thousand, ten thousand, twenty thousand . . . He is mad. He is foaming. He is quickly moving toward the girl in the dark. He has laid his hands on her shoulders and is madly imploring her in a hoarse voice. Deep inside him, something horrid that assumes the threatening anger of his father and the village seems to be pushing him. He is violently shaking Wamuhu, while his mind tells him that he is patting her gently. Yes. He is out of his mind. The figure has now reached fifty thousand shillings and is increasing. Wamuhu is afraid, extricates herself from him, the mad, educated son of a religious clergyman, and she runs. He runs after her and holds her, calling her by all sorts of endearing words. But he is shaking her, shake, shake, her, her—he tries to hug her by the neck, presses . . . She lets out one horrible scream and then falls on the ground. And so all of a sudden the struggle is over, the figures stop and John stands there trembling like the leaf of a tree on a windy day.

John, in the grip of fear, ran homeward. Soon everyone would know.

Responding to the Selection

1. What parallels do you see between the behavior of John and his father?

2. What is the possible significance of the story John's mother tells him at the beginning of the story?

3. Why does Wamuhu's father fear for the tribe?

4. What are some of the attitudes toward females that are revealed in this story?

5. What do you think will happen to John?

The Pig

Barbara Kimenye

WORLD LENS

♦♦♦

UGANDA

In the East African nation of Uganda, the Ganda people still make up the largest ethnic group. Prior to 1967, they had their own tribal kingdom, which they called Buganda. This monarchy was officially deposed upon the restructuring of Uganda.

Approximately sixteen percent of the Ugandan people practice the Muslim religion and so are forbidden to eat pork. The Qur'an, or Holy Book, says: "Forbidden to you (for food) are: dead meat, blood, the flesh of swine, and that on which hath been invoked a name other than that of Allah."

Old Kibuka had long believed that retirement was no sort of life for a man like himself, who would, so he modestly believed, pass for not a day over forty-five. He had held a responsible post at the Ggombolola Headquarters,[1] until the Government had sent somebody from the Public Service Commission to nose around the offices and root out all employees over retirement age. Then the next thing Kibuka knew, despite his youthfully dyed hair, he had a pension, a Certificate of Service, but no longer a job.

He still worried about the state his filing system must be in today, for having once called in at the Headquarters, merely to see if the youngster who had replaced him needed any advice or help, he had been appalled at the lack of order. Papers were scattered everywhere, confidential folders were open for all the world to read, and his successor was flirting madly with some pin-brained girl at the other end of the newly installed telephone.

The visit had not been anything near a success, for not even his former colleagues showed anything but superficial interest in what Kibuka had to say.

---

1 **Ggombolola Headquarters:** central administrative offices

So there he was, destined to waste the remainder of his life in the little cottage beside the Kalasanda stream, with plenty indeed to look back on, but not very much to look forward to, and his greatest friend, Yosefu Mukasa, was away in Budda County on business.

The self-pitying thought "I might as well be dead" kept recurring in his mind as he pumped his pressure stove to boil a kettle of tea. Then the noise of a car, grinding its way along the narrow, uneven track, heading in his direction, sent him eagerly to the door. It was his eldest grandson who climbed out of the battered Landrover. A tall, loose-limbed young man in a khaki shirt and blue jeans. Old Kibuka practically choked with happiness as his frail fingers were squeezed in a **sinewy** grip, and the bones of his shoulders almost snapped under an affectionate hug.

sinewy
strong; muscular

"What a wonderful surprise! Come in, my boy. I was just making a cup of tea."

"Grandfather, this is a very short visit. I'm afraid I can't stay more than a few minutes." The boy's voice was musically deep, very much like his grandfather's once had been, before the tremor of age had changed it. "I just came to see how you are getting on, and I brought you a present."

"That's very kind of you, son!" The unexpected visit and now a present: in a matter of seconds Kibuka had completely reversed his opinion that life was no longer worth living. He was aglow with excitement.

"Yes. It's one of the piglets from the Farm School. The sow doesn't seem able to feed this new litter, so I thought you might like one for eating; it should make an excellent meal."

The boy strode back to the Landrover and returned with a black, squealing bundle under his arm.

Kibuka was more delighted than ever. He had never seen so small a pig before, and he spent a good ten minutes marveling at its tiny twinkling eyes, its minute hoofs, and its wisp of a tail. When his grandson drove away, he waved happily from the doorstep, the piglet clutched tenderly to his chest.

He had told his grandson that he would take the creature up to the Mukasas and ask Miriamu to prepare it as a special "welcome home" supper for Yosefu, but he soon sensed a certain reluctance within himself to do this, because the piglet followed him about the house or squatted trustingly at his feet each time he sat down. Moreover, it obviously understood every word Kibuka said to it, for, whenever he spoke, it listened gravely with its dainty forefeet placed lightly upon his knee.

By nightfall Kibuka was enchanted with his new companion, and would have as much considered eating it as he would consider eating the beloved grandson who had given it to him. He fed the piglet little scraps of food from his own plate, besides providing it with a rich porridge mixture. Nevertheless, within a few days it was clear that the pig's appetite was increasing out of all proportion to its size, and Kibuka had to resort to collecting matoke peelings[2] in an old bucket from his friends and nearest neighbors.

The news that Kibuka was keeping a pig, the first ever actually reared in Kalasanda, caused something of a sensation. In no time at all there was little need for him to cart the bucket from house to house, because the women and children, on their way to draw water from the stream, made a practice of bringing the peelings and food scraps with them as part of the excuse for calling on him, and being allowed to fondle the animal and discuss its progress as if it were a dear relative with a delicate hold on life.

No pig had ever had it so good. Fortunately, it proved to be a **fastidiously** clean creature, and for this reason Kibuka allowed it to spend its nights at the foot of his bed, although he was careful not to let his neighbors know of this. The pig, naturally enough, positively flourished in this cozy atmosphere of good will and personal attention. From a squealing bundle small enough to be held in one hand, it quickly developed into a handsome, hefty porker with eyes which held the faintest glint of malice even when it was at its most affectionate with Kibuka.

However, as the weeks went by, its rapid growth was accompanied by a variety of problems. For instance, it required more and more food, and, having been reared on the leavings of

fastidiously
painstakingly; meticulously

No pig had ever had it so good.

---

2 **matoke peelings:** banana or plantain skins, a common food in Buganda

every kitchen in Kalasanda, was inclined to turn up its enormous snout at the idea of having to root in the shamba whenever it felt like something to eat. Every time it started to kick its empty dish about noisily, pausing now and then to glare balefully at old Kibuka and utter snorts of derision, the old man was driven to taking up his bucket and trudging forth to see if any scraps in the village had been overlooked.

Also, while Kibuka had at first secretly enjoyed the warmth of a cuddly little piglet lying across his feet each night, he found himself at a distinct disadvantage when that same piglet acquired a bulk of some fifty or so pounds, and still insisted upon ponderously hoisting itself onto his bed as of right. Worse still, along with the weight, the piglet also produced a snore which regularly kept poor Kibuka awake until dawn. It was a grave decision he was finally called upon to make, yet one on which he simply dare not waver: in future, the pig would have to stay outside, tethered to a tree.

Who suffered most, Kibuka or his pig, would be hard to tell, for the animal's lamentations, continuing throughout the night, were equal in strength to the black remorse and wealth of recrimination churning in Kibuka's bosom. That pig never knew how often it was near to being brought indoors and pacified with a bowl of warm milk.

During the day it still was free to roam about until, that is, it adopted the irritating habit of falling into the stream. There it would be, **placidly** ambling after Kibuka as he pottered in his small shamba, or gently napping in the shade of a coffee tree, and then, for no apparent reason, off it would go to the water's edge, and either fall or plunge in before anybody could say "bacon."

placidly
calmly; serenely

The Kalasanda stream had no real depth; many Kalasandans often bathed there or waded in; but sometimes, after a drop or two of rain, the current had more strength, and was quite capable of sweeping a child off its feet. The pig seemed always to choose such times for its immersion, and there wasn't anything anybody could really do as it spluttered and floundered with its hoofs flaying madly, and terror written plainly across its broad, black face.

At first, Kibuka would rush back and forth along the bank,

calling frantically in the hope that it would struggle towards him, but what usually happened in the end was that a particularly strong eddy would sweep it round the bend into a thicket of weeds and rushes, and then the children playing there would have a good half-hour's fun driving it home.

This happened so often that Kibuka was forced to keep the pig tethered day and night. He visualized the time when no children would be playing in the reeds, and the pig would perhaps become entangled, dragged under and drowned.

By way of compensation he decided upon a regular evening walk for the animal, so by and by Kalasanda became accustomed to the sight of Kibuka, slight yet patriarchal in his kanzu and black waistcoat,[3] sedately traversing the countryside with a huge black pig at the end of a rope, and only strangers saw anything out of the ordinary in it. Without doubt, these walks were a source of great pleasure and exercise to the pig, who found them a wonderful change from the all too familiar view of Kibuka's shamba. Unfortunately, the same could not be said of their effect on old Kibuka. To be frank, Kibuka's corns[4] were killing him, and the excruciating pain of every step sometimes brought tears to his eyes. Still, he tried to bear his discomfort with **stoic fortitude**, for, as he said to Daudi Kulubya, who showed concern over his limp, it was always the same before the heavy rains: in fact, his corns were as good as a barometer when it came to forecasting the weather. But he was always glad to return home, where he could sit for an hour with his poor feet in a bowl of hot water and try to keep his mind off the small fortune he was spending on corn plasters[5] brought to Kalasanda by the peddlers in the market.

How long this state of affairs would have continued is anybody's guess. There were occasions when Kibuka actually entertained the notion of parting with his pet at the first good offer from a reputable farmer or butcher. And yet, one trusting glance or gesture of affection from that waddling hunk of pork was enough for him to feel ashamed of what he regarded as his own treachery.

stoic
composed; unflappable

fortitude
courage; determination

---

3 **kanzu and black waistcoat:** the traditional clothing for Bugandan men, consisting of a long cotton outer garment and a black vest

4 **corns:** calluses on the toes and soles of the feet

5 **corn plasters:** bandages for one's calluses

The end came at last in the most unlikely manner. One minute there was Kibuka contemplating the sunset, and, incidentally, giving his feet a rest by one of the obscure paths leading to the Sacred Tree,[6] while the pig scratched happily at the root of a clump of shrubs, its head hidden by foliage, while its carcass, broadside on, barricaded the path, and then, seconds later, there was the snarl of a motorcycle engine, the horrible grinding of brakes, followed by a whirling kaleidoscope of disaster. Kibuka, pig, bike and rider seemed to explode in all directions. Each had a momentary vision of the others sailing through the air.

When Kibuka eventually dared to open his eyes and cautiously move each limb, he was relieved to find he was still in one piece, although one shoulder felt painfully bruised and there was blood on both his hands. The rider, whom he now recognized as a certain Nathaniel Kiggundu, did not appear to have fared very badly either. He was staggering out of a tangled mass of weeds, wiping mud off his face, and fingering a long tear in the knee of his trousers.

Somewhere from behind the hedge came the raucous cries of a pig in distress, and it was in this direction that both men headed, once they had regained their bearings. They were only just in time to see the injured animal give up the ghost and join its ancestors in that heavenly piggery which surely must exist somewhere above. There was scarcely a mark on it, but its head lay at a strange and awkward angle, so it can be safely assumed that it died of a broken neck.

Old Kibuka was terribly upset, and the accident had left him in a generally shaky condition. He sat down beside the dead animal and wondered what would happen next. Nathaniel Kiggundu, however, seeing Kibuka was comparatively unhurt, showed more concern over his motorcycle, which lay grotesquely twisted in a ditch. The inevitable crowd collected almost as soon as the pig expired, so there was much coming and going, first to stare at the fatal casualty, and then to stare at the motorbike. Nantondo kept up a running commentary, her version of how the accident happened, although nobody believed she had seen it, and by the time Musisi the Ggombolola Chief arrived on the

---

6 **Sacred Tree:** a local spiritual landmark

scene, she had fully adopted the role of Mistress of Ceremonies.

After taking a statement from Kiggundu, Musisi approached Kibuka and insisted upon taking him home in the Landrover. "You don't look at all well, Sir. Come. You can make your statement in the morning, when you have had a rest."

"But I can't leave my pig here." Kibuka refused to budge from the spot.

"Well, I can put it in the back of the Landrover, if you like. Only it would be better to have the butcher cut it up, because I don't think pork will keep for long in this weather."

The idea of eating the pig had never entered Kibuka's mind. While sitting beside the body, he had been seriously considering just whereabouts in the shamba he could bury it. Now he opened his mouth to tell Musisi in no uncertain terms that eating one's good friends was a practice reserved for barbarians: and then, he suddenly had a clear picture of himself struggling to dig a grave. He was sure no Kalasandans would want to help him do it. Then came the realization of the effect a perpetual reminder of his porking friend in his shamba would have on him. He did not think he could stand it. Far better, indeed, to let the past bury itself and, besides, why deprive his fellow villagers of a tasty treat? They were, after all, the people who had nourished the creature on their leftovers.

"Very well. Get somebody to carve it up and share it out among the people who eat pork, and do be sure to send a whole back leg up to the Mukasas," he said at last, suddenly feeling far too weary to care.

"Musa the butcher won't do it," Nantondo piped. "He's a Muslim."

"Well, I'll take it along to the Ggombolola Headquarters and ask one of the askaris[7] to carve it up. Anybody who wants pork must go there at about seven o'clock tonight," declared Musisi, and ordered two of the onlookers to help him lift the carcass into the back of his vehicle.

Back at his cottage, Kibuka rubbed his injured shoulder with a concoction he used to cure most of his ailments, be they loose bowels or a sore throat, and then sat brooding over a cup of tea.

---

7 **askaris:** native officers of the peace

He went to bed very early and awoke next day to find the sun well risen. He decided he had had the best night's sleep he had enjoyed for many a month. Musisi arrived as Kibuka was leaving home to see if the leg of pork had been safely delivered to Yosefu and Miriamu.

"No, I'm taking the meat there now, Sir," Musisi said. "Would you care to come with me?"

Kibuka gladly accepted the lift, although he declined the lump of pork Musisi had brought for him, personally. "You have it, son. I'm not a great lover of pork."

Miriamu went into raptures over the leg of pork, and Yosefu showed the keenest interest in the details of the accident. They pressed both Kibuka and Musisi to stay to lunch, but Musisi had to leave to attend a committee meeting in Mmengo, so only Kibuka remained. He and Yosefu, who lately had not seen as much of each other as usual, had plenty to discuss, and lunch was an exhilarating meal.

"I must say, you really are a wonderful cook!" Kibuka told Miriamu, helping himself to more food. Miriamu preened herself, shyly. "Well, that pork was as tender as a chicken, and very tasty, too!"

There was a moment of dismay when Kibuka realized he was eating and thoroughly enjoying the **succulence** of his late friend, but it quickly passed, and he continued piling his plate with meat, smiling to himself at the knowledge that there would be no need to take a walk in the late afternoon; he could have a good nap instead.

succulence
tastiness; richness

Responding to the Selection

1. In what ways are we asked to sympathize with Kibuka? Think about how that is different from identifying with him.

2. Is there anything this Bugandan village has in common with an American town of a similar size? Explain your answer.

3. What needs does Kibuka have that the pig fulfills?

4. What is the general tone of this story? Say which details and word choices lead you to make this conclusion.

The Pig   323

No Witchcraft for Sale

Doris Lessing

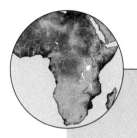

WORLD LENS

◆◆◆

ZIMBABWE/

ENGLAND

The farm where Doris Lessing grew up was typical for Africa: 3,000 acres of unfenced scrub bush—land covered with dense vegetation and undergrowth—and the open grasslands known as the veld. Only a few hundred acres were cultivated, with the rest populated by many kinds of wild game. Although Lessing moved to England as a young woman, she writes movingly about her childhood home in Africa.

Of this important writer, one literary critic said, "Lessing's stories challenge her readers to become more alert to the political ways of people." In the following story, the motivations for the white Africans and black Africans are shown to be at cross-purposes.

The Farquars had been childless for years when little Teddy was born; and they were touched by the pleasure of their servants, who brought presents of fowls and eggs and flowers to the homestead when they came to rejoice over the baby, exclaiming with delight over his downy golden head and his blue eyes. They congratulated Mrs. Farquar as if she had achieved a very great thing, and she felt that she had—her smile for the lingering, admiring natives was warm and grateful.

Later, when Teddy had his first haircut, Gideon the cook picked up the soft gold tufts from the ground and held them reverently in his hand. Then he smiled at the little boy and said: "Little Yellow Head." That became the native name for the child. Gideon and Teddy were great friends from the first. When Gideon had finished his work, he would lift Teddy on his shoulders to the shade of a big tree and play with him there, forming curious little toys from twigs and leaves and grass or shaping animals from wetted soil. When Teddy learned to walk it was often Gideon who crouched before him, clucking encouragement, finally catching him when he fell, tossing him up in the air till they both became breathless with laughter. Mrs. Farquar was fond of the old cook because of his love for her child.

There was no second baby; and one day Gideon said: "Ah, missus, missus, the Lord above sent this one; Little Yellow Head is the most good thing we have in our house." Because of the "we" Mrs. Farquar felt a warm impulse toward her cook, and at the end of the month she raised his wages. He had been with her now for several years; he was one of the few natives who had his wife and children in the compound and never wanted to go home to his kraal,[1] which was some hundreds of miles away. Sometimes a small piccanin,[2] who had been born the same time as Teddy, could be seen peering from the edge of the bush, staring in awe at the little white boy with his miraculous fair hair and Northern blue eyes. The two little children would gaze at each other with a wide, interested gaze, and once Teddy put out his hand curiously to touch the black child's cheeks and hair.

Gideon, who was watching, shook his head wonderingly, and said: "Ah, missus, these are both children, and one will grow up to be a baas,[3] and one will be a servant"; and Mrs. Farquar smiled and said sadly, "Yes, Gideon, I was thinking the same." She sighed. "It is God's will," said Gideon, who was a mission boy. The Farquars were very religious people, and this shared feeling about God bound servant and masters even closer together.

"Ah, missus, these are both children, and one will grow up to be a baas, and one will be a servant . . ."

Teddy was about six years old when he was given a scooter and discovered the intoxications of speed. All day he would fly around the homestead, in and out of flowerbeds, scattering squawking chickens and irritated dogs, finishing with a wide, dizzying arc into the kitchen door. There he would cry: "Gideon, look at me!" And Gideon would laugh and say: "Very clever, Little Yellow Head." Gideon's youngest son, who was now a herdsboy, came especially up from the compound to see the

---

1 **kraal:** a local village

2 **piccanin:** (also picaninny), a black child

3 **baas:** Afrikaans for "boss"

scooter. He was afraid to come near it, but Teddy showed off in front of him. "Piccanin," shouted Teddy, "get out of my way!" And he raced in circles around the black child until he was frightened and fled back to the bush.

"Why did you frighten him?" asked Gideon, gravely reproachful.

Teddy said defiantly: "He's only a black boy," and laughed. Then, when Gideon turned away from him without speaking, his face fell. Very soon he slipped into the house and found an orange and brought it to Gideon, saying: "This is for you." He could not bring himself to say he was sorry; but he could not bear to lose Gideon's affection either. Gideon took the orange unwillingly and sighed. "Soon you will be going away to school, Little Yellow Head," he said wonderingly, "and then you will be grown-up." He shook his head gently and said, "And that is how our lives go." He seemed to be putting a distance between himself and Teddy, not because of resentment, but in the way a person accepts something inevitable. The baby had lain in his arms and smiled up into his face; the tiny boy had swung from his shoulders and played with him by the hour. Now Gideon would not let his flesh touch the flesh of the white child. He was kind, but there was a grave formality in his voice that made Teddy pout and sulk away. Also, it made him into a man: With Gideon he was polite and carried himself formally, and if he came into the kitchen to ask for something, it was in the way a white man uses toward a servant, expecting to be obeyed.

But on the day that Teddy came staggering into the kitchen with his fists to his eyes, shrieking with pain, Gideon dropped the pot full of hot soup that he was holding, rushed to the child, and forced aside his fingers. "A snake!" he exclaimed. Teddy had been on his scooter and had come to a rest with his foot on the side of a big tub of plants. A tree snake, hanging by its tail from the roof, had spat full into his eyes. Mrs. Farquar came running when she heard the commotion. "He'll go blind," she sobbed, holding Teddy close against her. "Gideon, he'll go blind!" Already the eyes, with perhaps half an hour's sight left in them, were swollen up to the size of fists: Teddy's small white face was distorted by great purple oozing **protuberances**. Gideon said: "Wait a

protuberances
bulges; swellings

Africa

minute, missus, I'll get some medicine." He ran off into the bush.

Mrs. Farquar lifted the child into the house and bathed his eyes with permanganate. She had scarcely heard Gideon's words; but when she saw that her remedies had no effect at all, and remembered how she had seen natives with no sight in their eyes because of the spitting of a snake, she began to look for the return of her cook, remembering what she heard of the **efficacy** of native herbs. She stood by the window, holding the terrified, sobbing little boy in her arms, and peered helplessly into the bush. It was not more than a few minutes before she saw Gideon come bounding back, and in his hand he held a plant.

"Do not be afraid, missus," said Gideon, "this will cure Little Yellow Head's eyes." He stripped the leaves from the plant, leaving a small white fleshy root. Without even washing it, he put the root in his mouth, chewed it vigorously, and then held the spittle there while he took the child forcibly from Mrs. Farquar. He gripped Teddy down between his knees and pressed the balls of his thumbs into the swollen eyes, so that the child screamed and Mrs. Farquar cried out in protest: "Gideon, Gideon!" But Gideon took no notice. He knelt over the writhing child, pushing back the puffy lids till chinks of eyeball showed, and then he spat hard, again and again, into first one eye and then the other. He finally lifted Teddy gently into his mother's arms and said: "His eyes will get better." But Mrs. Farquar was weeping with terror, and she could hardly thank him: It was impossible to believe that Teddy could keep his sight. In a couple of hours the swellings were gone. The eyes were inflamed and tender, but Teddy could see. Mr. and Mrs. Farquar went to Gideon in the kitchen and thanked him over and over again. They felt helpless because of the gratitude: It seemed they could do nothing to express it. They gave Gideon presents for his wife and children, and a big increase in wages, but these things could not pay for Teddy's now completely cured eyes. Mrs. Farquar said: "Gideon, God chose you as an instrument for His goodness," and Gideon said: "Yes, missus, God is very good."

Now, when such a thing happens on a farm, it cannot be long before everyone hears of it. Mr. and Mrs. Farquar told their neighbors, and the story was discussed from one end of the

efficacy
effectiveness; power

No Witchcraft for Sale   327

district to the other. The bush is full of secrets. No one can live in Africa, or at least on the veld, without learning very soon that there is an ancient wisdom of leaf and soil and season—and, too, perhaps most important of all, of the darker tracts of the human mind—which is the black man's heritage. Up and down the district people were telling anecdotes, reminding each other of things that had happened to them.

"But I saw it myself, I tell you. It was a puff adder[4] bite. The kaffir's[5] arm was swollen to the elbow, like a great shiny black bladder. He was groggy after a half a minute. He was dying. Then suddenly a kaffir walked out of the bush with his hands full of green stuff. He smeared something on the place, and the next day my boy was back at work, and all you could see was the two small punctures in the skin."

This was the kind of tale they told. And, as always, with a certain amount of exasperation, because while all of them knew that in the bush of Africa are waiting valuable drugs locked in bark, in simple-looking leaves, in roots, it was impossible to ever get the truth about them from the natives themselves.

The story eventually reached town; and perhaps it was at a sundowner party, or some such function, that a doctor who happened to be there challenged it. "Nonsense," he said, "These things get exaggerated in the telling. We are always checking up on this kind of story, and we draw a blank every time."

Anyway, one morning there arrived a strange car at the homestead, and out stepped one of the workers from the laboratory in town, with cases full of test tubes and chemicals.

Mr. and Mrs. Farquar were flustered and pleased and flattered. They asked the scientist to lunch, and they told the story all over again, for the hundredth time. Little Teddy was there too, his blue eyes sparking with health, to prove the truth of it. The scientist explained how humanity might benefit if this new drug could be offered for sale, and the Farquars were even more pleased: They were kind, simple people who liked to think of something good coming about because of them. But when the scientist began talking of the money that might result, their manner showed

---

4 **puff adder:** a poisonous snake

5 **kaffir:** a derogatory term for black South Africans

discomfort. Their feelings over the miracle (that was how they thought of it) were so strong and deep and religious that it was distasteful to them to think of money. The scientist, seeing their faces, went back to his first point, which was the advancement of humanity. He was perhaps a trifle **perfunctory**: It was not the first time he had come salting the tail[6] of a fabulous bush secret.

Eventually, when the meal was over, the Farquars called Gideon into their living room and explained to him that this baas here was a Big Doctor from the Big City, and he had come all the way to see Gideon. At this Gideon seemed afraid; he did not understand; and Mrs. Farquar explained quickly that it was because of the wonderful thing he had done with Teddy's eyes that the Big Baas had come.

Gideon looked from Mrs. Farquar to Mr. Farquar and then at the little boy, who was showing great importance because of the occasion. At last he said grudgingly: "The Big Baas want to know what medicine I used?" He spoke incredulously, as if he could not believe his old friends could so betray him. Mr. Farquar began explaining how a useful medicine could be made out of the root, and how it could be put on sale, and how thousands of people, black and white, up and down the continent of Africa, could be saved by the medicine when that spitting snake filled their eyes with poison. Gideon listened, his eyes bent on the ground, the skin of his forehead puckering in discomfort. When Mr. Farquar had finished he did not reply. The scientist, who all this time had been leaning back in a big chair, sipping his coffee and smiling with skeptical good humor, chipped in and explained all over again, in different words, about the making of drugs and the progress of science. Also, he offered Gideon a present.

There was a silence after this further explanation, and then Gideon remarked indifferently that he could not remember the root. His face was sullen and hostile, even when he looked at the Farquars, whom he usually treated like old friends. They were beginning to feel annoyed, and this feeling **annulled** the guilt that had been sprung into life by Gideon's accusing manner. They were beginning to feel that he was unreasonable. But it was at that moment that they all realized that he would never give in. The

perfunctory
unenthusiastic; cursory

annulled
cancelled; nullified

---

6 **salting the tail:** investigating

magical drug would remain where it was, unknown and useless except for the tiny scattering of Africans who had the knowledge, natives who might be digging a ditch for the municipality in a ragged shirt and a pair of patched shorts but who were still born to healing, hereditary healers, being the nephews or sons of the old witch doctors, whose ugly masks and bits of bone and all the uncouth properties of magic were the outward signs of real power and wisdom.

The Farquars might tread on that plant fifty times a day as they passed from house to garden, from cow kraal to mealie[7] field, but they would never know it.

But they went on persuading and arguing, with all the force of their exasperation; and Gideon continued to say that he could not remember, or that there was no such root, or that it was the wrong season of the year, or that it wasn't the root itself, but the spit from his mouth that had cured Teddy's eyes. He said all these things one after another and seemed not to care they were contradictory. He was rude and stubborn. The Farquars could hardly recognize their gentle, lovable old servant in this ignorant, perversely obstinate African, standing there in front of them with lowered eyes, his hands twitching his cook's apron, repeating over and over whichever one of the stupid refusals first entered his head.

And suddenly he appeared to give in. He lifted his head; gave a long, blank, angry look at the circle of whites, who seemed to him like a circle of yelping dogs pressing around him; and said: "I will show you the root."

They walked single file away from the homestead down a kaffir path. It was a blazing December afternoon, with the sky full of hot rain clouds. Everything was hot: The sun was like a bronze tray whirling overhead, there was a heat shimmer over the fields, the soil was scorching underfoot, the dusty wind blew gritty and thick and warm in their faces. It was a terrible day, fit only for reclining on a veranda with iced drinks, which is where they would normally have been at that hour.

From time to time, remembering that on the day of the snake it had taken ten minutes to find the root, someone asked: "Is it

---

7 **mealie:** Indian corn, in Africa

much farther, Gideon?" And Gideon would answer over his shoulder, with angry politeness: "I'm looking for the root, baas." And indeed, he would frequently bend sideways and trail his hand among the grasses with a gesture that was insulting in its perfunctoriness. He walked them through the bush along unknown paths for two hours in that melting, destroying heat, so that the sweat trickled coldly down them and their heads ached. They were all quite silent; the Farquars because they were angry, the scientist because he was being proved right again; there was no such plant. His was a tactful silence.

At last, six miles from the house, Gideon suddenly decided they had had enough; or perhaps his anger evaporated at that moment. He picked up, without an attempt at looking anything but casual, a handful of blue flowers from the grass, flowers that had been growing plentifully all down the paths they had come. He handed them to the scientist without looking at him and marched off by himself on the way home, leaving them to follow him if they chose.

When they got back to the house, the scientist went to the kitchen to thank Gideon: he was being very polite, even though there was an amused look in his eyes. Gideon was not there. Throwing the flowers casually into the back of his car, the **eminent** visitor departed on his way back to his laboratory.

Gideon was back in his kitchen in time to prepare dinner, but he was sulking. He spoke to Mr. Farquar like an unwilling servant. It was days before they liked each other again.

The Farquars made enquiries about the root from their laborers. Sometimes they were answered with distrustful stares. Sometimes the natives said: "We do not know. We have never heard of the root." One, the cattle boy, who had been with them a long time and had grown to trust them a little, said: "Ask your boy in the kitchen. Now, there's a doctor for you. He's the son of a famous medicine man who used to be in these parts, and there's nothing he cannot cure." Then he added politely: "Of course, he's not as good as the white man's doctor, we know that, but he's good for us."

After some time, when the soreness had gone from between the Farquars and Gideon, they began to joke: "When are you

eminent
distinguished; high-ranking

going to show us the snake root, Gideon?" And he would laugh and shake his head, saying, a little uncomfortably: "But I did show you, missus, have you forgotten?"

Much later, Teddy, as a schoolboy, would come into the kitchen and say: "You old rascal, Gideon! Do you remember that time you tricked us all by making us walk miles all over the veld for nothing? It was so far my father had to carry me!"

And Gideon would double up with polite laughter. After much laughing, he would suddenly straighten himself up, wipe his old eyes, and look sadly at Teddy, who was grinning mischievously at him across the kitchen: "Ah, Little Yellow Head, how you have grown! Soon you will be grown-up with a farm of your own . . . "

Responding to the Selection

1. Do these characters seem authentic to you? Explain whether or not you believe the author has succeeded in developing believable, flesh-and-blood characters.

2. What does Gideon have to fear from the scientist's and family's request for his knowledge?

3. What changes do you see in the child Teddy's attitude toward blacks as the story develops? Give evidence from the story to support your answer.

4. Does this story imply anything about the position of white people in Africa? Explain your answer.

The Moment Before the Gun Went Off

Nadine Gordimer

WORLD LENS

♦♦♦

SOUTH AFRICA

Born to Jewish immigrants, Nobel Prize winner Nadine Gordimer was raised and educated in a racially divided South Africa. Her acclaimed body of fiction and nonfiction focuses mostly on the damage apartheid has done to people's humanity. Employing irony and strong atmosphere, she grounds her characters in a South Africa that is usually under seige, both politically and morally.

Despite this unromantic and often critical view of her country, Gordimer has sustained a deep vein of hopefulness throughout her career. Though apartheid was banned in 1994, South Africa still struggles with deep racial and economic divisions. And, Gordimer continues to be a powerful voice for equality and national pride.

Marais Van der Vyver shot one of his farm labourers, dead. An accident, there are accidents with guns every day of the week—children playing a fatal game with a father's revolver in the cities where guns are domestic objects, nowadays, hunting mishaps like this one, in the country—but these won't be reported all over the world. Van der Vyver knows his will be. He knows that the story of the Afrikaner[1] farmer— regional Party leader and Commandant of the local security commando—shooting a black man who worked for him will fit exactly *their* version of South Africa, it's made for them. They'll be able to use it in their boycott and divestment campaigns,[2] it'll be

---

1 **Afrikaner:** a nonnative African; a white settler, mainly of Dutch descent

2 **boycott and divestment campaigns:** successful local and worldwide economic protests against the ruling whites of South Africa

another piece of evidence in their truth about the country. The papers at home will quote the story as it has appeared in the overseas press, and in the back-and-forth he and the black man will become those crudely-drawn figures on anti-apartheid[3] banners, units in statistics of white brutality against the blacks quoted at the United Nations—he, whom they will gleefully be able to call "a leading member" of the ruling Party.

People in the farming community understand how he must feel. Bad enough to have killed a man, without helping the Party's, the government's, the country's enemies, as well. They see the truth of that. They know, reading the Sunday papers, that when Van der Vyver is quoted saying he is "terribly shocked," he will "look after the wife and children," none of those Americans and English, and none of those people at home who want to destroy the white man's power will believe him. And how they will sneer when he even says of the farm boy (according to one paper, if you can trust any of those reporters), "He was my friend, I always took him hunting with me." Those city and overseas people don't know it's true: farmers usually have one particular black boy they like to take along with them in the lands; you could call it a kind of friend, yes, friends are not only your own white people, like yourself, you take into your house, pray with in church and work with on the Party committee. But how can those others know that? They don't want to know it. They think all blacks are like the big-mouth agitators in town. And Van der Vyver's face, in the photographs, strangely opened by distress—everyone in the district remembers Marais Van der Vyver as a little boy who would go away and hide himself if he caught you smiling at him, and everyone knows him now as a man who hides any change of expression round his mouth behind a thick, soft moustache, and in his eyes by always looking at some object in hand, leaf of a crop fingered, pen or stone picked up, while concentrating on what he is saying, or while listening to you. It just goes to show what shock can do; when you look at the newspaper photographs you feel like apologizing, as if you had stared in on some room where you should not be.

---

3 **anti-apartheid:** against apartheid (Afrikaans for "apartness"), the system of segregated government in South Africa that was dismantled in 1994

There will be an inquiry; there had better be, to stop the assumption of yet another case of brutality against farm workers, although there's nothing in doubt—an accident, and all the facts fully admitted by Van der Vyver. He made a statement when he arrived at the police station with the dead man in his bakkie. Captain Beetge knows him well, of course; he gave him brandy. He was shaking, this big, calm, clever son of Willem Van der Vyver, who inherited the old man's best farm. The black was stone dead, nothing to be done for him. Beetge will not tell anyone that after the brandy Van der Vyver wept. He sobbed, snot running onto his hands, like a dirty kid. The Captain was ashamed, for him, and walked out to give him a chance to recover himself.

◆ ◆ ◆ ◆ ◆

Marais Van der Vyver left his house at three in the afternoon to cull a buck from the family of kudu[4] he protects in the bush areas of his farm. He is interested in wildlife and sees it as the farmers' sacred duty to raise game as well as cattle. As usual, he called at his shed workshop to pick up Lucas, a twenty-year-old farmhand who had shown mechanical aptitude and whom Van der Vyver himself had taught to maintain tractors and other farm machinery. He hooted, and Lucas followed the familiar routine, jumping onto the back of the truck. He liked to travel standing up there, spotting game before his employer did. He would lean forward, braced against the cab below him.

Van der Vyver had a rifle and .300 ammunition beside him in the cab. The rifle was one of his father's, because his own was at the gunsmith's in town. Since his father died (Beetge's sergeant wrote "passed on") no one had used the rifle and so when he took it from a cupboard he was sure it was not loaded. His father had never allowed a loaded gun in the house; he himself had been taught since childhood never to ride with a loaded weapon in a vehicle. But this gun was loaded. On a dirt track, Lucas thumped his fist on the cab roof three times to signal: look left. Having seen the white-ripple-marked flank of a kudu, and its fine horns raking through disguising bush, Van der Vyver drove rather fast over a pot-hole. The jolt fired the rifle. Upright, it was

---

4 **kudu:** African antelope

pointing straight through the cab roof at the head of Lucas. The bullet pierced the roof and entered Lucas's brain by way of his throat.

That is the statement of what happened. Although a man of such standing in the district, Van der Vyver had to go through the ritual of swearing that it was the truth. It has gone on record, and will be there in the **archive** of the local police station as long as Van der Vyver lives, and beyond that, through the lives of his children, Magnus, Helena and Karel—unless things in the country get worse, the example of black mobs in the towns spreads to the rural areas and the place is burned down as many urban police stations have been. Because nothing the government can do will appease the **agitators** and the whites who encourage them. Nothing satisfies them, in the cities: blacks can sit and drink in white hotels, now, the Immorality Act has gone, blacks can sleep with whites . . . It's not even a crime any more.

Van der Vyver has a high barbed security fence round his farmhouse and garden which his wife, Alida, thinks spoils completely the effect of her artificial stream with its tree-ferns beneath the jacarandas.[5] There is an aerial soaring like a flag-pole in the back yard. All his vehicles, including the truck in which the black man died, have aerials that swing their whips when the driver hits a pot-hole: they are part of the security system the farmers in the district maintain, each farm in touch with every other by radio, twenty-four hours out of twenty-four. It has already happened that **infiltrators** from over the border have mined remote farm roads, killing white farmers and their families out on their own property for a Sunday picnic. The pot-hole could have set off a land-mine, and Van der Vyver might have died with his farm boy. When neighbours use the communications system to call up and say they are sorry about "that business" with one of Van der Vyver's boys, there goes unsaid: it could have been worse.

It is obvious from the quality and fittings of the coffin that the farmer has provided money for the funeral. And an elaborate funeral means a great deal to blacks; look how they will deprive themselves of the little they have, in their lifetime, keeping up

archive
records; chronicles

agitators
instigators; rabble-rousers

infiltrators
intruders; spies

---

5 **jacarandas:** tropical trees with fragrant wood

BRASS SCULPTURE OF THE AKAN PEOPLE

payments to a burial society so they won't go in boxwood to an unmarked grave. The young wife is pregnant (of course) and another little one, wearing red shoes several sizes too large, leans under her jutting belly. He is too young to understand what has happened, what he is witnessing that day, but neither whines nor plays about; he is solemn without knowing why. Blacks expose small children to everything, they don't protect them from the sight of fear and pain the way whites do theirs. It is the young wife who rolls her head and cries like a child, sobbing on the breast of this relative and that.

All present work for Van der Vyver or are the families of those who work; and in the weeding and harvest seasons, the women and children work for him, too, carried—wrapped in their blankets, on a truck, singing—at sunrise to the fields. The dead man's mother is a woman who can't be more than in her late thirties (they start bearing children at puberty) but she is heavily mature in a black dress between her own parents, who were already working for old Van der Vyver when Marais, like their daughter, was a child. The parents hold her as if she were a prisoner or a crazy woman to be restrained. But she says nothing, does nothing. She does not look up; she does not look at Van der Vyver, whose gun went off in the truck, she stares at the grave. Nothing will make her look up; there need be no fear that she will look up; at him. His wife, Alida, is beside him. To show the proper respect, as for any white funeral, she is wearing the navy-blue-and-cream hat she wears to church this summer. She is always supportive, although he doesn't seem to notice it; this coldness and reserve—his mother says he didn't mix well as a child—she accepts for herself but regrets that it has prevented him from being nominated, as he should be, to stand as the Party's parliamentary candidate for the district. He does not let her clothing, or that of anyone else gathered closely, make contact with him. He, too, stares at the grave. The dead man's mother and he stare at the grave in communication like that between the black man outside and the white man inside the cab the moment before the gun went off.

◆ ◆ ◆ ◆ ◆

The moment before the gun went off was a moment of high excitement shared through the roof of the cab, as the bullet was to pass, between the young black man outside and the white farmer inside the vehicle. There were such moments, without explanation, between them, although often around the farm the farmer would pass the young man without returning a greeting, as if he did not recognize him. When the bullet went off what Van der Vyver saw was the kudu stumble in fright at the report[6] and gallop away. Then he heard the thud behind him, and past the window saw the young man fall out of the vehicle. He was sure he had leapt up and toppled—in fright, like the buck. The farmer was almost laughing with relief, ready

The moment before the gun went off was a moment of high excitement . . .

---

6 **report:** the loud noise of the gunfire

to tease, as he opened his door, it did not seem possible that a bullet passing through the roof could have done harm.

The young man did not laugh with him at his own fright. The farmer carried him in his arms, to the truck. He was sure, sure he could not be dead. But the young black man's blood was all over the farmer's clothes, soaking against his flesh as he drove.

How will they ever know, when they file newspaper clippings, evidence, proof, when they look at the photographs and see his face—guilty! guilty! they are right!—how will they know, when the police stations burn with all the evidence of what has happened now, and what the law made a crime in the past. How could they know that *they do not know.* Anything. The young black **callously** shot through the negligence of the white man was not the farmer's boy; he was his son.

callously
heartlessly; unfeelingly

Responding to the Selection

1. Look for elements of irony in this story—its tone, what happens in the plot, the stereotypes about blacks, and characterizations of Marais Van der Vyver. For example, how is the reference to South Africa's Immorality Act ironic here?

2. Note the details in the story that show as well as imply how blacks and whites lead different lives in apartheid South Africa.

3. Were you prepared for the ending? See if the author provides any clues in the story about its possible conclusion.

4. One of Gordimer's primary fictional themes is "alienation." How does the author explore alienation in the Van der Vyver family?

5. Why do you think the author has chosen this title? Reflect on the meaning and possible symbolism of "The Moment Before the Gun Went Off."

The Prisoner Who Wore Glasses

Bessie Head

WORLD LENS

♦♦♦

SOUTH AFRICA

South African Bessie Head was born in an insane asylum. Her white mother was placed there by her parents when they found out their daughter was pregnant with a black African's child. Head was raised by a poor adoptive family and excluded by both whites and blacks. After a life of terrible difficulties, Head and her son moved to Botswana, in self-imposed exile from her homeland.

The setting of the following story is the Eastern Cape, a province in southeastern South Africa where apartheid was in full force until its abolition in 1994. South African prisons were known for their brutality, not only between the warders and inmates, but among inmates themselves.

Scarcely a breath of wind disturbed the stillness of the day, and the long rows of cabbages were bright green in the sunlight. Large white clouds drifted slowly across the deep blue sky. Now and then they obscured the sun and caused a chill on the backs of the prisoners who had to work all day long in the cabbage field.

This trick the clouds were playing with the sun eventually caused one of the prisoners who wore glasses to stop work, straighten up and peer short-sightedly at them. He was a thin little fellow with a hollowed-out chest and comic knobbly knees. He also had a lot of fanciful ideas because he smiled at the clouds.

"Perhaps they want me to send a message to the children," he thought tenderly, noting that the clouds were drifting in the direction of his home some hundred miles away. But before he could frame the message, the warder[1] in charge of his work span[2] shouted:

"Hey, what you think you're doing, Brille?"

The prisoner swung round, blinking rapidly, yet at the same time sizing up the enemy. He was a new warder, named Jacobus Stephanus Hannetjie. His eyes were the color of the sky but they were frightening. A simple, primitive, brutal soul gazed out of them. The prisoner bent down quickly and a message was quietly passed down the line:

"We're in for trouble this time, comrades."

"Why?" rippled back up the line.

"Because he's not human," the reply rippled down, and yet only the crunching of the spades as they turned over the earth disturbed the stillness.

This particular work span was known as Span One. It was composed of ten men, and they were all political prisoners. They were grouped together for convenience, as it was one of the prison regulations that no black warder should be in charge of a political prisoner lest this prisoner convert him to his views. It never seemed to occur to the authorities that this very reasoning was the strength of Span One and a clue to the strange terror they aroused in the warders. As political prisoners they were unlike the other prisoners in the sense that they felt no guilt nor were they outcasts of society. All guilty men instinctively **cower**, which was why it was the kind of prison where men got knocked out cold with a blow at the back of the head from an iron bar. Up until the arrival of Warder Hannetjie, no warder had dared beat any member of Span One and no warder had lasted more than a week with them. The battle was entirely psychological. Span One was assertive and it was beyond the scope of white warders to handle assertive black men. Thus, Span One had got out of control. They were the best thieves and liars in the camp. They lived all day on raw cabbages. They chatted and smoked tobacco. And since they moved, thought and acted as one, they had perfected every technique of group concealment.

Trouble began that very day between Span One and Warder

cower
cringe; grovel

---

1 **warder:** the overseer

2 **work span:** a unit of prison workers

Hannetjie. It was because of the shortsightedness of Brille. That was the nickname he was given in prison and is the Afrikaans word for someone who wears glasses. Brille could never judge the approach of the prison gates, and on several previous occasions he had munched on cabbages and dropped them almost at the feet of the warder, and all previous warders had overlooked this. Not so Warder Hannetjie.

"Who dropped that cabbage?" he thundered.

Brille stepped out of line. "I did," he said meekly.

"All right," said Hennetjie. "The whole span goes three meals off."

"But I told you I did it," Brille protested.

The blood rushed to Warder Hannetjie's face, "Look 'ere," he said.

"I don't take orders from a kaffir. I don't know what kind of kaffir you think you are. Why don't you say Baas. I'm your Baas. Why don't you say Baas, hey?"

Brille blinked his eyes rapidly but by contrast his voice was strangely calm.

"I'm twenty years older than you," he said. It was the first thing that came to mind, but the comrades seemed to think it a huge joke. A titter swept up the line. The next thing Warder Hannetjie whipped out a knobkerrie[3] and gave Brille several blows about the head. What surprised his comrades was the speed with which Brille had removed his glasses or else they would have been smashed to pieces on the ground.

That evening in the cell Brille was very apologetic.

"I'm sorry, comrades," he said. "I've put you into a hell of a mess."

"Never mind, brother," they said. "What happens to one of us, happens to all."

"I'll try to make up for it, comrades," he said. "I'll steal something so that you don't go hungry."

Privately, Brille was very philosophical about his head wounds. It was the first time an act of violence had been perpetrated against him, but he had long been a witness of extreme, almost unbelievable human brutality. He had twelve

---

3 **knobkerrie:** a compact club

Africa

children and his mind traveled back that evening through the sixteen years of bedlam in which he had lived. It had all happened in a small drab little three-bedroomed house in a small drab little street in the Eastern Cape, and the children kept coming year after year because neither he nor Martha managed the contraceptives the right way and a teacher's salary never allowed moving to a bigger house and he was always taking exams to improve this salary only to have it all eaten up by hungry mouths. Everything was pretty horrible, especially the way the children fought. They'd get hold of each other's heads and give them a good bashing against the wall. Martha gave up somewhere along the line, so they worked out a thing between them. The bashings, biting and blood were to operate in full swing until he came home. He was to be the bogeyman,[4] and when it worked he never failed to have a sense of godhead[5] at the way in which his presence could change savages into fairly reasonable human beings.

Yet somehow it was this chaos and mismanagement at the center of his life that drove him into politics. It was really an ordered beautiful world with just a few basic slogans to learn along with the rights of mankind. At one stage, before things became very bad, there were conferences to attend, all very far away from home.

"Let's face it," he thought **ruefully**. "I'm only learning right now what it means to be a politician. All this while I've been running away from Martha and the kids."

And the pain in his head brought a hard lump to his throat. That was what the children did to each other daily and Martha wasn't managing, and if Warder Hannetjie had not interrupted him that morning, he would have sent the following message:

"Be good comrades, my children. Cooperate, then life will run smoothly."

The next day Warder Hannetjie caught this old man with twelve children stealing grapes from the farm shed. They were an enormous quantity of grapes in a ten-gallon tin, and for this misdeed the old man spent a week in the isolation cell. In fact,

ruefully
sadly; regretfully

---

4 **bogeyman:** the person who is scary or dreaded

5 **godhead:** being godlike

Span One as a whole was in constant trouble. Warder Hannetjie seemed to have eyes at the back of his head. He uncovered the trick about the cabbages; how they were split in two with the spade and immediately covered with earth and then unearthed again and eaten with split-second timing. He found out how tobacco smoke was beaten into the ground, and he found out how conversations were whispered down the wind.

For about two weeks Span One lived in **acute** misery. The cabbages, tobacco and conversations had been the **pivot** of jail life to them. Then one evening they noticed that their good old comrade who wore the glasses was looking rather pleased with himself. He pulled out a four-ounce packet of tobacco by way of explanation, and the comrades fell upon it with great greed. Brille merely smiled. After all, he was the father of many children. But when the last shred had disappeared, it occurred to the comrades that they ought to be puzzled. Someone said:

"I say, brother. We're watched like hawks these days. Where did you get the tobacco?"

"Hannetjie gave it to me," said Brille.

There was a long silence. Into it dropped a quiet bombshell.

"I saw Hannetjie in the shed today," and the failing eyesight blinked rapidly. "I caught him in the act of stealing five bags of fertilizer, and he bribed me to keep my mouth shut."

There was another long silence.

"Prison is an evil life," Brille continued, apparently discussing some irrelevant matter. "It makes a man contemplate all kinds of evil deeds."

He held out his hand and closed it.

"You know, comrades," he said. "I've got Hannetjie. I'll betray him tomorrow."

Everyone began talking at once.

"Forget it, brother. You'll get shot." Brille laughed.

"I won't," he said. "That is what I mean about evil. I am a father of children, and I saw today that Hannetjie is just a child and stupidly truthful. I'm going to punish him severely because we need a good warder."

The following day, with Brille as witness, Hannetjie confessed to the theft of the fertilizer and was fined a large sum of money.

acute
sharp; intense

pivot
hub; center

From then on Span One did very much as they pleased while Warder Hannetjie stood by and said nothing. But it was Brille who carried this to extremes. One day, at the close of work Warder Hannetjie said:

"Brille, pick up my jacket and carry it back to the camp."

"But nothing in the regulations says I'm your servant, Hannetjie," Brille replied coolly.

"I've told you not to call me Hannetjie. You must say Baas," but Warder Hannetjie's voice lacked conviction. In turn, Brille squinted up at him.

"I'll tell you something about this Baas business, Hannetjie," he said. "One of these days we are going to run the country. You are going to clean my car. Now, I have a fifteen-year-old son, and I'd die of shame if you had to tell him that I ever called you Baas."

Warder Hannetjie went red in the face and picked up his coat.

On another occasion Brille was seen to be walking about the prison yard, openly smoking tobacco. On being taken before the prison commander he claimed to have received the tobacco from Warder Hannetjie. All throughout the **tirade** from his chief, Warder Hannetjie failed to defend himself, but his nerve broke completely. He called Brille to one side.

tirade
tongue-lashing; long scolding speech

"Brille," he said. "This thing between you and me must end. You may not know it, but I have a wife and children, and you're driving me to suicide."

"Why don't you like your own medicine, Hannetjie?" Brille asked quietly.

"I can give you anything you want," Warder Hannetjie said in desperation.

"It's not only me but the whole of Span One," said Brille cunningly. "The whole of Span One wants something from you."

Warder Hannetjie brightened with relief.

"I think I can manage if it's tobacco you want," he said.

Brille looked at him, for the first time struck with pity and guilt. He wondered if he had carried the whole business too far. The man was really a child.

"It's not tobacco we want, but you," he said. "We want you on our side. We want a good warder because without a good warder we won't be able to manage the long stretch ahead."

Warder Hannetjie interpreted this request in his own fashion, and his interpretation of what was good and human often left the prisoners of Span One speechless with surprise. He had a way of slipping off his revolver and picking up a spade and digging alongside Span One. He had a way of producing unheard-of-luxuries like boiled eggs from his farm nearby and things like cigarettes, and Span One responded nobly and got the reputation of being the best work span in the camp. And it wasn't only taken from their side. They were awfully good at stealing **commodities** like fertilizer which were needed on the farm of Warder Hannetjie.

commodities
goods; merchandise

Responding to the Selection

1. Explain what you think is meant by this quote: "As political prisoners they were unlike the other prisoners in the sense that they felt no guilt nor were they outcasts of society."

2. What has Brille come to understand in prison about his family life?

3. In what ways does Warder Hannetjie remind Brille of a child?

4. What do you think is the theme of this story?

5. Bessie Head, the author, suffered greatly as a result of being of mixed-race heritage in apartheid South Africa. Do you believe this story offers any hope concerning relations between blacks and whites in her homeland?

UNIT REVIEW

Africa

Discussing

1. In both "Marriage Is a Private Affair" and "A Meeting in the Dark," young men fret that their fathers will disapprove of their potential wives. Compare these two stories, looking at how the personalities of the young men and their fathers help to shape the eventual outcomes.

2. Look at how whites and blacks regard each other in "No Witchcraft for Sale," "The Moment Before the Gun Went Off," and "The Prisoner Who Wore Glasses." How do they help to teach and support each other, and how do they fail? Think about what each group is trying to protect when it keeps something back from the other.

3. The stories "In the Shadow of War" and "Loyalties" are about the civil war in Nigeria, a war notable for its human massacres. Though strikingly different in tone, there are some things they have in common. What are some elements they share?

4. Do you think there is any significance to the fact that two of these selections come from apartheid South Africa? Why do you think this harsh political system inspired these writers?

5. "Pride" is a theme that runs through the poems in this unit. What do you think is the connection between this theme and Africa's history of colonial rule?

6. In many of these selections, people are not given respect or allowed to thrive as human beings. Point out the stories where lack of respect is a theme and try to determine why this conflict is so powerful for both writer and reader alike.

Writing

7. Write a speech in which you explain to an audience of your peers the origins of a deep-seated problem in your school, community, or other organization or group. Show them the relationships that explain why the present-day situation exists. Try to boost their hopes that things can change. This could be a serious problem or one more lighthearted. Nevertheless, use all the rhetorical skills at your command. When you are happy with the effectiveness of your writing, present it orally to the class.

8. Many of the writers in this unit have suffered from imprisonment or exile, both voluntary and involuntary. Write a letter from prison or from abroad, giving yourself the fictitious identity of a writer who has suffered as a result of the strong expression of his or her beliefs. To add authenticity to the letter, make sure you have a specific audience in mind and add plenty of realistic details of your surroundings.

Speaking

9. Africa has many exciting dramatists, such as Ama Ata Aidoo and Athol Fugard, as well as two writers represented by other genres in this book: Wole Soyinka and Ngugi wa Thiong'o. See if you can find a short one-act play or monologue by a contemporary African playwright and present it with as many of your classmates as required. Try to find work that will appeal to a general audience—drama that has universal themes and emotions.

Hands-on Activity

Do some research on African masks, getting help from the library, Internet, and other resources, including knowledgeable people in your area. Using plaster and paint, make your own mask, endowing it with a "spirit" that is personally meaningful. Discuss its meaning with your classmates before putting it on display with the others.

Personal Connections

After reading the selections in this unit, choose one of the following questions to write about in your journal.

1. Which characters or selections helped open your eyes to a new way of seeing the world?

2. What new understanding do you have about American culture, your family, or yourself?

3. Which differences among cultures do you think really matter? Explain.

RESEARCHING THE WORLD

General Research Subjects

The following general subjects are merely starting points for research. After choosing one that interests you, you will have to narrow your topic considerably.

Belief Systems
Celebrations and
   Ceremonies
Children and Family
Coming of Age
Courtship and Marriage
Crime and Justice
The Economy
Education

The Environment
Food
Famous Figures
Geography
Globalism
Important Events
Language
Literature and the Arts
The Media

Oppression and Exile
Popular Culture
Rural and Urban Life
Sports
Technology
Travel
Work and Leisure

Specific Research Topics

Pick from the following topics or use them as starting points for your research. Some topics can be applied to more than one country in this region; others pertain to a single country or group of people. Note that in order to be a manageable size, many of these topics will require further narrowing.

Arts/Leisure

- The Negritude movement
- Ethnic masks and sculpture
- *Griots*, or traveling storytellers
- Safari tourism
- African dances (ceremonial, folk, popular)

Culture/Geography

- Coming of age ceremonies
- Naming in Senegal
- Yoruba oral culture ("talking drums," praise-song)
- Body decorations (scarring, tattoos, jewelry)
- Wildlife (habitat, preservation, unique species)

History/Politics

- AIDS and famine crises
- Christian missionaries
- The slave trade (documents, diaries, pictures)
- The anti-apartheid movement
- Pan-Africanism

AUTHOR BIOGRAPHIES

Chinua Achebe (1930–) Albert Chinualumogu Achebe, an author of fiction, poetry, and essays, was born in Nigeria. His first novel, *Things Fall Apart* (1958), has been called a turning point in African literature. Previously, Africa had been mainly described and defined for the outside world by white authors. Achebe says that the myths and stories of African oral tradition have cultural uses. So he believes that "any good story, any good novel, should have a message, should have a purpose." In 1990, a serious automobile accident left Achebe paralyzed from the waist down. Because suitable medical care wasn't available in Nigeria, he was treated in a London hospital. After he recuperated, Achebe moved to the United States to write and teach.

David Diop (1927–1960) Although he was born in France, David Diop identified strongly with his African heritage. His mother was from Cameroon, his father from Senegal, and the family moved back and forth between French West Africa and France. In his collection of poems, *Coups de Pilon* (Pounding), Diop bitterly attacks slavery and colonialism, and praises the uniqueness of African experience. He had been recognized as a very promising poet when his life was cut short by a plane crash. Most of Diop's work was destroyed with him in the crash. The 22 poems published before his death appear in English translation in *Hammer Blows and Other Writings*.

Nadine Gordimer (1923–) Born in South Africa, Nadine Gordimer has always observed the moral and political complexities of her home country with a clear eye. Early on, she raised her voice against apartheid and injustice. When apartheid finally ended, she said it was "like a birth." Afterwards, Gordimer's writing—such as her novel *A Guest of Honour*—focused on the birth pains of the new society. In *The House Gun, July's People, My Son's Story,* and other works, she deals with the sometimes terrible choices made by people who find themselves in a changing world. Although Gordimer also writes nonfiction, she remarked, "Nothing I say in essays and articles will be as true as my fiction." Her work has been translated into more than thirty languages and has won many awards. In 1991, Gordimer became the first South African to be awarded the Nobel Prize for literature.

Bessie Head (1937–1986) The daughter of a white English woman and a black South African man, Bessie Head faced many problems under South Africa's former policy of apartheid. In 1964, Head moved to Botswana, where she spent 15 years in a refugee community, often living in poverty. However, she found the regularity of that life helpful. "In South Africa, all my life I lived in shattered little bits," she observed. "All those shattered bits began to grow together here . . . ." Head began writing, and published three novels, several collections of short stories, and two histories of African life. *A Question of Power* is an autobiographical novel describing her own bouts of depression and mental illness.

Barbara Kimenye (1940–) Originally from a small village in Uganda, Barbara Kimenye sets many of her stories in Kalasanda, a fictional village much like her own. She writes humorously, and sometimes satirically, about ordinary people in everyday situations. Her best-known stories are collected in *Kalasanda* and *Kalasanda Revisited*. Kimenye began writing short stories and a newspaper column when she was secretary to a Ugandan ruler. After a major political change in Uganda, she lived in England for several years. She is also a well-known author of children's books, including a series of adventure stories about a boy named Moses and his friends.

Doris Lessing (1919–) British author Doris Lessing was born in what is now Iran. Her family later moved to a farm in Rhodesia (now Zimbabwe), and many of her stories depict the harsh treatment of black Africans by whites. Always concerned with social and political matters, Lessing was a communist until she grew disenchanted with that movement. In 1949, she moved to

England. Lessing's many novels, short stories, memoirs, and other nonfiction have won awards internationally, and she has collaborated on operas with composer Philip Glass. Her most widely read work is *The Golden Notebook,* a novel about a woman writer's search for meaning. Lessing says, "If I don't write for any length of time, I get very irritable. If I had to stop, I would probably start wandering the streets, telling myself stories out loud."

Adewale Maja-Pearce (1953–) Nigerian journalist and author Adewale Maja-Pearce was raised in London. He was a boy during the Nigerian civil war (1967–1970) and the genocide that followed. Maja-Pearce has written about those tragedies with both humor and horror. He has also reported the stories of Rwandan refugees. Maja-Pearce has been severely critical of Western media, saying that they "stage-managed [suffering Africans] in the interests of careers."

Ben Okri (1959–) As a teenager, Nigerian author Ben Okri read African and European stories and myths, and also learned many tales from the oral traditions of his native culture. "We were all told stories as kids in Nigeria," he once said. "We had to tell stories that would keep one another interested, and you weren't allowed to tell stories that everybody else knew." At 14, Okri began writing poems, short stories, and essays. At 18, he had finished his first novel—*Flowers and Shadows.* With the manuscript in his suitcase, he went to London to study and work. Although sometimes penniless and homeless, he continued to write. *The Famished Road,* a novel about "spirit children" who are born over and over again, won the British Booker Prize in 1980.

Sembene Ousmane (1923–) Senegalese writer and film director Sembene Ousmane works in both French and Wolof, the main language of Senegal. Ousmane fought on the side of the French during World War II. He then became a dock worker in France, where he wrote his novel *Le Docker Noir* (The black docker). After studying film in Russia, he returned to Senegal to make films. His *La Noire de . . .* (Black girl)—the first feature made by an African filmmaker—won a prize at the 1966 Cannes Film Festival. However, because of his strong, often satirical, social commentary, Ousmane's work has sometimes been banned in his native country. Ousmane says ideas come to him when, "I see something, I tell myself, 'Wait, that's got to be told.'"

Léopold Sédar Senghor (1906–2001) Senegalese poet Léopold Sédar Senghor lived in Paris off and on during his life, and joined the French army when World War II began. Captured by the Germans, he was a prisoner of war for eighteen months, during which time he began writing poems. Senghor's first published collection was *Chants d'Ombre* (Songs of shadow). Later he became the first black man to be inducted into the French Academy, one of France's highest cultural achievements. Senghor also helped to found the Negritude movement, which he described as embodying "the totality of the cultural values of the Black world." From 1960 to 1980, this remarkable man was the democratically elected Catholic president of the new independent state of Senegal, a Muslim country.

Wole Soyinka (1934–) Poet, playwright, novelist, and essayist Akinwande Oluwole Soyinka was born in Nigeria and belongs to the Yoruba tribe. In 1967, he was put in prison for 27 months for political reasons. He wrote about this experience in his book *The Man Died: The Prison Notes of Wole Soyinka*. Once while he was in solitary confinement, a woman prisoner was mistakenly put in the same cell with him. At first, she feared that he was an interrogator. When she recognized him as a famous author, she began to weep. The woman helped him find new strength in himself, Soyinka recalled in an interview, "so she did me a lot more good than she could ever have guessed on that day." In 1986, he was awarded the Nobel Prize for literature. Soyinka went into a four-year exile in 1994 for opposing Nigeria's then totalitarian regime.

Ngugi wa Thiong'o (1938–) Kenyan author Ngugi wa Thiong'o started writing in English, then switched to his native Kikuyu. His name was originally James Thiong'o Ngugi, but he changed it as a symbol of his rejection of colonialism in Africa. Ngugi's work is highly political, often expressing his dislike of imperialism and capitalism. His popular Kikuyu play *I Will Marry When I Want* led to his arrest in Kenya. In his novel *Petals of Blood,* Ngugi points out that achieving a truly democratic society will require a struggle. But he has said, "'Struggle' is central to nature, to human art and to my history." In 1982, Ngugi left Kenya to live in London.

The Literature of the Middle East & South Asia

Laura Winkiel

Professor of English, Iowa State University, Ames, Iowa

For generations, the Middle East and South Asia have served as the intersection of many cultures and religions.

The Middle East is home to Arabic literature and Jewish literature from Israel. The spread of literature written in the Arabic language is linked to the rise of the Islamic religion in the 7th and 8th centuries. During this time, the Islamic Empire was the greatest empire in the world. Its language, religion, and literature extended throughout the Middle East, as far east as Afghanistan and as far west as Spain and Northern Africa. Arabic literature reflects the cultural influences of Africa, Europe, and Asia.

South Asia includes the gigantic subcontinent of India, one of the most ancient and diverse regions of the world. The people of modern India speak eighteen major languages and many other minor languages and dialects. They also practice all of the world's major religions, especially Hinduism, Buddhism, Jainism, and Islam. Throughout its long history, India has absorbed and transformed the cultures of the people who have conquered the region, including Greeks, Persians, Muslims, and Europeans. As a result, the Indian literary tradition is one of the world's oldest and richest.

With the exception of the European Crusades to Jerusalem in the eleventh through thirteenth centuries, the most striking European influence in both the Middle East and South Asia occurred only recently, in the eighteenth and nineteenth centuries. As French and English colonists invaded these territories, the people of the Middle East and South Asia became aware of Western forms of technology and modernization. For example, Muhammed Ali, who ruled Egypt from 1805 to 1848, sent his best students to Europe and commissioned the translation of various French texts into Arabic. These texts spread widely in the Middle East, broadening the scope of the Arab world to include Western forms of thought. But because Middle Eastern and South Asian cultures already had an established written culture and history, the works from their own heritage circulated alongside the European materials. Twentieth-century writers from this region have combined traditions to create a world literature that reflects Islamic and South Asian cultures as well as European traditions.

The combination of Western and Eastern thought and ways of life often produces creative literature of great beauty and insight, but sometimes results in conflict. The struggles are often between those peoples seeking to embrace modern ways such as Western food, clothing, and equality between men and women, and those seeking to preserve the Eastern traditions of religion, culture, trade, and traditional roles for the sexes.

The greatest symbol of Eastern resistance to Western ways of life is the veil. Muslim women who strictly practice their religion are instructed never to appear in public without having their hair and sometimes their face veiled and hidden from view. The purpose of this practice is to preserve women's purity and devotion to their husbands, brothers, and fathers. Wearing the veil is also a sign of resistance to the Western world, including the United States.

In a region of the world that has such a long history of conflict and that supports such a wide variety of religions, languages, cultures, and traditions, literature provides a window through which to view a rapidly changing world. Often, children, parents, and grandparents see the world very differently from each other in these stories and poems. These writers raise questions about globalization: is it best that the East should adapt the West's ways? What is lost when this occurs? How can the Middle East and South Asia adopt aspects of Western life without losing their heritage? These stories help us to understand the complex questions that Middle Easterners and South Asian people ask as they stand at a crossroads of cultural and religious change.

The Literature of the Middle East & South Asia

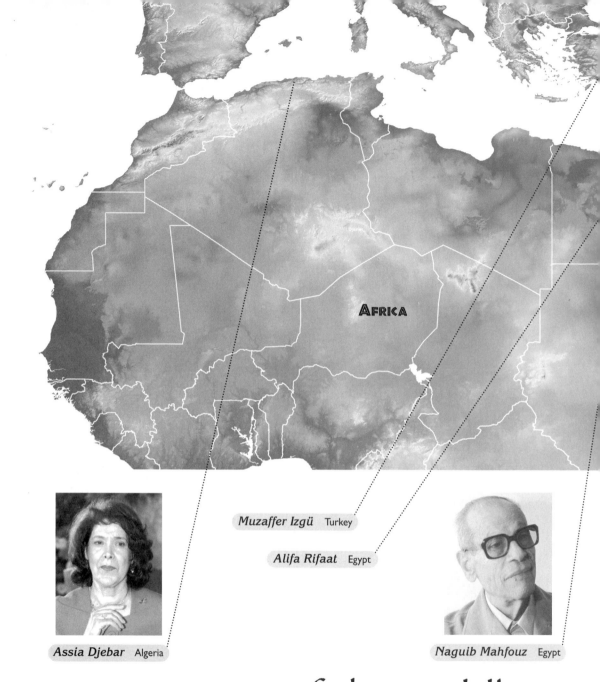

Muzaffer Izgü Turkey

Alifa Rifaat Egypt

Assia Djebar Algeria

Naguib Mahfouz Egypt

AFRICA

Literary Map of the Middle East & South Asia

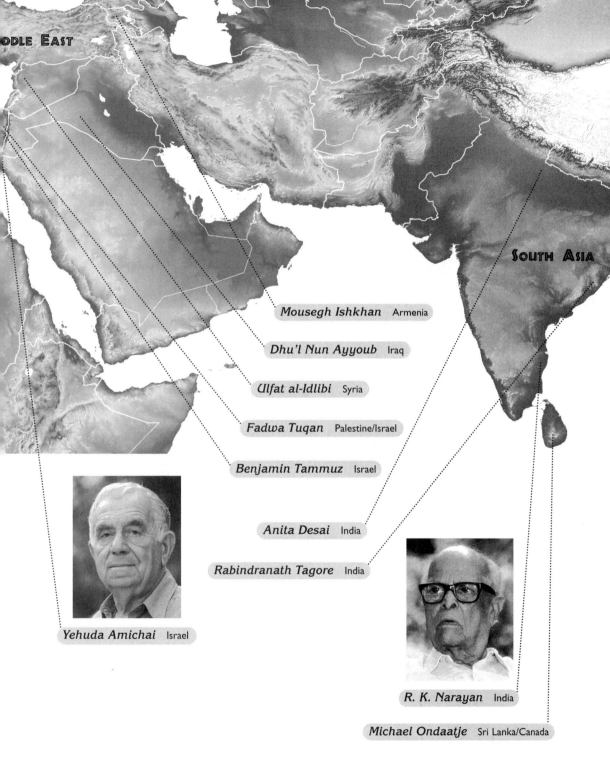

Middle East

Mousegh Ishkhan   Armenia

Dhu'l Nun Ayyoub   Iraq

Ulfat al-Idlibi   Syria

Fadwa Tuqan   Palestine/Israel

Benjamin Tammuz   Israel

Anita Desai   India

Rabindranath Tagore   India

Yehuda Amichai   Israel

South Asia

R. K. Narayan   India

Michael Ondaatje   Sri Lanka/Canada

My Father Writes to My Mother

Assia Djebar

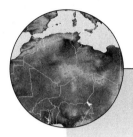

WORLD LENS

♦♦♦

ALGERIA

Using a pen name to escape her family's disapproval, Assia Djebar writes candidly about the status of women in the Middle East. In Algeria, Muslim women are unable to do many things that Western women may take for granted. In the following story, Djebar explores the reactions of her family and locals to the time when her father broke with tradition by writing to her mother.

proviso
condition; stipulation

Whenever my mother spoke of my father, she, in common with all the women in her town, simply used the personal pronoun in Arabic corresponding to "him." Thus, every time she used a verb in the third person singular which didn't have a noun subject, she was naturally referring to her husband. This form of speech was characteristic of every married woman, from fifteen to sixty, with the **proviso** that in later years, if the husband had undertaken the pilgrimage to Mecca,[1] he could be given the title of "Hajj."

Everybody, children and adults, especially girls and women, since all important conversations took place among the womenfolk, learnt very quickly to adapt to this rule whereby a husband and wife must never be referred to by name.

After she had been married a few years, my mother gradually learnt a little French. She was able to exchange a few halting words with the wives of my father's colleagues who had, for the most part, come from France and, like us, lived with their families in the little block of flats set aside for the village teachers.

---

1 **pilgrimage to Mecca:** the visit made by Muslims to the birthplace of the prophet Muhammad at the Mecca in Saudi Arabia

I don't know exactly when my mother began to say, "*My husband* has come, *my husband* has gone out . . . I'll ask *my husband*," etc. Although my mother did make rapid progress in the language, in spite of taking it up fairly late in life, I can still hear the evident awkwardness in her voice betrayed by her labored phraseology,[2] her slow and deliberate enunciation at that time. Nevertheless, I can sense how much it cost her modesty to refer to my father directly in this way.

It was as if a floodgate had opened within her, perhaps in her relationship with her husband. Years later, during the summers we spent in her native town, when chatting in Arabic with her sisters or cousins, my mother would refer to him quite naturally by his first name, even with a touch of superiority. What a daring innovation! Yes, quite unhesitatingly—I was going to say, **unequivocally**—in any case, without any of the usual **euphemisms** and verbal **circumlocutions**. When her aunts and elderly female relations were present, she would once more use the traditional formalities, out of respect for them; such freedom of language would have appeared **insolent** and **incongruous** to the ears of the pious old ladies.

Years went by. As my mother's ability to speak French improved, while I was still a child of no more than twelve, I came to realize an **irrefutable** fact: namely that, in the face of all these womenfolk, my parents formed a couple. One thing was an even greater source of pride in me: when my mother referred to any of the day-to-day incidents of our village life—which in our city relatives' eyes was very backward—the tall figure of my father— my childhood hero—seemed to pop up in the midst of all these women engaged in idle chit-chat on the age-old patios to which they were confined.

My father, no one except my father; none of the other women ever saw fit to refer to their menfolk, their masters who spent the day outside the house and returned home in the evening, **taciturn**, with eyes on the ground. The nameless uncles, cousins, relatives by marriage, were for us an unidentifiable collection of individuals to all of whom their spouses alluded impartially in the masculine gender.

unequivocally
clearly; unambiguously

euphemisms
polite expressions; delicacies

circumlocutions
roundabout expressions

insolent
disrespectful; arrogant

incongruous
improper; inappropriate

irrefutable
inarguable; undeniable

taciturn
not talkative; quiet by nature

---

2 **phraseology:** a method of putting one's words together

With the exception of my father . . . My mother, with lowered eyes, would calmly pronounce his name "Tahar"—which, I learned very early, meant "The Pure"—and even when a suspicion of a smile flickered across the other women's faces or they looked half ill at ease, half indulgent, I thought that a rare distinction lit up my mother's face.

imperceptible
unobservable; unperceivable

These harem conversations ran their **imperceptible** course: my ears only caught those phrases which singled my mother out above the rest. Because she always made a point of bringing my father's name into these exchanges, he became for me still purer than his given name **betokened**.

betokened
indicated; showed

One day something occurred which was a **portent** that their relationship would never be the same again—a commonplace enough event in any other society, but which was unusual to say the least with us: in the course of an exceptionally long journey away from home (to a neighboring province, I think), my father wrote to my mother—yes, to my mother!

portent
sign; forewarning; presage

He sent her a postcard, with a short greeting written diagonally across it in his large, legible handwriting, something like "Best wishes from this distant region" or possibly, "I am having a good journey and getting to know an unfamiliar region," etc. and he signed it simply with his first name. I am sure that, at the time, he himself would not have dared add any more intimate formula above his signature, such as "I am thinking of you," or even less, "Yours affectionately." But, on the half of the card reserved for the address of the recipient, he had written "Madame" followed by his own surname, with the possible addition—but here I'm not sure—"and children," that is to say we three, of whom I, then about ten years old, was the eldest . . .

The radical change in customs was apparent for all to see: my father had quite brazenly written his wife's name, in his own handwriting, on a postcard which was going to travel from one town to another, which was going to be exposed to so many masculine eyes, including eventually our village postman—a Muslim postman to boot—and, what is more, he had dared to refer to her in the western manner as "Madame So-and-So . . . ," whereas, no local man, poor or rich, ever referred to his wife and children in any other way than by the vague periphrasis: "the household."

So, my father had "written" to my mother. When she visited her family she mentioned this postcard, in the simplest possible words and tone of voice, to be sure. She was about to describe her husband's four or five days' absence from the village, explaining the practical problems this had posed: my father having to order the provisions just before he left, so that the shopkeepers could deliver them every morning; she was going to explain how hard it was for a city woman to be isolated in a village with very young children and cut off in this way . . . . But the other women had interrupted, exclaiming, in the face of this new reality, this almost incredible detail:

"He wrote to you, *to you*?"

"He wrote his wife's name and the postman must have read it? Shame! . . . "

"He could at least have addressed the card to his son, for the principle of the thing, even if his son is only seven or eight!"

My mother did not reply. She was probably pleased, flattered even, but she said nothing. Perhaps she was suddenly ill at ease, or blushing from embarrassment; yes, her husband had written to her, in person! . . . The eldest child, the only one who might have been able to read the card, was her daughter: so, daughter or wife, where was the difference as far as the addressee was concerned?

"I must remind you that I've learned to read French now!"

This postcard was, in fact, a most daring manifestation of affection. Her modesty suffered at that very moment that she spoke of it. Yet, it came second to her pride as a wife, which was secretly flattered.

The murmured exchanges of these segregated women struck a faint chord with me, as a little girl with observing eyes. And so, for the first time, I seem to have some intuition of the possible happiness, the mystery in the union of a man and a woman.

My father had dared "to write" to my mother. Both of them referred to each other by name, which was **tantamount** to declaring openly their love for each other, my father by writing to her, my mother by quoting my father henceforward without false shame in all her conversations.

tantamount
equal; equivalent

Responding to the Selection

1. In what way does the author's father behave radically?

2. What are some of the many things you learn about the relations between and differences among men and women in the Algerian village culture Djebar describes?

3. Who do you think is taking a greater risk—the father, with his actions, or the mother, with hers? Explain.

4. Do you think having such a family may have influenced this Arabic woman to become a writer? Explain.

5. Point to evidence in the story of conflicts, both external and internal.

Another Evening at the Club

Alifa Rifaat

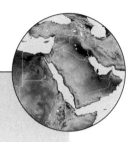

As a girl growing up in Egypt, Alifa Rifaat was not allowed to pursue an education, despite her desire to do so. Instead, she was forced to marry her cousin, who refused to let her publish her writing. She wrote in secret until her husband passed away, and then she published her hidden collection of 18 short stories. Many of her stories reflect on the oppression of women by their husbands and society. Rifaat believes that this results from misinterpreting the Islamic holy book, the Koran.

WORLD LENS

♦♦♦

EGYPT

In a state of tension, she awaited the return of her husband. At a loss to predict what would happen between them, she moved herself back and forth in the rocking chair on the wide wooden verandah that ran along the bank and occupied part of the river itself, its supports being fixed in the river bed, while around it grew grasses and reeds. As though to banish her apprehension, she passed her fingers across her hair. The spectres of the eucalyptus trees ranged along the garden fence rocked before her gaze, with white egrets[1] slumbering on their high branches like huge white flowers among the thin leaves.

The crescent moon rose from behind the eastern mountains and the peaks of the gently stirring waves glistened in its feeble rays, intermingled with threads of light leaking from the houses of Manfalout scattered along the opposite bank. The coloured bulbs fixed to the trees in the garden of the club at the far end of the town stood out against the surrounding darkness. Somewhere over there her husband now sat, most likely engrossed in a game of chess.

---

1 **egrets:** herons, water-loving birds with long necks and legs

It was only a few years ago that she had first laid eyes on him at her father's house, meeting his gaze that weighed up her beauty and priced it before offering the dowry.[2] She had noted his eyes ranging over her as she presented him with the coffee in the Japanese cups that were kept safely locked away in the cupboard for important guests. Her mother had herself laid them out on the silver-plated tray with its elaborately embroidered spread. When the two men had taken their coffee, her father had looked up at her with a smile and had told her to sit down, and she had seated herself on the sofa facing them, drawing the end of her dress over her knees and looking through lowered lids at the man who might choose her as his wife. She had been glad to see that he was tall, well-built and clean-shaven except for a thin greying moustache. In particular she noticed the well-cut coat of English tweed and the silk shirt with gold links. She had felt herself blushing as she saw him returning her gaze. Then the man turned to her father and took out a gold case and offered him a cigarette.

"You really shouldn't, my dear sir," said her father, patting his chest with his left hand and extracting a cigarette with trembling fingers. Before he could bring out his box of matches Abboud Bey had produced his lighter.

"No, after you, my dear sir," said her father in embarrassment. Mingled with her sense of excitement at this man who gave out such an air of worldly self-confidence was guilty shame at her father's inadequacy.

After lighting her father's cigarette Abboud Bey sat back, crossing his legs, and took out a cigarette for himself. He tapped it against the case before putting it in the corner of his mouth and lighting it, then blew out circles of smoke that followed each other across the room.

"It's a great honour for us, my son," said her father, smiling first at Abboud Bey, then at his daughter, at which Abboud Bey looked across at her and asked:

"And the beautiful little girl's still at secondary school?"

She lowered her head modestly and her father had answered:

"As from today she'll be staying at home in readiness for your

---

2 **dowry:** the gift or payment a man pays to his bride's family

happy life together, Allah[3] permitting," and at a glance from her father she had hurried off to join her mother in the kitchen.

"You're a lucky girl," her mother had told her. "He's a real find. Any girl would be happy to have him. He's an Inspector of Irrigation though he's not yet forty. He earns a big salary and gets a fully furnished government house wherever he's posted, which will save us the expense of setting up a house—and I don't have to tell you what our situation is—and that's besides the house he owns in Alexandria where you'll be spending your holidays."

Samia had wondered to herself how such a splendid suitor had found his way to her door. Who had told him that Mr. Mahmoud Barakat, a mere clerk at the Court of Appeal, had a beautiful daughter of good reputation?

The days were then taken up with going the rounds of Cairo's shops and choosing clothes for the new grand life she would be living. This was made possible by her father borrowing on the security of his government pension. Abboud Bey, on his part, never visited her without bringing a present. For her birthday, just before they were married, he bought her an emerald ring that came in a plush box bearing the name of a well-known jeweller in Kasr el-Nil Street. On her wedding night, as he put a diamond bracelet round her wrist, he had reminded her that she was marrying someone with a brilliant career in front of him and that one of the most

. . . one of the most important things in life was the opinion of others, particularly one's equals and seniors.

important things in life was the opinion of others, particularly one's equals and seniors. Though she was still only a young girl she must try to act with suitable dignity.

"Tell people you're from the well-known Barakat family and that your father was a judge," and he went up to her and gently patted her cheeks in a fatherly, reassuring gesture that he was often to repeat during their times together.

Then, yesterday evening, she had returned from the club

---

3 **Allah:** the Muslim religion's Supreme Being

somewhat light-headed from the bottle of beer she had been required to drink on the occasion of someone's birthday. Her husband, noting the state she was in, hurriedly took her back home. She had undressed and put on her nightgown, leaving her jewellery on the dressing-table, and was fast asleep seconds after getting into bed. The following morning, fully recovered, she slept late, then rang the bell as usual and had breakfast brought to her. It was only as she was putting her jewellery away in the wooden and mother-of-pearl box that she realized her emerald ring was missing.

Could it have dropped from her finger at the club? In the car on the way back? No, she distinctly remembered it last thing at night, remembered the usual difficulty she had in getting it off her finger. She stripped the bed of its sheets, turned over the mattress, looked inside the pillow cases, crawled on hands and knees under the bed. The tray of breakfast lying on the small bedside table caught her eye and she remembered the young servant coming in that morning with it, remembered the noise of the tray being put down, the curtains being drawn, the tray then being lifted up again and placed on the bedside table. No one but the servant had

entered the room. Should she call her and question her?

Eventually, having taken two aspirins, she decided to do nothing and await the return of her husband from work.

Directly he arrived she told him what had happened and he took her by the arm and seated her down beside him:

"Let's just calm down and go over what happened."

She repeated, this time with further details, the whole story.

"And you've looked for it?"

"Everywhere. Every possible and impossible place in the bedroom and the bathroom. You see, I remember distinctly taking it off last night."

He grimaced at the thought of last night, then said:

"Anybody been in the room since Gazia when she brought in the breakfast?"

"Not a soul. I've even told Gazia not to do the room today."

"And you've not mentioned anything to her?"

"I thought I'd better leave it to you."

"Fine, go and tell her I want to speak to her. There's no point in your saying anything but I think it would be as well if you were present when I talk to her."

Five minutes later Gazia, the young servant girl they had recently employed, entered behind her mistress. Samia took herself to a far corner of the room while Gazia stood in front of Abboud Bey, her hands folded across her chest, her eyes lowered.

"Yes, sir?"

"Where's the ring?"

"What ring are you talking about, sir?"

"Now don't make out you don't know. The one with the green stone. It would be better for you if you hand it over and then nothing more need be said."

"May Allah blind me if I've set eyes on it."

He stood up and gave her a sudden slap on the face. The girl reeled back, put one hand to her cheek, then lowered it again to her chest and made no answer to any of Abboud's questions. Finally he said to her:

"You've got just fifteen seconds to say where you've hidden the ring or else, I swear to you, you're not going to have a good time of it."

As he lifted up his arm to look at his watch the girl flinched slightly but continued in her silence. When he went to the telephone Samia raised her head and saw that the girl's cheeks were wet with tears. Abboud Bey got through to the Superintendent of Police and told him briefly what had occurred.

"Of course I haven't got any actual proof but seeing that no one else entered the room, it's obvious she's pinched it. Anyway I'll leave the matter in your capable hands—I know your people have their ways and means."

He gave a short laugh, then listened for a while and said: "I'm really most grateful to you."

He put down the receiver and turned round to Samia:

"That's it, my dear. There's nothing more to worry about. The Superintendent has promised me we'll get it back. The patrol car's on the way."

♦ ♦ ♦ ♦ ♦

The following day, in the late afternoon, she'd been sitting in front of her dressing-table rearranging her jewellery in its box when an earring slipped from her grasp and fell to the floor. As she bent to pick it up she saw the emerald ring stuck between the leg of the table and the wall. Since that moment she had sat in a state of panic awaiting her husband's return from the club. She even felt tempted to walk down to the water's edge and throw it into the river so as to be rid of the unpleasantness that lay ahead.

At the sound of the screech of tyres rounding the house to the garage, she slipped the ring onto her finger. As he entered she stood up and raised her hand to show him the ring. Quickly, trying to choose her words but knowing that she was expressing herself clumsily, she explained what an extraordinary thing it was that it should have lodged itself between the dressing-table and the wall, what an extraordinary coincidence she should have dropped the earring and so seen it, how she'd thought of ringing him at the club to tell him the good news but . . .

She stopped in mid-sentence when she saw his frown and added weakly: "I'm sorry. I can't think how it could have happened. What do we do now?"

He shrugged his shoulders as though in surprise.

"Are you asking me, my dear lady? Nothing of course."

"But they've been beating up the girl—you yourself said they'd not let her be till she confessed."

Unhurriedly, he sat himself down as though to consider this new aspect of the matter. Taking out his case, he tapped a cigarette against it in his accustomed manner, then moistened his lips, put the cigarette in place and lit it. The smoke rings hovered in the still air as he looked at his watch and said:

"In any case she's not got all that long before they let her go. They can't keep her for more than forty-eight hours without getting any evidence or a confession. It won't kill her to put up with things for a while longer. By now the whole town knows the servant stole the ring—or would you like me to tell everyone: 'Look, folks, the fact is that the wife got a bit tiddly on a couple of sips of beer and the ring took off on its own and hid itself behind the dressing-table.'? What do you think?"

"I know the situation's a bit awkward . . . "

"Awkward? It's downright ludicrous. Listen, there's nothing to be done but to give it to me and the next time I go down to Cairo I'll sell it and get something else in its place. We'd be the laughingstock of the town."

He stretched out his hand and she found herself taking off the ring and placing it in the outstretched palm. She was careful that their eyes should not meet. For a moment she was on the point of protesting and in fact uttered a few words:

"I'd just like to say we could . . . "

Putting the ring away in his pocket, he bent over her and with both hands gently patted her on the cheeks. It was a gesture she had long become used to, a gesture that promised her continued security, that told her that this man who was her husband and the father of her child had also taken the place of her father who, as though assured that he had found her a suitable substitute, had followed up her marriage with his own funeral. The gesture told her more eloquently than any words that he was the man, she the woman, he the one who carried the responsibilities, made the decisions, she the one whose role it was to be beautiful, happy, carefree. Now, though, for the first time in their life together the gesture came like a slap in the face.

Directly he removed his hands her whole body was seized with an uncontrollable trembling. Frightened he would notice, she rose to her feet and walked with deliberate steps towards the large window. She leaned her forehead against the comforting cold surface and closed her eyes tightly for several seconds. When she opened them she noticed that the café lights strung between the trees on the opposite shore had been turned on and that there were men seated under them and a waiter moving among the tables. The dark shape of a boat momentarily blocked out the café scene; in the light from the hurricane lamp hanging from its bow she saw it cutting through several of those floating islands of Nile waterlilies that, rootless, are swept along with the current.

Suddenly she became aware of his presence alongside her.

"Why don't you go and change quickly while I take the car out? It's hot and it would be nice to have supper at the club."

"As you like. Why not?"

By the time she had turned round from the window she was smiling.

Translated by Denys Johnson-Davies

Responding to the Selection

1. What does this story have to say about the relations between the rich and poor in Egypt?

2. What are some ways Samia might have acted differently after recovering her ring?

3. This story has a wealth of sensory details—images that appeal to the senses of sight, sound, touch, taste, and smell. Find one or two that you particularly like and say what it adds to the story.

4. There are rewards to being the wife of Abboud Bey. What are they?

The Happy Man

Naguib Mahfouz

In 1988 Naguib Mahfouz, one of Egypt's most celebrated and prolific writers, became the first Arabic writer to win the Nobel Prize for literature. His fiction documents the vast changes in Egypt during the 20th century, paying special attention to social and philosophical concerns. In the following story, he engages readers with a classic "What if . . . ?" question. What if, despite life's annoyances and tragedies, a man wakes up and finds himself deliriously happy? For the average Egyptian, happiness might seem elusive given the problems of the Middle East conflict, religious and political infighting, and a ravaged economy.

WORLD LENS

◆◆◆

EGYPT

He woke up in the morning and discovered that he was happy. "What's this?" he asked himself. He could not think of any word which described his state of mind more accurately and precisely than happy. This was distinctly peculiar when compared with the state he was usually in when he woke up. He would be half-asleep from staying so late at the newspaper office. He would face life with a sense of strain and contemplation. Then he would get up, whetting his determination to face up to all inconveniences and withstand all difficulties.

Today he felt happy, full of happiness, as a matter of fact. There was no arguing about it. The symptoms were quite clear, and their vigor and obviousness were such as to impose themselves on his senses and mind all at once. Yes, indeed; he was happy. If this was not happiness, then what was? He felt that his limbs were well proportioned and functioning perfectly. They were working in superb harmony with each other and with the world around him. Inside him, he felt a boundless power, an **imperishable** energy, an ability to achieve anything with confidence, precision, and

imperishable
enduring; unending

It was as if he were no longer troubled or bothered by fear, anxiety, sickness, death, argument, or the question of earning a living.

obvious success. His heart was overflowing with love for people, animals, and things and with an all-engulfing sense of optimism and joy. It was as if he were no longer troubled or bothered by fear, anxiety, sickness, death, argument, or the question of earning a living. Even more important than that, and something he could not analyze, it was a feeling which penetrated to every cell of his body and soul; it played a tune full of delight, pleasure, serenity, and peace and hummed in its incredible melodies the whispering sound of the world which is denied to the unhappy.

He felt drunk with ecstasy and savored it slowly with a feeling of surprise. He asked himself where it had come from and how; the past provided no explanation, and the future could not justify it. Where did it come from, then, and how? How long would it last? Would it stay with him till breakfast? Would it give him enough time to get to the newspaper office? Just a minute though, he thought . . . it won't last because it can't. If it did, man would be turned into an angel or something even higher. So he told himself that he should devote his attention to savoring it, living with it, and storing up its nectar before it became a mere memory with no way of proving it or even being sure that it had ever existed.

He ate his breakfast with relish, and this time nothing distracted his attention while he was eating. He gave "Uncle" Bashir, who was waiting on him, such a beaming smile that the poor man felt rather alarmed and taken aback. Usually he would only look in his direction to give orders or ask questions, although on most occasions he treated him fairly well.

"Tell me, Uncle Bashir," he asked the servant, "am I a happy man?"

The poor man was startled. He realized why his servant was confused; for the first time ever he was talking to him as a colleague or friend. He encouraged his servant to forget about his worries and asked him with unusual insistence to answer his question.

"Through God's grace and favor, you are happy," the servant replied.

"You mean, I should be happy. Anyone with my job, living in my house, and enjoying my health should be happy. That's what you want to say. But do you think I'm really happy?"

The servant replied, "You work too hard, Sir"; after yet more insistence, "It's more than any man can stand . . . ."

He hesitated, but his master gestured to him to continue with what he had to say.

"You get angry a lot," he said, "and have fierce arguments with your neighbors . . . ."

He interrupted him by laughing loudly. "What about you," he asked, "don't you have any worries?"

"Of course, no man can be free of worry."

"You mean that complete happiness is an impossible quest?"

"That applies to life in general . . . ."

How could he have dreamed up this incredible happiness? He or any other human being? It was a strange, unique happiness, as though it were a private secret he had been given. In the meeting hall of the newspaper building, he spotted his main rival in this world sitting down thumbing through a magazine. The man heard his footsteps but did not look up from the magazine. He had undoubtedly noticed him in some way and was therefore pretending to ignore him so as to keep his own peace of mind. At some circulation meetings, they would argue so violently with each other that sparks would begin to fly and they would exchange bitter words. One stage more, and they would come to blows. A week ago, his rival had won in the union elections and he had lost. He had felt pierced by a sharp, poisoned arrow, and the world had darkened before his eyes. Now here he was approaching his rival's seat; the sight of him sitting there did not make him excited, nor did the memories of their dispute spoil his composure. He approached him with a pure and carefree heart, feeling drunk with his incredible happiness; his face showed an expression full of tolerance and forgiveness. It was as though he were approaching some other man toward whom he had never had any feelings of **enmity**, or perhaps he might be renewing a friendship again. "Good morning!" he said without feeling any **compunction**.

The man looked up in amazement. He was silent for a few moments until he recovered, and then returned the greeting curtly. It was as though he did not believe his eyes and ears.

He sat down alongside the man. "Marvelous weather today . . . ," he said.

"Okay . . . ,"the other replied guardedly.

"Weather to fill your heart with happiness."

His rival looked at him closely and cautiously. "I'm glad that you're so happy . . . ," he muttered.

"**Inconceivably** happy . . . ," he replied with a laugh.

"I hope," the man continued in a rather hesitant tone of voice, "that I shan't spoil your happiness at the meeting of the administrative council . . . ."

"Not at all. My views are well known, but I don't mind if the members adopt your point of view. That won't spoil my happiness!"

"You've changed a great deal overnight," the man said with a smile.

"The fact is that I'm happy, inconceivably happy."

The man examined his face carefully. "I bet your dear son has changed his mind about staying in Canada?" he asked.

"Never, never, my friend," he replied, laughing loudly. "He is still sticking to his decision . . . ."

"But that was the principal reason for your being so sad . . . ."

"Quite true. I've often begged him to come back out of pity for me in my loneliness and to serve his country. But he told me that he's going to open an engineering office with a Canadian partner; in fact, he's invited me to join him in it. Let him live where he'll be happy. I'm quite happy here—as you can see, inconceivably happy . . . ."

The man still looked a little doubtful. "Quite extraordinarily brave!" he said.

"I don't know what it is, but I'm happy in the full meaning of the word."

Yes indeed, this was full happiness; full, firm, weighty, and vital. As deep as absolute power, widespread as the wind, fierce as fire, bewitching as scent, **transcending** nature. It could not possibly last.

The other man warmed to his display of affection. "The truth is," he said, "that I always picture you as someone with a fierce and violent temperament which causes him a good deal of trouble and leads him to trouble other people."

"Really?"

"You don't know how to make a truce, you've no concept of intermediate solutions. You work with your nerves, with the marrow in your bones. You fight bitterly, as though any problem is a matter of life and death!"

"Yes, that's true."

He accepted the criticism without any difficulty and with an open heart. His wave expanded into a boundless ocean of happiness. He struggled to control an innocent, happy laugh which the other man interpreted in a way far removed from its pure motives.

"So then," he asked, "you think it's necessary to be able to take a balanced view of events, do you?"

"Of course. I remember, by way of example, the argument we had the day before yesterday about racism. We both had the same views on the subject; it's something worth being zealous about, even to the point of anger. But what kind of anger? An intellectual anger, abstract to a certain extent; not the type which shatters your nerves, ruins your digestion, and gives you **palpitations**. Not so?"

"That's obvious; I quite understand . . . ." He struggled to control a second laugh and succeeded. His heart refused to renounce one drop of its joy. Racism, Vietnam, Palestine[1] . . . . no problem could assail that fortress of happiness which was encircling his heart. When he remembered a problem, his heart **guffawed**. He was happy. It was a **tyrannical** happiness, despising all misery and laughing at any hardship; it wanted to laugh, dance, sing, and distribute its spirit of laughter, dancing, and singing among the various problems of the world.

---

1 **Racism, Vietnam, Palestine:** conflicts with long histories of violence and injustice

He could not bear to stay in his office at the newspaper; he felt no desire to work at all. He hated the very idea of thinking about his daily business and completely failed to bring his mind down from its stronghold in the kingdom of happiness. How could he possibly write about a trolley bus falling into the Nile when he was so intoxicated by this frightening happiness? Yes, it really was frightening. How could it be anything else, when there was no reason for it at all, when it was so strong that it made him exhausted and paralyzed his will—apart from the fact that it had been with him for half a day without letting up in the slightest degree?

He left the pages of paper blank and started walking backwards and forwards across the room, laughing and cracking his fingers . . . .

He felt slightly worried; it did not penetrate deep enough to spoil his happiness but paused on the surface of his mind like an abstract idea. It occurred to him that he might recall the tragedies of his life so that he could test their effect on his happiness. Perhaps they would be able to bring back some idea of balance or security, at least until his happiness began to flag a little. For example, he remembered his wife's death in all its various aspects and details. What had happened? The event appeared to him as a series of movements without any meaning or effect, as though it had happened to some other woman, the wife of another man, in some distant historical age. In fact, it had a contagious effect which prompted a smile and then even provoked laughter. He could not stop himself laughing, and there he was guffawing, ha . . . ha . . . ha!

The same thing happened when he remembered the first letter his son had sent him saying that he wanted to emigrate to Canada. The sound of his guffaws as he paraded the bloody tragedies of the world before him would have attracted the attention of the newspaper workers and passersby in the street had it not been for the thickness of the walls. He could do nothing to dislodge his happiness. Memories of unhappy times hit him like waves being thrown onto a sandy beach under the golden rays of the sun.

He excused himself from attending the administrative council and left the newspaper office without writing a word. After lunch, he lay down on his bed as usual but could not sleep. In fact, sleep seemed an impossibility to him. Nothing gave him any indication that it was coming, even slowly. He was in a place alight and gleaming, resounding with sleeplessness and joy. He had to calm down and relax, to quiet his senses and limbs, but how could he do it? He gave up trying to sleep and got up. He began to hum as he was walking around his house. If this keeps up, he told himself, I won't be able to sleep, just as I can't work or feel sad. It was almost time for him to go to the club, but he did not feel like meeting any friends. What was the point of exchanging views on public affairs and private worries? What would they think if they found him laughing at every major problem? What would they say? How would they picture things? How would they explain it? No, he did not need anyone, nor did he want to spend the evening talking. He should be by himself and go for a long walk to get rid of some of his excess vitality and think about his situation. What had happened to him? How was it that this incredible happiness had overwhelmed him? How long would he have to carry it on his shoulders? Would it keep depriving him of work, friends, sleep and peace of mind? Should he resign himself to it? Should he abandon himself to the flood to play with him as the whim took it? Or should he look for a way out for himself through thought, action, or advice?

◆ ◆ ◆ ◆

When he was called into the examination room in the clinic of his friend, the specialist in internal medicine, he felt a little alarmed. The doctor looked at him with a smile. "You don't look like someone who's complaining about being ill," he said.

"I haven't come to see you because I'm ill," he told the doctor in a hesitant tone of voice, "but because I'm happy!"

The doctor looked piercingly at him with a questioning air.

"Yes," he repeated to underline what he had said, "because I'm happy!"

There was a period of silence. On one side there was anxiety, and on the other, questioning and amazement.

"It's an incredible feeling which can't be defined in any other way, but it's very serious . . . ."

The Happy Man   379

The doctor laughed. "I wish your illness was contagious," he said, prodding him jokingly.

"Don't treat it as a joke. It's very serious, as I told you. I'll describe it to you . . . ."

He told him all about his happiness from the time he had woken up in the morning till he had felt compelled to visit him.

"Haven't you been taking drugs, alcohol, or tranquilizers?"

"Absolutely nothing like that."

"Have you had some success in an important sphere of your life—work . . . love . . . money?"

"Nothing like that either. I've twice as much to worry about as I have to make me feel glad . . . ."

"Perhaps if you were patient for a while . . . ."

"I've been patient all day. I'm afraid I'll be spending the night wandering around . . . ."

The doctor gave him a precise, careful, and comprehensive examination and then shrugged his shoulders in despair. "You're a picture of health," he said.

"And so?"

"I could advise you to take a sleeping pill, but it would be better if you consulted a nerve specialist . . . ."

The examination was repeated in the nerve specialist's clinic with the selfsame precision, care, and comprehensiveness. "Your nerves are sound," the doctor told him. "They're in enviable condition!"

"Haven't you got a plausible explanation for my condition?" he asked hopefully.

"Consult a gland specialist!" the doctor replied, shaking his head.

The examination was conducted for a third time in the gland specialist's clinic with the same precision, care, and comprehensiveness. "I congratulate you!" the doctor told him. "Your glands are in good condition."

He laughed. He apologized for laughing, laughing as he did so. Laughter was his way of expressing his alarm and despair.

He left the clinic with the feeling that he was alone; alone in the hands of his tyrannical happiness with no helper, no guide, and no friend. Suddenly, he remembered the doctor's sign he sometimes saw from the window of his office in the newspaper building. It was true that he had no confidence in psychiatrists even though he had read about the significance of psychoanalysis.[2] Apart from that, he knew that their **tentacles** were very long and they kept their patients tied in a sort of long association. He laughed as he remembered the method of cure through free association[3] and the problems which it eventually uncovers. He was laughing as his feet carried him toward the psychiatrist's clinic, and imagined the doctor listening to his incredible complaints about feeling happy, when he was used to hearing people complain about hysteria, schizophrenia,[4] anxiety, and so on.

tentacles
feelers; long, flexible appendages

"The truth is, Doctor, that I've come to see you because I'm happy!"

He looked at the doctor to see what effect his statement had had on him but noticed that he was keeping his composure. He felt ridiculous. "I'm inconceivably happy . . . ," he said in a tone of confidence.

"The truth is, Doctor, that I've come to see you because I'm happy!"

He began to tell the doctor his story, but the latter stopped him with a gesture of his hand. "An overwhelming, incredible, **debilitating** happiness?" he asked quietly.

debilitating
weakening; crippling

He stared at him in amazement and was on the point of saying something, but the doctor spoke first. "A happiness which has made you stop working," he asked, "abandon your friends, and detest going to sleep? . . ."

"You're a miracle!" he shouted.

"Every time you get involved in some misfortune," the psychiatrist continued quietly, "you dissolve into laughter? . . ."

"Sir . . . are you familiar with the invisible?"

"No!" he said with a smile. "Nothing like that. But I get a

---

2 **psychoanalysis:** a kind of therapy in which a patient explores his or her unconscious psychological state

3 **free association:** the expression of one's thoughts without censorship in an attempt to reach one's unconscious

4 **schizophrenia:** a serious mental illness; a schizophrenic's sense of reality is severely distorted.

similar case in my clinic at least once a week!"

"Is it an epidemic?" he asked.

"I didn't say that, and I wouldn't claim that it's been possible to analyze one case into its primary elements as yet."

"But is it a disease?"

"All the cases are still under treatment."

"But are you satisfied without any doubt that they aren't natural cases? . . ."

"That's a necessary assumption for the job; there's only . . ."

"Have you noticed any of them to be deranged in . . . ," he asked anxiously, pointing to his head.

"Absolutely not," the doctor replied convincingly. "I assure you that they're all intelligent in every sense of the word . . . ."

The doctor thought for a moment. "We should have two sessions a week, I think," he said.

"Very well . . . ," he replied in resignation.

"There's no sense in getting alarmed or feeling sad . . . ."

Alarmed, sad? He smiled, and his smile kept on getting broader. A laugh slipped out, and before long, he was dissolving into laughter. He was determined to control himself, but his resistance collapsed completely. He started guffawing loudly . . . .

Translated by Akef Abadir and Roger Allen

Responding to the Selection

1. What would be difficult about being happy at all times? Try to imagine times in your own life when being happy would be inappropriate or a burden.

2. Does this man have to forget anything in order to be happy? Think about areas in his life that may merit a different response.

3. Are there elements of satire in this story? Name some things in society that the author is trying to criticize through humor.

4. Find two words to describe this character without reverting to the adjective "happy."

An Arab Shepherd Is Searching for His Goat on Mount Zion[1]

Yehuda Amichai

WORLD LENS

♦♦♦

ISRAEL

An Arab shepherd is searching for his goat on Mount Zion
and on the opposite mountain I am searching
for my little boy.
An Arab shepherd and a Jewish father
both in their temporary failure.
Our voices meet above the Sultan's Pool[2]
in the valley between us. Neither of us wants
the child or the goat to get caught in the wheels
of the terrible *Had Gadya*[3] machine.

Afterward we found them among the bushes
and our voices came back inside us, laughing and crying.
Searching for a goat or a son

---

1 **Mount Zion:** a hill located in Jerusalem

2 **Sultan's Pool:** a low-lying pool outside Jerusalem's famous walls

3 *Had Gadya:* Hebrew for "one kid." A Passover poem illustrates a chain of events in which a goat is bitten by a cat which is bitten by a dog, and so forth. The poem is about the cycle of retribution.

has always been in the beginning
of a new religion in these mountains.

Responding to the Selection:

1. There are mixed emotions in this poem. How does this relate to the larger issue of the Israeli-Palestinian conflict?

2. What do you think is meant by the last lines of the poem: "Searching for a goat or a son / has always been in the beginning of a new religion in these mountains"?

3. Why is the allusion to *Had Gadya* appropriate to the theme of this poem?

4. A narrative poem tells a story, or in this case, an anecdote. How might the story of this poem be different if politics and religion didn't come between the two fathers?

The Swimming Contest

Benjamin Tammuz

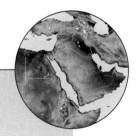

Like most Middle Easterners, Benjamin Tammuz dreamed of a time when there could be peace in his homeland. Many of Tammuz's stories, including "The Swimming Contest," examine the complexities of the tension between Arabs and Israelis. A journalist as well as fiction writer, Tammuz at one time was involved in the Canaanite movement, which sought to make Israel a Hebrew nation rather than a Jewish one. His stories at that time were characterized as utopian, reflecting his hope for an end to the hostilities between Jews and Arabs in Israel.

WORLD LENS

◆ ◆ ◆

ISRAEL

One hot summer's day many years ago I was sitting in the kitchen at home, staring out of the window. The chill of the red floor tiles seeped into my bare feet. With my elbows leaning on the oilcloth-covered table, I let my eyes stray outside. The rooms were pervaded by the afternoon stillness and I felt dreamily at peace.

Suddenly, galloping hoofbeats sounded down the road and a black Arab horse-cab—the kind that plied the roads before cars took over—came into view; it was like those cabs we used to hire to drive us to the Jaffa railway station when we travelled up to Jerusalem to spend Passover[1] with Grandmother.

The horses drew nearer and were reined in outside our house, and the Arab cabman alighted and knocked at our door. I jumped up to open it, and a musty smell filled the kitchen—a smell of horses and far-off places. The cabman's shoulders blocked out the light and prevented the **sultry** heat from forcing its way inside.

He handed me a letter. I glanced at it and saw it was in French, which I could not read. My mother entered and took the letter,

sultry
sweltering; torrid

---

1 **Passover:** the Jewish holiday in spring that commemorates the exodus of the Jews from Egypt, led by Moses

and her face lit up. She asked the cabman in and placed a slice of cold watermelon and a fresh *pita*[2] on the table before him. Leaning his whip against the wall, the Arab thanked her for her kindness, sat down at the table, and began taking large bites out of the watermelon, filling the air with the smacking of his lips. My mother told me that the letter was from the old Arab woman who lived in the orange grove. She wrote that she was well again and her pains had left her, and that she had been cured by my mother's hands, which she kissed from afar. She also wrote that now that summer had come and she had heard our holidays would soon be coming round, she hoped my mother would be able to get away from her other patients and come with her son to stay at her house in the orange grove.

◆ ◆ ◆ ◆ ◆

The sun was about to sink into the sea as we left the house and climbed into the cab. The cabman folded back the rounded leather hood, and as we sank into the deep, soft seat I was instantly overwhelmed by a sensation of travelling to distant parts. The Arab climbed onto his high perch, whistled to his horses, and flicked his whip in the air. The springs creaked, the seat sank and surged up again beneath us like an ocean swell, and a farewell whinny rose on the air. With a wrench of wheels the cab moved off, its rumble over the pitted road sounding like a joyful melody.

Before long we had left the Hassan-Beq Mosque behind and were plunging through the alleyways of the Manshieh quarter.[3] Smells of cooking assailed our nostrils: waves of *za'tr*,[4] of roast mutton, of fried aubergine[5] and mint-spiced salad washed over us in turn. The cabman's voice filled the air, sounding warnings right and left, coaxing street-hawkers to move out of our path, bawling at the **urchins** who squatted in the middle of the road. The horses trotted in a lively, unbroken rhythm, their brown shiny rumps swaying from side to side. The horse on the right, without

urchins
children; scamps

---

2 **pita:** Middle Eastern pocket bread

3 **quarter:** an urban district

4 **za'tr:** a spice combination of thyme, sesame seeds, and ground sumac

5 **aubergine:** eggplant

The Middle East & South Asia

breaking his stride, pricked up his tail and dropped his dung. Turning around on his lofty seat, the cabman threw us an apologetic smile and remarked that horses were shameless ill-bred creatures and we must excuse them.

We jogged along pleasurably and restfully in our seats till the city lay behind us and the horses were drawing the cab laboriously along a track of reddish sand lined with hedgerows of cactus and acacia. Waves of heat rose from the sand, settling beside us onto the cool seat. The sun must already have dipped into the sea, for beyond the orange groves the skies glowed crimson and a chilly dusk descended all around. Suddenly the horses stopped and made water on the sand in unison.

Again the cab lurched forward. A quiver rippled the horses' hides as their hooves struck a stretch of limestone-paved road, lined by cypresses on either side. Before us stood an archway of whitewashed stone, enclosing a large, closed wooden gate with a small wicket set in it. Near the wicket stood a girl of about my age, wearing a white frock and a pink ribbon in her hair. As the cab drew up at the gate she bolted inside, and the cabman said, "We're there!"

♦ ♦ ♦ ♦ ♦

You don't see such courtyards any more. And if you should happen to come to a place where there once was such a courtyard, you will only find a scene of wartime destruction: heaps of rubble and rafters, with cobwebs trying to impart an air of antiquity to what only yesterday still breathed and laughed.

But in those days the courtyard was in good repair and throbbing with life. It was square-shaped and enclosed on three sides by a two-storey building, with stables and barns occupying the lower storey. Black and red hens roamed about the yard, their clucking mingling with the neighing of horses. On the second floor was a pump-house, and next to it a pool-like reservoir into which water splashed from a pipe leading from the pump. Goldfish gathered near the outlet, darting among the bubbles created by the jet of water. A wooden parapet[6] railed in a long veranda that always lay in the shade. A coloured glass door led

6 **parapet:** a low protective barrier

from the veranda into a central reception room, from which numerous doors opened onto the living rooms, the kitchen and the pantries.

In the center of the room stood a long table surrounded by upholstered armchairs. In anticipation of our arrival that day, their white linen dust-covers had been removed and lay folded in neat piles in a corner. Earthenware vases painted red and gold were arranged about the room; they contained large paper roses and lilies, some of them fashioned into strange, unflowerlike shapes. One vase, its paint long faded, had been brought there on the wedding day of the elderly mistress of the house.

From gilt wooden frames on the walls stared the portraits of sword-bearing men in fezes. The old lady led my mother up to one of the pictures and said, "My husband, may he rest in peace! His father built this house. Now we live here during the summer and go back to Jaffa for the winter."

With a sigh my mother replied, "My husband's no longer alive, either. But his house and his father's house aren't here; everything remained over there, abroad, and I live in a rented apartment summer and winter."

"That's because you are newcomers, immigrants," the old lady said. "But with the help of God you'll thrive and build yourselves houses. You're hard-working people and your hands are blessed."

My mother caught the hint and threw her a grateful look, but I blurted out: "But it's not true that we're driving the Arabs out. We are out for peace, not war."

"We are out for peace, not war."

Placing her hand on my head, the old lady said, "It all depends on the individual; everyone who wants peace will live in peace."

At that moment the young girl appeared in the doorway.

◆ ◆ ◆ ◆ ◆

"Come over here, Nahida," the old lady said, "and kiss the hand of the *hakima*[7] who cured your grandmother. And this is her son."

Nahida came hesitantly into the room and stood in front of

---

7 **hakima:** female doctor

The Middle East & South Asia

my mother. My mother embraced her and kissed her on the cheek, and a flush suffused the girl's dark complexion. She hung her head and remained silent.

"Our Nahida is shy," the old lady said, "but her heart is kind."

Hitching up her white skirt, Nahida sat down in an armchair. The rest of us sat down, too, as though permitted to do so now that the most honoured person among us was seated.

The old lady made a remark in French and my mother laughed. Again Nahida blushed and I noticed her eyeing me to see whether I understood French.

"I don't understand a word," I told her. "What are they saying?"

"My grandmother says you and I would make a fine couple."

"Rubbish!" I answered and stared at the floor.

"You can go and play," the old woman said. "We're not keeping you."

I got up and followed Nahida out onto the veranda. We went and sat down at the edge of the pool.

"Do you believe in God?" I asked her. "Because I don't, not at all."

"I do, and I have a place in the grove where I go and pray. If we become friends, I'll take you there and I'll show you there's a God."

"Then you fast in the month of Ramadan?"[8] I asked. "I eat even on Yom Kippur."[9]

"I don't fast because I'm still too young. Do you rest on the Sabbath?"

"That depends," I answered. "I rest if I've got nothing else to do. Not because there's a God, but just if I feel like it."

"But I love God," Nahida said.

"Then we certainly won't make a couple unless you stop believing."

Nahida was about to make some retort when we heard the gate open, and two men entered the yard. Nahida leapt up and rushed over to them, throwing her arms around the neck of the

---

8 **Ramadan:** the Muslim holy days, a month of fasting during daylight hours

9 **Yom Kippur:** the Day of Atonement, a Jewish holiday on which believers fast and pray for forgiveness of their sins

older man, who wore a fez and European clothes.

"Daddy, we have visitors!" she cried.

"I know," her father replied. "The *hakima* has come to see us."

I stood up and waited for them to mount the steps to the pool. The second man, who wore a *keffiyeh*[10] and *agal*[11] and looked about eighteen, was Nahida's uncle, her father's brother. He came up first and held out his hand to greet me. Nahida's father patted my cheek and ushered me into the house.

We had supper out on the veranda. We were served large dishes of fried potatoes, sliced aubergine in tomato sauce and diced salted cheese, and a bowl of pomegranates and watermelons. There was a heap of hot *pitas* in the centre of the table.

Nahida's uncle—his name was Abdul-Karim—asked me if I was in the Haganah.[12] When I told him that was a secret, he laughed and said it was an open secret which the whole country knew about.

"Abdul-Karim is studying at the College of the Mufti," Nahida's father told us. "And he's in constant fear of your Haganah."

Abdul-Karim's face darkened and he kept silent; but the old lady, his mother, laid her hand on his arm and said, "My Abdul-Karim is a fine, loyal man. Don't you tease him."

Abdul-Karim kissed his mother's hand and said nothing. Just then, a shaggy sheepdog appeared on the veranda and wriggled under the table, butting against the tangle of legs as it looked for a spot to lie down. Finally it came to rest with its head on Nahida's feet and its tail on mine; it kept licking Nahida's feet, and its wagging tail tickled mine. The tickling made me smile and I turned to explain to Nahida why I was smiling, but when I saw she was taking my smile as a mark of friendship, I kept quiet.

When supper was over, Nahida's father said to his brother:

"Abdul-Karim my brother, go and show the children what you've brought from town."

Motioning to Nahida and myself to follow him, Abdul-Karim

---

10 **keffiyeh:** (also kaffiyah), an Arabic head covering

11 **agal:** the cord that holds the keffiyeh in place

12 **Haganah:** an underground military organization in Israel from 1920 to 1948

went into a toolshed in the orange grove and came out with a brand-new shotgun.

"We'll go hunting rabbits tomorrow," he said. "Know how to fire a gun?"

"A little," I told him. "We can have a shooting match if you like."

"We had a swimming match here in the pool last week," Nahida said, "and my uncle beat them all."

"I'll take you on at swimming too, if you like," I said.

"*Ahlan usahlan!*"[13] Abdul-Karim agreed. "Tomorrow morning, then. Now let's get back to the house and listen to some songs. We have a gramophone."

Back in the house, Abdul-Karim put on a record, wound the handle and adjusted the soundbox. The sound of a *kamanji*[14] and drum and cymbals issued forth, immediately followed by an Arab song, sung in a sweet **plaintive** voice, with delicate, floating trills. Abdul-Karim sprawled back contentedly in his armchair, his face beaming. When the record ended he put on another, though to me it seemed as though the same song was being played over again. This went on again and again till I got bored and slipped out to another room where my mother was chatting with the old lady. But that bored me too, so I went out to the veranda and gazed at the pool and the orange grove beyond. A large moon hung just above the treetops and a chill rose from the water in the pool. Some night bird was calling nearby, but stopped whenever the gramophone fell silent. As a yawn escaped me, I thought regretfully of my pals at home who were probably roasting potatoes on a fire under the electricity pylon,[15] having pilfered the wood from the nearby sausage factory. What had made me come here, I asked myself.

Nahida found a queer way of waking me up next morning. They had a fat, lazy cat in the house, which Nahida dropped onto my face while I was asleep. I leapt out of bed and flung the cat back into her lap. That was how we started our second day in the house in the orange grove. I was still brushing my teeth when

plaintive
melancholy; mournful

---

13 *"Ahlan usahlan!":* a traditional welcoming phrase in Arabic

14 *kamanji:* a banjo-like stringed instrument

15 **pylon:** steel tower carrying the electric lines

Abdul-Karim came into the kitchen and said, "What about our swimming race?" "I'm ready," I told him.

We hurried through breakfast, got into bathing trunks and went outside. My mother, the old lady, and Nahida's father had already drawn up chairs at the side of the pool to watch the race.

"Ready, steady . . . go!" Nahida called out, and Abdul-Karim and I dived in. Either because I was over-excited or I wasn't used to fresh water, I sank to the bottom like a stone, and by the time I had recovered sufficiently to surface Abdul-Karim was already halfway across. I saw my mother bending over the parapet and heard her calling out to me, "Don't be afraid! Swim fast!" I started swimming, but it was no use. By the time I reached the pipe leading from the pump-house, Abdul-Karim was already sitting on the parapet on the far side, squeezing the water out of his hair.

"You beat me in the pool," I told him. "But I'll take you on at anything else, if you want."

"At what?" he asked.

"Let's say at arithmetic."

"Why not?" he answered, and told Nahida to fetch some paper and pencils. When Nahida came back with them, I tore a sheet of paper into two halves, and on each I wrote down seven million, nine hundred and eighty-four thousand, six hundred and ninety-eight multiplied by four million, nine hundred and eighty-six thousand, seven hundred and fifty-nine.

"Let's see who figures that out first," I said.

Taking a pencil, Abdul-Karim started jotting down figures, and so did I. I was through before he was and handed my sheet to Nahida's father to check. It turned out I had made a mistake. Then Abdul-Karim handed over his paper and it turned out that he had gone wrong, too.

"Then let's have a general knowledge competition," I challenged Abdul-Karim. "For instance: who discovered America?"

"Columbus," Abdul-Karim answered.

"Wrong!" I said. "It was Amerigo Vespucci, and that's why it's called America!"

"He beat you!" Nahida called to her uncle. "You see, he beat you!"

"He beat me in America," Abdul-Karim said, "but I beat him *right here*, in the pool."

"You wait till I'm grown up and then I'll beat you right here in the pool," I told him.

Nahida seemed about to nod her agreement, but thought better of it and looked at her uncle to see what he was going to answer to that.

"If he ever manages to beat me here in the pool," Abdul-Karim said, "it will be very bad indeed. It will be bad for you too, Nahida. Bad for all of us."

We didn't get his meaning and I wanted to tell him to cut out his philosophizing; but I didn't know how to say that in Arabic, so I kept quiet.

Later we went hunting rabbits in the orange grove.

II

Many years had gone by and summer had come round once again. Tired out after that year's work, I was looking for some place where I could take a fortnight's[16] rest. Packing a small valise, I traveled up to Jerusalem, only to find all the boarding houses full. Finally, wearied by rushing about the city, I boarded a bus bound for the Arab village of Ein Karem. As I took my seat, I started wondering what I would do there and what had made me go there of all places.

At the end of the main street stood a domed building, with a fountain gushing out from under its floor. Opposite, on a hillside that sloped up to the Russian monastery on its summit, in the shade of a clump of sycamores, some men sat on low wooden stools, sipping coffee and puffing at their *narghiles*.[17] I walked over and sat down on one of the stools, and when the waiter came over to take my order, I asked him if he knew of a family that would be willing to put me up for a couple of weeks.

"I don't know of one," the lad answered. "But maybe the owner does."

The café proprietor came over to have a look at me. "A family

---

16 **fortnight's:** two weeks'

17 ***narghiles:*** hookahs, or water-pipes for smoking tobacco

to put you up?" he said. "What for?"

"To take a rest," I answered. "I'm tired and I'm looking for somewhere to rest."

"And how much are you willing to pay?" he asked.

"As much as I have to," I replied.

The proprietor sent the lad to the house of a certain Abu-Nimr. Before long he came back and said:

"Go up that way. Abu-Nimr is willing."

Picking up my valise, I trudged up the hillside, wondering all the time what had made me come to this place. I entered a courtyard and knocked at the door of the house indicated. A tall, bald Arab of about forty-five came out and said, "Welcome! Come right in."

I let him precede me down a long, cool passage and into a small room, almost entirely taken up by a tall, wide bed.

"If you like it, you're very welcome," Abu-Nimr said.

"It's very nice," I said. "How much will it cost?"

"I don't know. My wife will tell you that," he said and left the room.

I unpacked my valise and sat down on the bed, instantly sinking into the soft bedding, which billowed up to my elbows. There was a deep stillness all around, pervaded by the familiar smells of frying oil, mint leaves, black coffee, rosewater and cardamom seeds. I felt my face break into a smile as my ears strained to catch a sound that was missing in order to complete a dim, distant memory.

Suddenly I heard a tap turned on in the kitchen and the sound of gushing water made me hold my breath: water gushing from a pipe into a pool!

I got up and went out to the yard. There was no pool, not even orange trees; but there was something about the apple and plum trees, some quality of strangeness peculiar to an Arab homestead. It was obvious that the courtyard had not evolved all at once, that each generation had added something of its own. One man had planted the apple tree by the water tap, another the mulberry tree near the dog kennel, and in time the garden had sprouted up to tell its masters' life stories. I stood listening, my fantasy peopling the courtyard with Nahida and her grandmother, with Abdul-

Karim, with the horse-cab that would suddenly draw to a halt outside the gate and the horses that would stand and urinate.

♦ ♦ ♦ ♦ ♦

That evening I was invited to join the family at supper, and Abu-Nimr introduced me to the people who sat round the table: his round-faced, bustling wife, who smiled into space without resting her eyes on me; his two sons, aged thirteen and fifteen, who attended high school in the city; his plump, white-skinned daughter, married to a policeman who was away from home all week, and who came home loaded with a wicker basket containing a trussed pigeon, apples from Betar, and a dozen eggs commandeered from some villager who happened to call at the police station.

The food that was served was no more than a continuation of that faraway supper in the orange grove. At that moment I realized what I had come there for.

After supper the strains of an Arab song rose from the gramophone. Abu-Nimr asked me whether I would care to show his boys how to operate the English typewriter he had bought in the city the day before. I sat down to instruct the lads, who set about their task with tremendous awe while their parents looked on, their hearts overflowing with pride. After a while their mother brought me a glass of cocoa and urged me to take a little rest. The gramophone was still playing, and as I sipped my drink Nahida's voice came back to me and Abdul-Karim's features formed themselves before my eyes, and out of the gloom in the passage there rose the sounds of my mother chatting with the old lady. It was then that I knew that I had been waiting all these years for just this moment, that I would relive our stay at the house in the orange grove.

♦ ♦ ♦ ♦ ♦

Again the years went by. We were in the grip of war with the Arabs. I was serving in a company that was lined up to storm Tel Arish, an Arab stronghold in the Jaffa dunes, east of the city.

We had launched an abortive attack there several weeks before which had cost us twenty-six men. This time we felt sure of

success and looked forward to the battle as a fierce retaliation.

We set out from Holon at midnight, and soon began crawling in the direction of the Tel Arish buildings. The sand dunes afforded excellent cover, and we slipped across them effortlessly and soundlessly. A west wind carried the Jaffa smells over to us, but later the wind veered round behind us, from the new estates going up in Holon, breathing the smell of new, white houses on our backs. The sand beneath us surrendered the sun's warmth it had absorbed during the day, telling of the days of light we had known among the white houses, and **auguring** the liberty and joy that would again be ours once victory had been gained.

auguring
signifying; foretelling

♦♦♦♦♦

When the Arabs spotted us it was too late for them to do anything about it. We were already within grenade-range of their position, and we stormed it from three sides. One of our first grenades burst inside their forward machine gun nest, putting all its crew

The Middle East & South Asia

out of action. We charged inside and raked the village with the German machine gun. The Arabs there panicked and rushed out of the houses, only to be cut down by our riflemen, who lay in ambush on our two flanks to the north and south. This left the Arabs only one escape route, westwards, and it appeared that some of them managed to slip through in that direction and escape into the cover of the nearby orange grove—the same grove where, about twenty years before, I had spent a few days with the old lady's family.

I had been expecting things to turn out like that, for that was how it had been planned. The house in the orange grove was our second objective that night. We didn't know whether there were any soldiers there, but we were quite sure that any we failed to destroy at the Tel Arish position would easily be able to reorganize and entrench themselves in the stone building and courtyard. It seemed that they had kept a reserve force in the house in the orange grove, for heavy fire was opened upon us from that direction, and there were other indications that fortified positions there were ready to go into action in the event that Tel Arish should fall.

Our luck didn't hold out there, however: the battle continued till dawn and we lost six men. This only heightened our desire for revenge, and besides, we still outnumbered them. Soon the defence of the house showed signs of weakening and the fire gradually slackened off. At dawn we rushed the courtyard, got through as far as the stables and laid a charge of high explosives, then withdrew. A few moments later there was a violent clap of thunder and the wing of the house next to the pool collapsed into a heap of rubble. This was immediately followed by the groans of the wounded and cries of surrender. We re-mustered[18] in the courtyard and shouted to the Arabs to come out and surrender.

◆ ◆ ◆ ◆ ◆

I was not surprised to see Abdul-Karim. He seemed to have expected this, too, though that was something I had never dared to imagine. I recognized him straight away. I went up to him and called his name. When I explained who I was, he gave a weary

---

18 **re-mustered:** came together again

smile of recollection.

"Nahida . . . is she here too?" I asked him.

"No," he said. "The family has left Jaffa."

Some of the boys listened to our conversation in surprise.

"D'you know him?" our officer asked me.

"I know him," I said.

"Can he give us any important information?"

"Maybe," I said. "But let me settle an old score with him first."

"Want to finish him off?" the officer asked me.

"No," I told him. "I just want to talk to him."

The boys burst out laughing at this. Abdul-Karim, who hadn't understood what we were saying, must have taken offence, for his hands trembled with suppressed fury.

I hastened to explain to him that I wanted to talk to him alone.

"You're the victors," he said. "We do as we're told."

"As long as I haven't beaten you in the pool," I told him, "there's no telling who is the victor."

Abdul-Karim smiled. He seemed to have got my meaning.

Our officer didn't seem to get it, however, for he ordered Abdul-Karim to be taken into the orange grove, where the prisoners were being rounded up. I went up to the pool and sat down on the parapet. Our reinforcements from Bat-Yam and Holon began to appear and the orderlies set about attending to the wounded in the courtyard. I stripped and entered the water. It was warm and dirty: it must have been a long time since the pipe overhead had jetted water from the well pump.

Stretching out my arms, I swam across the pool, then back again. I closed my eyes and waited to hear my mother's voice, urging me on: "Don't be scared! Swim fast!" But instead, I heard Abdul-Karim say: "You beat me in America, but I beat you *right here*, in the pool."

"You beat me in America, but I beat you *right here*, in the pool."

Just then I heard a shot from the orange grove. My heart missed a beat. I knew Abdul-Karim had been killed. Leaping out of the water, I pulled on my trousers and rushed into the grove. There was some commotion and the officer was yelling:

"Who the hell fired that shot?"

"My gun went off," one of the boys said.

When he saw me coming up the officer said, "We've lost that information, damn it! They've killed that Arab of yours."

"We've lost it," I said.

I went over to Abdul-Karim's body and turned it over. He looked as though he had seen me swimming in the pool a few moments ago. His was not the expression of a man who had lost.

There, in the courtyard, it was I, all of us, who were the losers.

Translated by Joseph Schachter

Responding to the Selection

1. Use two or three adjectives to describe the first meeting between the narrator and Abdul-Karim. How does it foreshadow the ending of the story?

2. What is ironic about such fierce conflict existing in the context of the Holy Lands?

3. Consider whether the story's ending was inevitable, given the nature of the conflict—two parties who feel they have an equal and historical claim to disputed homelands. What do you make of the next-to-last sentence, "His was not the expression of a man who had lost"?

4. Why do you think the narrator wants to return to the orange grove when he is a grown man?

Song of Becoming

Fadwa Tuqan

WORLD LENS

♦♦♦

PALESTINE/
ISRAEL

Since 1948, Israel has been warring with its neighbors over land. Israelis and Palestinians, in particular, have been caught up in violent disputes over the Israeli-occupied territories of the West Bank and Gaza, which the Palestinians claim as their own. Although Palestinian author Fadwa Tuqan did not set out to write about politics, she found it difficult to avoid, having witnessed so much persecution in her native land.

They're only boys
who used to frolic and play
launching rainbowed kites
on the western wind,
their blue-red-green kites
whistling, leaping,
trading easy laughter and jokes
dueling with branches, pretending to be
great heroes in history.

Suddenly now they've grown,
grown more than the years of a normal life,
merged with secret and passionate words,
carried love's messages like the Bible or Quran,[1]
to be read in whispers.
They've grown to become trees
plunging deep roots into earth,
stretching high towards the sun.
Now their voices are ones that reject,
that knock down and build anew.

---

1 **Quran:** (also Koran), the Muslim holy book

Anger smouldering on the fringes of a blocked horizon,
invading classrooms, streets, city quarters,
centering on squares,
facing sullen tanks with streams of stones.

Now they shake the gallows of dawn
assailing the night and its flood.
They've grown more than the years of a life
to become the worshipped and the worshippers.

When their torn limbs merged with the stuff of our earth,
they became legends,
they grew into vaulting bridges,
they grew and grew, becoming
larger than all poetry.

Translated by Naomi Shihab Nye

Responding to the Selection

1. Consider the fact that as a young girl, the author of this poem faced severe punishment as a result of the unwanted attentions of a boy. What does it say about both the poet and the culture she is from that she could write such a loving and evocative poem about males?

2. Why do you think the poet brings up both the Bible and the Quran?

3. Why do the boys who have been "dueling with branches" turn into trees? Discuss the symbolic meaning of this transformation.

4. Think of the ways in which the poet reminds you of the boys' vulnerability and dreams. What is her purpose?

The Women's Baths

Ulfat al-Idlibi

WORLD LENS

•••

SYRIA

The "grandmother of modern Syrian literature," Ulfat al-Idlibi began publishing her stories and literary criticism in 1950. Considering one out of two females in Syria could not read or write, this was a remarkable accomplishment, even for a girl from a wealthy family.

The tradition of public baths is a rich one. Baths were popular for many reasons: they epitomized the Muslim concern for cleanliness and love of water, and they allowed customers to be pampered. They were also important meeting places, especially for women. Important rites of passage, such as births, puberty, and marriage, were often celebrated with a trip to the bathhouse. Today, despite modern plumbing, the baths continue to be a lavish experience.

Our household was troubled by an unusual problem: my grandmother, who had passed the age of seventy, insisted on taking a bath at the beginning of every month at the public baths, or market baths as she used to call them.

In my grandmother's opinion the market baths had a delicious ambience about them which we, who had never experienced it, could not appreciate.

For our part we were afraid that the old lady might slip on the wet floor of the baths—this has often happened to people who go there—and break her leg, as her seventy years had made her bones dry and stiff; or she might catch a severe chill coming outside from the warm air of the baths and contract a fatal illness as a result. But how could we convince this stubborn old lady of the **cogency** of these arguments?

It was quite out of the question that she should give up a custom to which she had adhered for seventy years, and she had

cogency
force; validity

done so without ever once having been stricken with the mishaps we feared. Grandmother had made up her mind that she would keep up this custom as long as she was able to walk on her own two feet, and her tenacity in clinging to her point of view only increased the more my mother tried to reason with her.

Yet Mother never tired of criticizing her mother-in-law, arguing with her and attempting to demonstrate the silliness of her views, even if only by implication. Whenever the subject of the public baths came up my mother proceeded to enumerate their shortcomings from the standpoints of health, of society, and even of economics.

The thing which really annoyed Mother was that my grandmother monopolized our only maid from the early morning onward on the day she went to the baths. She would summon her to her room to help her sweep it and change the sheets and do up the bundles to take to the baths. Then she would set out with her and would not bring her back until around sunset, when our maid would be exhausted and hardly able to perform her routine chores.

In our house I was the observer of a relentless, even though hidden, struggle between mother-in-law and daughter-in-law: between my grandmother, who clung to her position in the household and was resolved under no circumstances to relinquish it, and my mother, who strove to take her place.

Although girls usually side with their mother, I had a strong feeling of sympathy for my grandmother: old age had caught up with her since her husband had died some time before and left her a widow, and little by little her authority in the home shrank as my mother's authority gradually extended. It is the law of life: one takes, then one hands over to another in one's turn. But that does not mean we obey the law readily and willingly.

I used to feel a certain prick of pain when I saw Grandmother retire alone to her room for long hours after being defeated in an argument with Mother. I would sometimes hear her talking bitterly to herself, or I would see her monotonously shaking her head in silence, as though she were rehearsing the book of her long life, reviewing the days of her past, when she was the unchallenged mistress of the house, with the last word. I would often see her vent the force of her resentment on her thousand-bead rosary as her nervous fingers told its beads and she repeated the prayer to herself:

"Oh merciful God, remove this affliction!"

And who could this "affliction" be but my mother?

Then little by little she would calm down and forget the cause of her anger. There is nothing like the **invocation** of God for purifying the soul and enabling it to bear the hardships of life.

invocation
petitioning; appealing to

One day when I saw my grandmother getting her things ready to go to the market baths I had the idea of accompanying her, thinking that perhaps I might uncover the secret which attracted her to them. When I expressed my wish to accompany her she was very pleased, but my mother did not like this sudden impulse at all, and said, in my grandmother's hearing, "Has the craze for going to the market baths affected you as well? Who knows—you may catch some infection, like scabies or something, and it will spread around the family."

Thereupon my father broke in with the final word: "What is the matter with you? Let her go with her grandmother. All of us went to the public baths when we were young and it never did any of us any harm."

My mother relapsed into a grudging silence, while my grandmother gave an exultant smile at this victory—my father rarely took her side against my mother.

Then Grandmother led me by the hand to the room where her massive trunk was kept. She produced the key from her pocket and opened the trunk in my presence—this was a great honor for me, for the venerable trunk had never before been opened in the presence of another person—and immediately there wafted out of it a strange yet familiar scent, a scent of age, a smell of the distant past, of years which have been folded up and stored away. Grandmother drew out of the depths of the trunk a bundle of red velvet, the corners of which were embroidered with pearls and sequins.

She opened it in front of me and handed me a wine-colored bathwrap decorated with golden stars. I had never set eyes on a more beautiful robe. She also gave me a number of white towels decorated around the edges with silver thread, saying "All these

The Middle East & South Asia

are brand new; no one has ever used them. I have saved them from the time I was married. Now I'm giving them to you as a present, since you are going to the baths with me. Alas . . . poor me. Nobody goes with me now except the servants."

She gave a deep, heart-felt sigh. Then she called the servant to carry the bundle containing our clothes and towels, and the large bag which held the bowl, the soap, the comb, the sponge-bag, and loofah,[1] the soil of Aleppo,[2] and the henna which would transform my grandmother's white hair to jet black. She put on her shawl, and we made our way toward the baths, which were only a few paces from our house. Times without number I had read the words on the little plaque which crowned the low, unpretentious door as I passed by: "Whoever the Divine Blessing of health would achieve, should turn to the Lord and then to the baths of Afif."

We entered the baths.

The first thing I noticed was the female "intendant." She was a stout woman, sitting on the bench to the right of persons coming in. In front of her was a small box for collecting the day's revenue. Next to it was a *nargileh* decorated with flowers. It had a long mouthpiece which the intendant played with between her lips, while she looked at those around her with a proprietorial air. When she saw us she proceeded to welcome us without stirring from her place. Then she summoned Umm Abdu, the bath attendant. A woman hastened up and gave us a perfunctory welcome. She had penciled eyebrows, eyes painted with *kohl*,[3] and was dressed very neatly. She had adorned her hair with two roses and a sprig of jasmine. She was very **voluble**, and was like a spinning-top, never motionless, and her feet in her Shabrawi clogs made a rhythmic clatter on the floor of the baths. Her function was that of hostess to the bathers. She came up to my grandmother and led her to a special bench resembling a bed. Our maid hastened to undo one of our bundles, drawing out a small prayer rug which she spread out on the bench. My grandmother sat down on it to get undressed.

voluble
talkative; effusive

---

1 **loofah:** a kind of sponge

2 **soil of Aleppo:** a type of perfumed clay used for hair-washing

3 ***kohl:*** a dark powder used for eye makeup

I was fascinated by what I saw around me. In particular my attention was drawn to the spacious hall called *al-barani*.[4] In the center of it was a gushing fountain. Around the hall were narrow benches on which were spread brightly-colored rugs where the bathers laid their things. The walls were decorated with mirrors, yellowed and spotted with age, and panels on which were inscribed various maxims. On one of them I read, "Cleanliness is part of Faith."

4 **al-barani:** a public bath's outermost hall

The Middle East & South Asia

My grandmother urged me to undress. I took off my clothes and wrapped myself in the wine-colored bath-wrap, but as I was not doing it properly Umm Abdu came and helped me. She secured it around my body and then drew the free end over my left shoulder, making it appear like an Indian sari.

Then she helped my grandmother down from her bench, and conducted us toward a small door which led into a dark corridor, calling out at the top of her voice, "Marwah! Come and look after the Bey's mother!"

With a sigh a shape suddenly materialized in the gloom in front of me: it was a grey-haired, emaciated woman of middle age with a face in which suffering had engraved deep furrows. She was naked except for a faded cloth which hung from her waist to her knees. She welcomed us in a nasal tone, prattling on although I could not catch a single syllable of what she was saying, thanks to the babble of **discordant** voices which filled my ears and the hot thick steam which obstructed my sight; and there was a smell which nearly made me faint, the like of which I had never encountered in my life before. I felt nauseous, and was almost sick, leaning against the maid for support.

discordant
inharmonious; conflicting

Nevertheless, in a few moments I grew accustomed to the odor and it no longer troubled me; my eyes, also, became accustomed to seeing through the steam.

We reached a small hall containing a large stone basin. A number of women circled around in it, chatting and washing at the same time. I asked my grandmother: "Why don't we join them?"

She replied: "This is the *wastani*;[5] I have hired a cubicle in the *juwani*.[6] I am not accustomed to bathing with the herd."

I followed her through a small door to the *juwani*, and found myself looking with confused curiosity at the scene that presented itself. There was a large rectangular hall, at each corner of which stood a large basin of white marble. Women sat around each one, busily engrossed in washing, scrubbing, and rubbing, as though they were in some kind of race. I raised my eyes to look at the ceiling, and saw a lofty dome with circular openings, glazed with

---

5 *wastani:* a public bath's interior hall

6 *juwani:* a public bath's innermost hall

crystal, through which enough light filtered to illuminate the hall. The uproar here was at its worst—there was a clashing of cans, the splashing of water, and the clamor of children.

My grandmother paused for a moment to greet a friend among the bathers, while I found myself following a violent quarrel which had arisen between two young women. I understood from the women around them that they were two wives of a **polygamous** marriage, who had met face to face for the first time at the baths. The furious quarrel led at length to an exchange of blows with metal bowls. Luckily a spirit of **chivalry** among some of the bathers induced them to separate the two warring wives before they could satisfy their thirst for revenge.

As we advanced a little way the howling of a small child drowned the hubbub of the hall. Its mother had put it on her lap, twisting one of its legs around her and proceeding to scrub its face with soap and pour hot water over it until its skin was scarlet red. I averted my gaze, fearing the child would expire before my eyes.

We reached the cubicle, and I felt a sense of oppression as we entered it. It consisted of nothing but a small chamber with a basin in the front. Its one advantage was that it screened those taking a bath inside from the other women.

We were received in the cubicle by a dark, stout woman with a pockmarked face and a harsh voice. She was Mistress Umm Mahmud. She took my grandmother from the attendant Marwah, who was being assailed by shouts from every direction:

"Cold water, Marwah, cold water, Marwah!"

The poor woman set about complying with the bathers' requests for cold water, dispensing it from two big buckets which she filled from the fountain in the outer hall. She was so weighed down with the buckets that she aroused pity in those who saw her struggle.

I turned back to Grandmother and found her sitting on the tiled floor in front of the basin. She had rested her head between the hands of Umm Mahmud, who sat behind her on a sort of wooden chair which was only slightly raised above the level of the floor. She proceeded to scour Grandmother's head with soap seven consecutive times—not more, not less.

I stood at the door of the cubicle, entertained by the scene presented by the bathers. I watched the younger women coming

polygamous
having more than one mate at one time

chivalry
courtesy; honor

and going, from time to time going into the outer hall for the sake of diversion, their fresh youthfulness showing in their proud swaying gait. In their brightly colored wraps decorated with silver thread they resembled Hindu women in a temple filled with the fragrance of incense. Little circles of light fell from the dome onto their tender-skinned bodies, causing them to glisten.

I found the sight of the older women depressing: they sat close to the walls chatting with one another, while the cream of henna on their hair trickled in black rivulets along the wrinkles of their foreheads and cheeks, as they waited impatiently for their turn to bathe.

Suddenly I heard shrill exclamations of pleasure. I turned toward their source, and saw a group of women gathered around a pretty young girl, loudly expressing their delight at some matter.

Mistress Umm Mahmud said to me: "Our baths are doing well today: we have a bride here, we have a woman who has recently had a child, and we have the mother of the Bey—may God spare her for us!"

It was no wonder that my grandmother swelled with pride at being mentioned in the same breath with a bride and a young mother.

I enjoyed standing at the door of the cubicle watching the bride and her companions. Then I caught sight of a fair well-built woman enveloped in a dark blue wrap, giving vent to overflowing joy with little shrieks of delight. I realized from the words she was singing that she must be the bride's mother:

> "Seven bundles I packed for thee, and the eighth
>   in the chest is stored;
> To Thee, Whom all creatures need, praise be, oh
>   Lord!"

A young woman, a relative or friend of the bride, replied:

> "Oh maiden coming from the *wastani*, with thy
>   towel all scented.
> He who at thy wedding shows no joy, shall die an
>   infidel,[7] from Paradise prevented!"

---

7 **infidel:** a nonbeliever

The bride's mother continued the song:

> "The little birds chirp and flutter among the trellis'd
>   leaves;
> How sweet the bride! The bath upon her brow now
>   pearly crowns of moisture weaves.
> Thou canst touch the City Gate with thy little finger
>   tip, though it is so high;
> I have waited long, long years for this day's coming
>   nigh!"

But the best verse was reserved for the bridegroom's mother:

> "Oh my daughter-in-law! I take thee as my
>   daughter!
> The daughters of Syria are many, but my heart only
>   desires and wishes for thee!
> Pistachios, hazels and dates: the heart of the
>   envious has been sore wounded;
> Today we are merry, but the envious no merriment
>   shall see!"

"The daughters of Syria are many, but my heart only desires and wishes for thee!"

The singing finished as the bride and her companions formed a circle around a tray upon which had been placed cakes of Damascene[8] mincemeat, and a second one filled with various kinds of fruit. The bride's mother busied herself distributing the cakes right and left, and one of them fell to my share also!

In a far corner a woman was sitting with her four children around a large dish piled with *mujaddarah*[9] and pickled turnips, their preoccupation with their meal rendering them completely oblivious to what was going on around them in the baths. When the dish had been emptied of food the mother took from a basket by her side a large cabbage. Gripping its long green leaves, she raised it up and then brought it down hard on the tiled floor, until it split apart and scattered into fragments. The children

---

8 **Damascene:** from Damascus, the Syrian capital
9 *mujaddarah:* a rice and lentil dish popular in Syria

tumbled over reach other to snatch them up and greedily devoured them, savoring their fresh taste.

Then my attention was diverted by a pretty girl, about fifteen or sixteen years old, sitting on a bench along the wall of the boiler-house. She seemed impatient and restless, as though she found it hard to tolerate the pervasive heat. She was surrounded by three women, one of whom, apparently her mother, was feverishly fussing over her. She began to rub over her body a yellow ointment which exuded a scent of ginger (it was what was called "strengthening ointment"). My grandmother explained to me that it reinforced the blood vessels of a new mother, and restored her to the state of health she had enjoyed before having her child.

The attendant Umm Abdu came up to us and inquired after our comfort. She brought us both glasses of licorice sherbet as a present from the intendant. Then she lit a cigarette for my grandmother, who was obviously regarded as a patron of distinction.

It was now my turn. My grandmother moved aside, and I sat down in her place, entrusting my head to the attentions of Umm Mahmud for a thorough rubbing. After I had had my seven soapings I sat down before the door of the cubicle to relax a little. I was amused to watch the bath attendant Marwah scrubbing one of the bathers. Her right hand was covered with coarse sacking, which she rubbed over the body of the woman sitting in front of her. She began quite slowly, and then sped up, and as she did so little grey wicks began to appear under the sacking, which quickly became bigger and were shaken to the floor.

After we had finished being loofah-ed and rubbed, Umm Mahmud asked me to come back to her to have my head soaped an additional five times. I surrendered to her because I had promised myself that I would carry out the bathing rites through all their stages and degrees as protocol dictated, whatever rigors I had to endure in the process!

I was not finished until Umm Mahmud had poured the last basinful of water over my head, after anointing it with "soil of Aleppo," the scent of which clung to my hair for days afterwards.

Umm Mahmud rose, and standing at the door of the cubicle,

called out in her harsh voice: "Marwah! Towels for the Bey's mother!"

With a light and agile bound Marwah was at the door of the *wastani*, calling out in a high-pitched tone, like a cockerel:[10] "Umm Abdu! Towels for the Bey's mother!" Her shout mingled with that of another "Mistress" who was standing in front of a cubicle opposite ours, likewise demanding towels for her client.

Umm Abdu appeared, clattering along in her Shabrawi clogs, with a pile of towels on her arm which she distributed among us, saying as she did: "Blessings upon you . . . Have an enjoyable bath, if God wills!"

Then she took my grandmother by the arm and led her to the *barani*, where she helped her to get up onto the high bench, and then to dry herself and get into her clothes.

Grandmother stood waiting her turn to pay her bill. There was a heated argument going on between the intendant and a middle-aged woman who had three girls with her. I gathered from what was being said that the usual custom was for the intendant to charge married women in full, but that widows and single women paid only half the normal fee. The lady was claiming that she was a widow, and her daughters were all single. The intendant listened to her skeptically, and obviously could not believe that the eldest of the girls was single, in that she was an adult and was very beautiful. But at last she was forced to accept what the woman said after the latter had sworn the most solemn oath that what she was saying was the truth.

My grandmother stepped forward and pressed something into the intendant's hand, telling her: "Here's what I owe you, with something extra for the cold water and the attendance."

The intendant peered down at her hand and then smiled; in fact she seemed very pleased, for I heard her say to my grandmother: "May God keep you, Madam, and we hope to see you every month."

Then my grandmother distributed tips to the attendant, the "Mistress," and Marwah, as they emerged from the *juwani* to bid her good-bye.

I have never known my grandmother to be so generous and

---

10 **cockerel:** a young rooster

The Middle East & South Asia

open-handed as on the day which we spent at the market baths. She was pleased and proud as she listened to the blessings called down on her by those who had received her **largesse**. Then she gave me an intentionally lofty look, as if to say: "Can you appreciate your grandmother's status now? How about telling your mother about *this*, now that she's begun to look down her nose at me?"

As she left the baths there was a certain air of haughtiness in her step, and she held herself proudly upright, although I had only known her walk resignedly, with a bent back, at home.

Now she was enjoying the esteem which was hers only when she visited the

At last I understood their secret . . .

market baths. At last I understood their secret . . .

Responding to the Selection

1. Describe the "ambience," as the narrator puts it, of the women's baths. Point out some details that you find interesting.

2. What do you think the grandmother seeks at the women's baths?

3. Is conflict between the grandmother and mother inevitable? Consider with whom you sympathize most, the grandmother or the mother.

4. What does the granddaughter learn at the women's baths?

Wanted: A Town Without a Crazy

Muzaffer Izgü

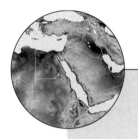

WORLD LENS

•••

TURKEY

Modern Turkey is poised between the developed and the developing worlds. At present, its government is lobbying to join the European Economic Union and become partners with its European neighbors. Nevertheless, 99 percent of the population is Muslim, and its history and people are steeped in Islamic culture. Like many countries situated in the Middle East, Turkey has seen the rise of Muslim fundamentalism in recent years, creating problems for the secular government, schools, and civic life, in some cases. Despite this revival, the Turkish people are accustomed to a tolerant form of Muslim worship. Turks are as fond of tradition as they are optimistic about their prospects in the modern world.

On the table crouched someone my age with a messy beard and untidy hair. Using the broom in his hand sometimes as a guitar, sometimes as a microphone, his singing and dancing had the people in the coffeehouse dying with laughter. My brother-in-law explained, "That's our town crazy."

He did a little act between verses. Moving the broom handle forward and back and making a series of sounds, then holding the handle in his mouth, undulating his hips and dancing, the loony shouted, "Dem dérula, dem dérula!"[1] The crowd picked up the tempo, became exuberant and from time to time shouted, "Hurrah for Crazy Hilmi!"

For a moment, the name Hilmi stuck in my mind. Could this Hilmi be that *same* Hilmi? Even behind a tangled beard, the face resembled his. The squinty eyes, the forehead protruding like a

---

1 **"Dem dérula, dem dérula!":** a nonsense phrase, in Turkish

The Middle East & South Asia

fist, ears like the back of a shovel, even the arms, long like a bear's, were his.

"Look here!" I told my brother-in-law, "I probably know this crazy guy."

"You wouldn't know him," he replied. "This is your first visit to this town, so where could you have met him?"

"Is he from around here?"

"By God, I really don't know. I've lived here for three years and he was here when I came."

At this point the loony finished his concert, walked among the tables and after collecting fifty piastres from this one, a lira[2] from that and a "Get outa here!" from others, he left, **crestfallen**. I had to find out, so I arose quickly. I not only knew this man, but knew him well, having worked with him seven years previously in the same district office. After handing in my resignation and leaving, I had heard no news of Hilmi Bey again. But the Hilmi Bey I knew was a very serious-minded, sober man. I fell in behind him and just as he "lifted" a handful of chestnuts from a bag at the grocery store, saying, "Hilmi Bey!" I caught him.

crestfallen
downcast; disappointed

He threw me a guilty glance then turned to the grocer. After the grocer pressed eight or ten more chestnuts into his hand, he said to me, "He brings good luck. Whatever store he takes something from does very good business that day."

Hilmi Bey moved off from there in a hurry; he was almost running. I started running too. I intended to learn whether this was my Hilmi or some other Hilmi. He was running toward the gardens. They say that a lunatic's strength is superior but I managed to keep close behind him. When he speeded up, I ran even faster to try and catch up with him. Finally, however, I lost him in a wooded area and started calling, "Hilmi Bey! Hilmi Bey!"

No answer. Who knew which tree he was hiding behind! After calling a few times, I heard his crazy laugh close by. There he was. He appeared from behind a bush and grinned.

"Hilmi Bey," I repeated.

"Huh!"

Right, it was him . . . Yet inside I still had doubts. Approaching

---

2 **piastres . . . lira:** former Turkish coins. The piastre is one hundredth of a lira.

closer, I said, "See here, Hilmi Bey, what's the matter with you?"

"Hey," he replied, "I'm the town lunatic."

"Are you really crazy?"

He laughed again. "When you heard my laugh, you really thought at first that I was loony." He bounded over the bush to my side and placed before me things he took out of his pockets: candy, chestnuts, expensive cigarettes, nylon ribbons, a big chocolate bar, four large oranges, some first-class glasses, then he unwound from around his waist, three meters of greatcoat cloth . . . Hilmi's pockets could completely stock a sundries[3] shop.

"Tell me," I insisted, "when did you lose your mind?"

"Come on, lose what mind! Thank God there's nothing wrong with my head."

"Are you really all right?"

"Of course I'm all right. I understood when you resigned from the civil service, it was because there was nothing in it. If we paid the rent we couldn't eat or if we ate we couldn't pay the rent so I took a month's leave, rolled up my sleeves, and started searching for a town without a lunatic. Wearing a heavy overcoat, dark glasses, and carrying a large suitcase, I went from town to town. Every place I went, my first task was to find out if the place had a crazy. If they told me there was, I immediately moved on. In twenty-five days I went through nearly a hundred towns, but each one had a loony. Though I struggled and economized, I was down to my last piastre when finally I came to this town. I sat down in a coffeehouse and, after drinking a tea, called the waiter: 'Brother, I wonder if this town happens to have a lunatic.' "

♦ ♦ ♦ ♦ ♦

"'Where, sir? Here? Eight years ago, we had a cuckoo but ever since he got run over by a truck, the whole town has missed him greatly. What a great guy he was, our cuckoo. He sang songs in the coffeehouses, wandered through the neighborhoods tying cloth on this door and that and played music when there was a wedding, using his nose for a pipe and his chest for a drum. It happened one Friday, Sefer the truckdriver ran him over. Believe me, we gave Crazy Davut a funeral that the town won't even give

---

3 **sundries:** miscellaneous items

Mayor Riza Bey when he dies."

"The waiter heaved a great sigh, 'Ah, ah, after Davut left there was no joy in town. Where could you find another loony like him?'

"Well, after this conversation I left for home and my family. After packing a few things, I said to my wife, 'Well, tell me good-bye.'

"Surprised, she asked, 'Where are you going?'

"'I'm going crazy. I found a town without a lunatic.'

"'Sounds like you're already loony!'

"'Would you listen to her! Of course I've gone mad!'

"'Very well. So what will *we* do?'

"'You'll be the wife and children of a loony.'

"So to enter the town with the honor and glory befitting a loony, I had to start with my clothes. First, I went and had an extra long, bright red topcoat made. I smeared it with mud to make it look old and ripped holes in it left and right. Then I went to the flea market and bought piles of worthless old money and bizarre medals. These I pinned here and there on the coat. Around my waist I bound a thick belt and hung a frying pan to one end on a cord. The frying pan was to be my guitar. I hung things all around my belt: a ladle, wooden spoons, a potty, an old electric clock, a women's umbrella, a cast-iron stove-lid. Clanging and rattling all over, I boarded the bus. The people on the minibus broke into laughter, so I stood up, and using my frying pan as a guitar, sang all the songs I knew. Laughing and clapping, they were so light-hearted it was indescribable. Some threw oranges for me to eat, others gave me candy, and some money. Not only that, the bus driver not only failed to ask me for the fare but invited me to his home: 'Where have you been all this time? Come every day, the food and drinks are on me.'

♦ ♦ ♦ ♦ ♦

"I got off the bus in town to the same laughter. As soon as I landed, eight or ten kids followed me. Their numbers grew to fifty, one hundred. You know kids! Everyone heard about me from them; that's how my fame spread through the town from the first day.

"'Did you hear, huh? A cuckoo came to town.'

"'Man, is he loony. Davut couldn't hold a candle to him!'

"God bless them! From that first day, I drank tea free, coffee too. I ate the best food in the restaurants free, and in addition, they gave me pocket money. It kills me to think that while these poor people were suffering all those years from the lack of a loony, I was putting numbers on documents, kowtowing when I entered the director's office, and wasting all that time for a mere thousand lira a month. If I'd known, wouldn't I have come to this town long before?

"The people are so happy at finding a loony that they don't even ask who or what he is or even where he comes from. Now when I enter the mayor's office, I don't say *selam* or hello and don't even bother to knock. I walk right in, lean against the mayor's arm then settle myself into an easy chair. After thrusting an expensive cigarette into my hand, he lights it with his own lighter and orders me a coffee. While I drink my coffee, he asks, 'You have any problems or anything, Hilmi?'

"I grin. So that means I have no difficulties. As I'm leaving the mayor puts his hand into his pocket and slips me a fiver. From there I go to the director of finance and from there to the doctor, then to the commissar.[4] God bless them, they stick fives and tens into my pockets. Then I go out among tradesmen. Grinning, I enter the shops and tug at the owners' sleeves; they quickly open the drawer, saying, 'May your fortune be bountiful, God willing, Hilmi.' They take out a ten or a five and hand it to me. If my hand happens to brush a bolt of cloth, they immediately tell an apprentice to cut off a couple of meters for me. I wind the two meters around my waist and enter a second store. Then the health services. It's as if they're at my beck and call. Recently, I developed a pain, so I lay down in the middle of the road. In an instant, God, what a commotion broke loose!

◆ ◆ ◆ ◆ ◆

"People rushed there crying, 'Our loony's fallen ill!' You won't believe it; not only the doctor but also the mayor came. People flocked around saying, 'Please, doctor, if you haven't made a diagnosis, let's get a taxi and take him to town. We have a pretty

---

4 **commissar:** a public official charged with maintaining citizen loyalty

good loony and in return for our respect, God blesses our pocketbooks.'

"For a week I was treated like a king in the hospital. The mayor came to visit me three times, and the townspeople every day. What a departure I had from the hospital! It was as if one of the country's greats had had an important operation and was returning from the brink of death."

"Very well," I said, "what about your wife and children? How are they getting along?"

He grinned again: "I disappear for two or three days a month; the town is used to this. They say the poor fellow is having another fit of nervous agitation so he takes off in order not to bring any harm on the townspeople. As a matter of fact, I send some of the money and things I've collected by mail and others I forward to a place agreed upon with my wife. Thus my family gets along very well. One of my sons is attending the university and a daughter has finished high school. We bought a flat in an apartment building and my wife has it furnished to suit her heart's desire."

"OK," I continued, "but when are you going to put an end to this lunacy?"

He grinned: "Are you nuts? There are lots of professional lunatics in this country. One of them would snatch my spot, so I can't leave town. What's more, I'm sort of used to this insanity."

As he leaped up and skipped away, he said, "Don't tell anyone. Even if you did, they wouldn't believe you!"

Responding to the Selection

1. Does Hilmi degrade himself by acting as the town crazy? Explain your answer.

2. Irony is a contrast between what one expects or what appears to be and what actually is. Where is there irony in this story?

3. Do you think Americans would treat poor and unconventional people like Hilmi with the same degree of respect as his adopted townspeople? Say why or why not.

The Armenian Language Is the Home of the Armenian

Moushegh Ishkhan

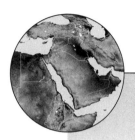

WORLD LENS

•••

ARMENIA

Armenia's history is drenched in blood. A small country caught between the Islamic and Christian worlds, it has been subject to constant invasions. In 1915, 1.5 million Armenians died in a Turkish massacre, launching a migration that emptied Armenian villages and tore apart countless families. In 1988, an earthquake brought a death toll of 25,000–50,000 people. Despite their traumas, the Armenians are proud proponents of their heritage and place a very high value on all earmarks of culture: books, education, and music.

The Armenian language is the home
and haven where the wanderer can own
roof and wall and nourishment.
He can enter to find love and pride,
locking the hyena and the storm outside.
For centuries its architects have toiled
to give its ceilings height.
How many peasants working
day and night have kept
its cupboards full, lamps lit, ovens hot.
Always rejuvenated, always old, it lasts
century to century on the path
where every Armenian can find it when he's lost
in the wilderness of his future, or his past.

Translated by Diana der Hovanessian

Responding to the Selection

1. In what ways is the Armenian language like a home to Armenians? Consider how your own language is like a home to you.

2. Time is often referred to in this poem about the Armenian language. Considering the Armenians' history of disruption and exile, what does it add to the poem to refer to time?

3. The English-only movement in the United States has risen in part due to the waves of non-English speaking immigrants to this country in the last few decades. Its adherents would like to see English be the language of all official transactions and would like immigrants to learn English as quickly as possible so they assimilate into U.S. culture. How do you think they might respond to this poem and why?

THE REFUGEES, Marc Chagall, 1976

From Behind the Veil

Dhu'l Nun Ayyoub

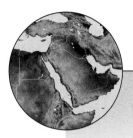

A veil is worn by many Muslim women, especially those in Middle Eastern cultures. These women are obliged to observe laws requiring them to cover their bodies while in public places. The rise of fundamentalism in recent years has returned the veil's popularity as a headdress and symbol of Muslim pride, religiosity, and feminine modesty.

WORLD LENS

♦♦♦

IRAQ

The street, although wide, was inconveniently full of strollers passing to and fro. The situation was not helped by the sleek swift cars, which sped by from time to time. They carried wealthy occupants, young women and ladies, who, protected from the curiosity of the outside world, displayed radiant faces. Their shining gaze roved across the street, smiling or frowning as they took in sights which pleased or displeased them.

Among the surging crowd was an amazing mixture of different clothes and contrasting shapes, which, if nothing else, serve to emphasize the varying tastes of these passers-by.

A European who had never been to the East before might be excused for thinking that its people were in the middle of a great festival. As time goes by, however, he is moved to say in amazement, "What long carnival celebrations you have in this country!" Our Western friend would think that people wear these amazing clothes for a festival, just as they would do in his own country.

You can also see women in the crowd, both veiled and unveiled. A man can be surprised to find himself turning involuntarily towards those figures, wearing long silk gowns, which give them such an enticing and alluring shape, and make the observer yearn to uncover the magic and the secrets which lie beneath them.

His desire is only increased when his gaze falls on the filmy veil. Behind it he can catch a fleeting glimpse of fine features and penciled eyebrows, which serve to inflame the fires of his heart. It makes him want to devote the rest of his life to the exploration of this world full of shame-faced beauty.

Ihsan was one of those who would stroll along with the crowd displaying his smart and tasteful suit over his slim figure, patting his dark gleaming hair whenever he felt that the evening breezes had ruffled it, or spread a curl over his clear forehead.

This Ihsan was a young man of eighteen, good-looking with

fine features which made him attractive to a number of women. Naturally he was aware of his appeal and attraction, and he had the youthful capacity to exploit it. That's why you can see him now, with his eyes wandering in search of a **quarry**.

Ihsan was not interested in chasing unveiled girls. They exuded poise, which he found unattractive, and they were always looking anxiously to avoid criticism so they never looked the passers-by directly in the face. They would walk by without turning their heads, paying no attention to the expressions of flattery which came

Ihsan was not interested in chasing unveiled girls.

their way from the **gallants**, who, after getting as much out of them as a dog gets out of barking at clouds, would give them no further attention.

This is the reason that makes Ihsan always sidle up to the girls with the long cloaks and the secret little movements which attract him: the burning sighs and the gentle laughter and the concealed glances.

Siham had gone out on the evening of that day as usual to take the air and stroll through the streets. This evening stroll had become a part of her life to such an extent that it was now indispensable. She couldn't remember exactly the date when she first set out to saunter through the street, and did not really know the reason why she kept up her evening appointments. If she did, she did not admit it. Whatever the case, no sooner had Siham seen the bustle in the middle of the street than she headed for the pavement. She looked cautiously left and right until she saw Ihsan in the distance, and suddenly she felt the blood coursing through her veins.

She found herself unconsciously moving towards him until she was almost parallel with him, saw him staring at her from top to bottom, and felt a tremor throughout her body. When she saw his burning stare almost penetrating the cloak which covered her slender body her heart beat violently. She was used to seeing him every day at this time, and she used to stare at him freely each time until she had memorized his face. Of late, she had begun to feel her heart pounding whenever she saw him, and her face flushed with confusion. There was nothing to stop her from

The Middle East & South Asia

feasting her eyes on him, however, because she knew that the veil covered her face and concealed the overwhelming attraction she felt for him.

We cannot be certain what it was that made this youth know that the girl was interested in him, and whether his first overture to her came in the course of one of his habitual overtures, which he made to any girl. Whatever it was, he went up to the girl boldly on that first day, and sidled up to her, greeted her, and saw her turning round to look at him cautiously before hurrying on her way.

He knew immediately that she was not angry with him, and emboldened, he carried on behind her and saw her going into one of the public parks. She knew that he was following her, and hastened on her way, trembling with conflicting emotions of joy, fear, and caution.

He followed her into the park for a short distance, until he saw her sitting on her own, behind a big tree. He went up to her and spoke to her smilingly.

"Good evening."

"Good evening," she replied shyly.

Then she raised her veil from her brown face and her dark eyes, and Ihsan was captivated by the long dark eyelashes which cast a shadow over her features.

The features of her face were fine, and inspired the beholder with the strongest feelings of awe and worship. She was fearful and breathless, turning from side to side like a timid gazelle.[1] She knew that what she was doing amounted to an unpardonable crime, but drew comfort from one thing—the knowledge that this boy had not seen her before and did not know her. She was having an adventure, nothing more, and she was drawn into it by her youth and by the warm blood which coursed in her veins.

The boy's mind worked on some expressions of flattery and endearment. For his opening shot, he ventured: "I've seen you often, as you've passed by this street and then gone to walk among the trees. I wasn't able to talk to you because I respect you, and your whole appearance tells me that you are from a good family."

---

1 **gazelle:** a small antelope noted for its graceful motion

She replied, a little resentfully: "But I suppose you always try to talk with ordinary girls as well? Why don't you just chase the common girls, and satisfy your passions on them?"

"I'm sorry, really, I don't mean you any harm. But I'm alone, as you see, and I can't find a companion to share my walks with me. I saw that you were the only girl who found pleasure in these strolls, and so I felt that there was a link between us. Anyway, if you find my presence unpleasant in any way, I'll move off right now."

He made a move to get up, but she checked him and asked: "Do you know who I am?"

"I haven't the least idea, but this doesn't stop me from believing that I share your spirit," he replied softly.

"If you want to accompany me on these innocent walks, I don't see any objection," she mused. "There's no harm in strolling around with you for an hour or so, at intervals which we can agree on, on condition that you promise me that you won't try to follow me and try to find out who I am. I don't want you trying to contact me at any other times."

"I respect your wish and I shall honour it," he replied formally.

The two of them sat side by side on one of the stone benches, and a deep silence reigned over them, in which each felt the beating of their own hearts. This silence continued for a long time. Both of them had been overcome by the novelty of their strange and singular situation.

Ihsan, however, was a youth accustomed to flirtations, although he realized that this time he was faced with a girl who was pure and virtuous. There was something about her, a certain strength of purpose and character, which confused him, and stopped him from going too far. His mind worked to collect his thoughts and to rescue him from the situation into which he had unwittingly walked.

At length, he spoke, somewhat confused.

"What is your name, please?"

"Have you forgotten my condition that you should not try to identify me?"

"Of course. I'm sorry. But surely . . . in view of our future friendship . . . ?

"Have you forgotten? We live in a society in which this situation is unforgivable. If my people knew anything of this they'd kill me. While society is like this, we must learn to deceive. We must use the follies of our society in order to break its shackles!"

"What a penetrating mind you have!" said Ihsan admiringly.

"Thank you. Time's getting on and I must be getting back to the house. I will see you again in two days."

As she said goodbye he tried to put his arm around her waist, but she **rebuffed** him sharply. Then she relented slightly, saying: "I don't know who you are. You might be one of those mean boys who take delight in trapping girls for their own pleasure and sport."

rebuffed
snubbed; rejected

She went back to the house invigorated, but somewhat disturbed, for she had broken with the most binding and serious of traditions in one fell swoop. She didn't understand how it had begun and how it had ended, until it seemed to her that everything that had happened that day was a disturbing dream.

She threw her cloak on one side, and went to help her mother with the housework. She flattered her mother, made herself agreeable, and took delight in carrying out her orders and her arrangements. When her father returned home from work she welcomed him with smiling face, then she went to her room to get on with her studies.

She set about her work mechanically, with nervous high spirits, and had disturbing dreams at night.

The meetings went on longer, and the subjects of their conversations diversified. The relationship between them developed, and things became deeply involved. She no longer felt that there was anything strange or unusual about the meetings, but she kept her head, using her lively mind to conceal her relationship with this boy, and to prevent him from trying to find out who she was and getting in touch with her.

♦ ♦ ♦ ♦ ♦

One day Siham was sitting with her father, talking to him after supper, while he was scanning the evening paper. His eye fell on a long article about women who had abandoned the veil, and,

heresies
fallacies; dissenting beliefs

deciding to have his daughter's view, he read the article out loud. No sooner had he finished than Siham roundly abused the author for trying to break with convention and introduce modern **heresies**. Her father felt a greatly increased regard for his intelligent, well-brought-up daughter, who obviously knew the value of traditions and respected them. Such a difference between her and the rest of her irresponsible, scandalous friends, who, no sooner had they learned to read and write, went around throwing overboard society's conventions without shame or respect!

Impulsively, he moved towards his daughter and kissed her forehead.

"God preserve you as a treasure for your father."

When she reached her room Siham could barely stop herself from laughing out loud. She picked up her veil and danced with glee, then stopped in the middle of the room and began to whisper to the veil: "You black shroud, you know how I despise you and make use of you to keep him apart from me! I don't care about you, and I feel nothing for you. I defy you. But I love you too. These poor girls take refuge behind you in order to preserve their virginity, and their honour, and good morals. If they were more truthful they would say that they love you because you hide faults and scandals. I love you because you help me to enjoy my life in a way that only those who wear the veil can appreciate. I pity those wretched unveiled women. I scorn them."

Translated by S. Al-Bazzazz

Responding to the Selection

1. What are some of the tensions in this story? Choose one conflict—social, family, male-female, or internal—and explore the distance between rules and expectations and what people want for themselves.

2. What do you learn in this story about the many uses of the veil in modern Islamic societies?

3. Do you have sympathy for the young woman? Explain why or why not.

4. What might strict Muslims find disturbing about Western courtship behavior?

Five Hours to Simla

Anita Desai

WORLD LENS

◆◆◆

INDIA

Then, miraculously, out of the pelt of yellow fur that was the dust growing across the great northern Indian plain, a wavering grey line emerged. It might have been a cloud bank looming, but it was not—the sun blazed, the earth shrivelled, the heat burnt away every trace of spring's **beneficence**. Yet the grey darkened, turned bluish, took on substance.

beneficence
kindness; generosity

"Look—mountains!"

"Where?"

"I can't see any mountains."

"Are you blind? Look, look up—not down, fool!"

A scuffle broke out between the boys on the sticky grime of the Rexine[1]-covered front seat. It was quietened by a tap on their heads from their mother in the back. "Yes, yes, mountains. The Himalayas.[2] We'll be there soon."

"Huh." A sceptical grunt from the driver of the tired, dust-buried grey Ambassador car. "At least five more hours to Simla." He ran his hand over the back of his neck where all the dirt of the road seemed to have found its way under the wilting cotton collar.

"Sim-la! Sim-la!" the boys set up a chant, their knees bouncing

---

1 **Rexine:** artificial leather

2 **Himalayas:** an extensive mountain range in Asia, which includes Mount Everest, the highest mountain in the world

up and down in unison.

Smack, the driver's left hand landed on the closest pair, bringing out an instant stain of red and sudden, sullen silence.

"Be quiet!" the mother hissed from the back unnecessarily.

The Ambassador gave a sudden lurch, throwing everyone forwards. The baby, whose mouth had been glued to the teat of a bottle like a fly to syrup, came unstuck and wailed with indignation. Even their mother let out a small involuntary cry. Her daughter, who had been asleep on the back seat, her legs across her mother's lap, now stirred.

"Accident!" howled the small boy who had been smacked, triumphantly.

But it was not. His father had stopped just short of the bicycle rickshaw[3] ahead, which had just avoided running into the bullock[4] cart carrying farmers' families to market. A bus, loaded with baggage and spilling over with passengers, had also ground to a halt with a shrieking of brakes. Ahead of it was a truck, wrapped and folded in canvas sheets that blocked all else from sight. The mountains had disappeared and so had the road.

After the first **cacophony** of screeching brakes and grinding gears, there followed the comparatively **static** hum of engines, and drivers waited in exasperation for the next lurch forwards. For the moment there was a lull, curious on that highway. Then the waiting very quickly began to fray at the edges. The sun was beating on the metal of the vehicles, and the road lay flattened across the parched plain, with no trees to screen it from the sun. First one car horn began to honk, then a bicycle rickshaw began to clang its bell, then a truck blared its musical horn, and then the lesser ones began to go pom-pom, pom-pom almost in harmony, and suddenly, out of the centre of all that noise, a long, piercing wail emerged.

The two boys, the girl, the baby, all sat up, shocked. More so when they saw what their father was doing. Clenching the wheel with both hands, his head was lowered on to it, and the blare of the horn seemed to issue out of his fury.

The mother exclaimed.

cacophony
din; clamor

static
steady; unchanging

---

3 **rickshaw:** a passenger cart pulled by a human being

4 **bullock:** a young bull

The father raised his head and banged on the wheel, struck it. "How will we get to Simla before dark?" he howled.

The mother exclaimed again, shocked. "But we'll be moving again in a minute."

As if to contradict her, the driver of the truck stalled at the top of the line, swung himself out of the cabin into the road. He'd turned off his engine and stood in the deeply rutted dust, fumbling in his shirt pocket for cigarettes.

Other drivers got out of and down from their vehicles: the bullock-cart driver lowered himself from the creaking cart; the bicycle-rickshaw driver descended; the bus driver got out and stalked, in his sweat-drenched khakis, towards the truck driver standing at the head of the line; and they all demanded, "What's going on? Breakdown?"

The truck driver watched them approach but was lighting his cigarette and didn't answer. Then he waved an arm—his movements were leisurely, elegant, quite unlike what his driving had been—and said, "Stone throw. Somebody threw a stone. Hit windshield. Cracked it."

The father in the Ambassador had also joined them in the road. Hands on his hips, he demanded, "So?"

"So?" said the truck driver, narrowing his eyes. They were grey in a tanned face, heavily outlined and elongated with kohl, and his hair was tied up in a bandanna with a long loose end that dangled upon his shoulder. "So we won't be moving again till the person who did it is caught, and a *faisla* is made—a settlement."

Immediately a babble broke out. All the drivers flung out their hands and arms in angry, demanding gestures, their voices rose in questioning, in **cajoling**, in argument. The truck driver stood looking at them, watching them, his face **inscrutable**. Now and then he lifted the cigarette to his mouth and drew a deep puff. Then abruptly he swung around, clambered back into the cabin of his truck and started the engine with a roar at which the others fell back, their attitudes slackening in relief, but then he wheeled the truck around and parked it squarely across the highway so no traffic could get past in either direction. The highway at that point had narrowed to a small culvert across a dry stream-bed full of stones. Now he clambered up the bank of the culvert and sat

cajoling
coaxing; wheedling

inscrutable
unknowable; indecipherable

down, his legs wide apart in their loose and not too clean pyjamas,[5] regarding the traffic piling up in both directions as though he was watching sheep filing into a pen.

The knot of drivers in the road began to grow, joined by many of the passengers demanding to know the cause of this **impasse**.

impasse
deadlock; stalemate

"Dadd-ee! Dadd-ee!" the small boys yelled, hanging out of the door their father had left open and all but falling out into the dust. "What's happened, Dadd-ee?"

"Shut the door!" their mother ordered sharply but too late. A yellow pye-dog came crawling out of the shallow ditch that ran alongside the road and, spying an open door, came slinking up to it, thin, hairless tail between its legs, eyes showing their whites, hoping for bread but quite prepared for a blow instead.

The boys drew back on seeing its exploring snout, its teeth bared ready for a taste of bread. "Mad dog!" shouted one. "Mad dog!" bellowed the other.

"Shh!" hissed their mother.

Since no one in the car dared drive away a creature so dangerous, someone else did. A stone struck its ribs, and with a yelp it ducked under the car to hide, but already the next beggar was at the door, throwing himself in with much the same mixture of leering enquiry and cringing readiness to withdraw. "Bread," he whined, stretching out a bandaged hand. "*Paisa, paisa.* Mother, mother," he pleaded, seeing the mother cower in her seat with the baby. The children cowered too.

They knew that if they remained thus for long enough and made no move towards purse or coin, he would leave; he couldn't afford to waste too much time on them when there were so many potential donors lined up so conveniently along the highway. The mother stared glassily ahead through the windscreen at the heat beating off the metal bonnet.[6] The children could not tear their eyes away from the beggar—his sores, his bandages, his crippled leg, the flies gathering . . .

When he moved on, the mother raised a corner of her sari to her mouth and nose. From behind it she hissed: "Shut-the-door!"

Unsticking their damp legs from the moist, adhesive seat, the

---

5 **pyjamas:** the loose top and pants favored by Indian men in tropical climates

6 **bonnet:** the Anglo-Indian term for a car hood

The Middle East & South Asia

boys scrambled to do so. As they leaned out to grab the door however, and the good feel of the blazing sun and the open air struck at their faces and arms, they turned around to plead, "Can we get out? Can we go and see what's happening?"

So **ardent** was their need that they were about to fall out of the open door when they saw their father detaching himself from the knot of passengers and drivers standing in the road and making his way back to them. The boys hastily edged back until he stood leaning in at the door. The family studied his face for signs; they were all adept at this, practising it daily over the breakfast table at home, and again when he came back from work. But this situation was a new one, a baffling one: they could

ardent
intense; passionate

Five Hours to Simla   433

not read it, or his position on it.

"What's happening?" the mother asked faintly at last.

"Damn truck driver," he swore through dark lips. "Some boy threw a rock—probably some goatherd in the field—and cracked his windscreen. He's parked the truck across the road, won't let anyone pass till there's a *faisla*. Says he won't move till the police come and get him compensation. Stupid damn fool— what compensation is a goatherd going to pay, even if they find him?"

The mother leaned her head back. What had reason to do with men's tempers? she might have asked. Instead, she sighed, "Is there a policeman?"

"What—here? In this forsaken desert?" her husband retorted, drawing in harsh breaths of overheated, dust-laden air as if he were breathing in all the stupidity around him. He could see passengers climbing down from the bus and the bullock cart, climbing across the ditch into the fields, and fanning out—some to lower their trousers, others to lift their saris behind the thorn bushes. If the glare was not playing tricks with his eyes, he thought he saw a puff of dust in the distance that might have been raised by goats' hooves.

"Take me to see, Dadd-ee, take me to see," the boys had begun to clamour, and to their astonishment he stood aside and let them climb out and even led them back to the truck that stood **imperviously** across the culvert.

The mother opened and shut her mouth silently. Her daughter stood up and hung over the front seat to watch the disappearing figures. In despair, she cried, "They're gone!"

"Sit down! Where can they go?"

"I want to go too, Mumm-ee, I want to go too-oo."

"Be quiet. There's nowhere to go."

The girl began to wail. It was usually a good strategy in a family with loud voices, but this time her grievance was genuine: her head ached from the long sleep in the car, from the heat beating on its metal top, from the lack of air, from the glare and from hunger. "I'm hung-gree," she wept.

"We were going to eat when we reached Solan," her mother reminded her. "There's such a nice-nice restaurant at the railway

imperviously
*impassably; not
allowing entrance
or exit*

station in Solan. Such nice-nice omelettes they make there."

"I want an omelette!" wailed the child.

"Wait till we get to Solan."

"When will we reach it? *When?*"

"Oh, I don't know. Late. Sit down and open that basket at the back. You'll find something to eat there."

But now that omelettes at Solan had been mentioned the basket packed at home with Gluco biscuits and potato chips held no attraction for the girl. She stopped wailing but sulked instead, sucking her thumb, a habit she was supposed to have given up but which resurfaced for comfort when necessary.

She did not need to draw upon her thumb juices for long. The news of the traffic jam on the highway had spread. From somewhere—it seemed from nowhere for there was no village bazaar, market place or stall visible in that dusty **dereliction**— wooden barrows came trundling along towards the waiting traffic, bearing freshly cut lengths of sugar cane; bananas already more black than yellow from the sun that baked them; peanuts in their shells roasting in pans set on embers. Men, women and children were climbing over the ditch like phantoms, materializing out of the dust, with baskets on their heads filled not only with food but with amusements as well—a trayload of paper toys painted **indigo** and violent pink, small bamboo pipes that released rude noises and a dyed feather on a spool. Kites, puppets, clay carts, wooden toys and tin whistles. The vendors milled around the buses, cars and rickshaws, and were soon standing at their car window, both vocally and manually proffering goods for sale.

The baby let drop its narcotic rubber teat, delighted. Its eyes grew big and shone at all it saw flowering about it. The little girl was perplexed, wondering what to choose from so much till the perfect choice presented itself in a rainbow of colour: green, pink and violet, her favourites. It was a barrow of soft drinks, and nothing on this day of gritty dust, yellow sun and frustrating delay could be more enticing than those bottles filled with syrups in those dazzling floral colours which provoked in her a scream of desire.

"Are you mad?" her mother said promptly. "You think I'll let

> **dereliction**
> *area of neglect or abandonment*

> **indigo**
> *deep reddish blue*

you drink a bottle full of typhoid and cholera[7] germs?"

The girl gasped with disbelief at being denied. Her mouth opened wide to issue a protest, but her mother went on. "After you have your typhoid-and-cholera injection, you may. You want a nice, big typhoid-and-cholera injection first?"

The child's mouth was still open in contemplation of the impossible choice when her brothers came plodding back through the dust, each carrying a pith[8]-and-bamboo toy—a clown that jounced upon a stick and a bird that whirled upon a pin. Behind them the father slouched morosely. He had his hands deep in his pockets, and his face was lined with a frown deeply embedded with dust.

"We'll be here for hours," he informed his wife through the car window. "A rickshaw driver has gone off to the nearest *thana* to find a policeman who can put sense into that damn truck driver's thick head." Despondently he threw himself into the driver's seat and sprawled there. "Must be a hundred and twenty degrees," he sighed.

"Pinky, where is the water bottle? Pass the water bottle to Daddy," commanded the mother solicitously.

He drank from the plastic bottle, tilting his head back and letting the water spill into his mouth. But it was so warm it was hardly refreshing, and he spat the last mouthful out of the car window into the dust. A scavenging chicken alongside the tyre skipped away with a squawk.

All along the road, in the stationary traffic, drivers and passengers were searching for shade, for news, for some sign of release. Every now and then someone brought information on how long the line of cars and trucks now was. Two miles in each direction was the latest estimate, at least two miles.

◆ ◆ ◆ ◆ ◆

Up on the bank of the culvert the man who had caused it all sat sprawling, his legs wide apart. He had taken off his bandanna, revealing a twist of cotton wool dipped in fragrant oil that was

---

7 **typhoid and cholera:** infectious diseases affecting the intestines, often fatal

8 **pith:** the soft, inner part of a plant stem

tucked behind his ear. He had bought himself a length of sugar cane and sat chewing it, ripping off the tough outer fibre with strong flashing teeth, then drawing the sweet syrup out of its soft white inside and spitting out, with relish, the pale fibre sucked dry. He seemed deliberately to spit in the direction of those who stood watching in growing frustration.

"Get hold of that fellow! *Force* him to move his truck," somebody suddenly shouted out, driven to the limit of his endurance. "If he doesn't, he'll get the thrashing of his life."

"Calm down, Sirdarji," another placated him with a light laugh to help put things back in perspective. "Cool down. It's hot, but you'll get your cold beer when you get to Solan."

"When will that be? When my beard's gone grey?"

"Grey hair is nothing to be ashamed of," philosophized an elder who had a good deal of it to show. "Grey hair shows patience, forbearance, a long life. That is how to live long—patiently, with forbearance."

"And when one has work to do, what then?" the Sikh demanded, rolling up his hands into fists. The metal bangle on his wrist glinted.

"Work goes better after a little rest," the elder replied, and demonstrated by lowering himself on to his haunches and squatting there on the roadside like an old bird on its perch or a man waiting to be shaved by a roadside barber. And, like an answer to a call, a barber did miraculously appear, an itinerant barber who carried the tools of his trade in a tin box on his head. No one could imagine where he had emerged from, or how far he had travelled in search of custom. Now he squatted and began to unpack a mirror, scissors, soap, blades, even a small rusty cigarette tin full of water. An audience stood watching his expert moves and flourishes and the evident pleasure these gave the elder.

Suddenly the truck driver on the bank waved a hand and called, "Hey, come up here when you've finished. I could do with a shave too—and my ears need cleaning."

There was a gasp at his **insolence**, and then indignant protests.

"Are you planning to get married over there? Are we not to

insolence
boldness; disrespect

move till your bride arrives and the wedding is over?" shouted someone.

This had the wrong effect: it made the crowd laugh. Even the truck driver laughed. He was somehow becoming a part of the conspiracy. How had this happened?

In the road, the men stood locked in bafflement. In the vehicles, the tired passengers waited. "Oo-oof," sighed the mother. The baby, asleep as if stunned by the heat, felt heavy as lead in her arms. "My head is paining, and it's time to have tea."

"Mama wants tea, mama wants tea!" chanted her daughter, kicking at the front seat.

"Stop it!" her father snapped. "Where is the kitchen? Where is the cook? Am I to get them out of the sky? Or is there a well filled with tea?"

The children all burst out laughing at the idea of drawing tea from a well, but while they giggled helplessly, a *chai wallah*[9] did appear, a tray with glasses on his head, a kettle dangling from his hand, searching for the passenger who had called for tea.

There was no mention of cholera or typhoid now. He was summoned, glasses were filled with milky, sweet tea and handed out, the parents slurped thirstily, and the children stared, demanding sips, then flinching from the scalding liquid.

Heartened, the father began to thrash around in the car, punch the horn, stamp ineffectually on the accelerator. "Damn fool," he swore. "How can this happen? How can this be allowed? Only in this bloody country. Where else can one man hold up four miles of traffic?"

Handing back an empty glass, the mother suggested, "Why don't you go and see if the policeman's arrived?"

"Am I to go up and down looking for a policeman? Should I walk to Solan to find one?" the man fumed. His tirade rolled like thunder out of the white blaze of the afternoon. The children listened, watched. Was it getting darker? Was a thundercloud approaching? Was it less bright? Perhaps it was evening. Perhaps it would be night soon.

"What will we do when it grows dark?" the girl whimpered. "Where will we sleep?"

---

9 *chai wallah:* a person employed to serve tea

The Middle East & South Asia

"Here, on the road!" shouted the boys. "Here on the road!" Their toys were long since broken and discarded. They needed some distraction. Their sister could easily be moved to tears by mentioning night, jackals, ghosts that haunt highways, robbers who carry silk handkerchiefs to strangle their victims . . .

♦♦♦♦♦

Suddenly, one of the drivers, hitching up his pyjamas and straightening his turban, came running back towards the stalled traffic, shouting, "They're moving! The policeman's come! They'll move now! There'll be a *faisla!*"

Instantly the picture changed from one of discouragement, despair and approaching darkness to animation, excitement, hope. All those loitering in the road leaped back into their vehicles, and in a moment the air was filled with the roar of revving engines as with applause.

The father too was pressing down on the accelerator, beating upon the steering wheel, and the children settling into position, all screaming, "Sim-la! Sim-la!" in unison.

But not a single vehicle moved an inch. None could. The obstructing truck had not been moved out of the way. The driver still sprawled on the bank, propped up on one elbow now, demanding of the policeman who had arrived, "So? Have you brought me compensation? NO? Why not? I told you I would not move till I received compensation. So where is it? Hah? What is the *faisla*? Hah?"

The roar of engines faltered, hiccuped, fell silent. After a while, car doors slammed as drivers and passengers climbed out again. Groups formed to discuss the latest development. What was to be done now? The elder's philosophical patience was no longer entertained. No one bandied jokes with the villain on the bank any more. Expressions turned grim.

Suddenly the mother wailed, "We'll be here all night," and the baby woke crying: it had had enough of being confined in the suffocating heat; it wanted air, it wanted escape. All the children began to whine. The mother drew herself up. "We'll have to get something to eat," she said and called over to her husband standing in the road, "Can't you get some food for the children?"

He threw her an irritated look over his shoulder. Together with the men in the road, he was going back to the culvert to see what could be done. There was an urgency about their talk now, their suggestions. Dusk had begun to creep across the fields like a thicker, greyer layer of dust. Some of the vendors lit kerosene lamps on their barrows, so small and faint that they did nothing but accentuate the darkness. Some of them were disappearing over the fields, along paths visible only to them, having sold their goods and possibly having a long way to travel. All that could be seen in the dark were the lighted pinpricks of their cigarettes.

What the small girl had most feared did now happen—the long, mournful howl of a jackal lifted itself out of the stones and thorn bushes and unfurled through the dark towards them. While she sat mute with fear, her brothers let out howls of delight and began to imitate the invisible creature's call.

The mother was shushing them fiercely when they heard the sound they had given up hope of hearing: the sound of a moving vehicle. It came roaring up the road from behind them—not at all where they had expected—overtaking them in a cloud of choking dust. Policemen in khaki, armed with steel-tipped canes, leaned out of it, their moustaches bristling, their teeth gleaming, eyes flashing and ferocious as tigers. And the huddled crowd stranded on the roadside fell aside like sheep; it might have been they who were at fault.

But the police truck overtook them all, sending them hurriedly into the ditch for safety, and drew up at the culvert. Here the police jumped out, landing with great thuds on the asphalt, and striking their canes hard upon it for good measure. The truck's headlights lit up the bank with its **pallid** wash.

pallid
pale; colorless

Caught in that illumination, the truck driver rose calmly to his feet, dusted the seat of his pyjamas, wound up the bandanna round his head, all in one fluid movement, and without a word leaped lightly back into the driver's seat of his truck. He turned the key, started the engine, manoeuvred into an onward position and, while his audience held its disbelieving breath, set off towards the north.

After a moment they saw that he had switched on his lights. He had also turned on his radio, and a song could be heard.

Father, I am leaving your roof,
To my bridegroom's home I go . . .

His tail lights could be seen dwindling in the dark. The police swung around, flourishing their canes. "Get on! *Chalo!*" they bellowed. "*Chalo, chalo*, get on, all of you," and they did.

Responding to the Selection

1. Describe how this story shows the collision of modern and traditional values in late 20th-century India.

2. Traffic backed up on a busy highway is a recipe for conflict, no matter what part of the world. Nevertheless, it seems unlikely the events in "Five Hours to Simla" would occur in the United States. What do you think the response to the Indian truck driver would be if he acted similarly on a highway in the United States?

3. How does the author intensify the mood of frustration in this story?

4. Name the main conflict in this story and state whether it is external or internal. How does the family deal with this particular conflict?

The Cabuliwallah
(The Fruit Seller from Cabul) [1]

Rabindranath Tagore

WORLD LENS

◆◆◆

INDIA

The author of India's national anthem, Rabindranath Tagore was admired by other Indians for his writing as well as his model citizenship. This Nobel Prize-winning author spoke out bravely against colonialism, going so far as to reject a knighthood from Britain's crown. In his writing, Tagore seeks to interweave strands of traditional Indian culture with Western influences.

Mini, my five-year-old daughter, cannot live without chattering. I really believe that in all her life she has not wasted one minute in silence. Her mother is often vexed at this and would stop her prattle, but I do not. To see Mini quiet is unnatural and I cannot bear it for long. Because of this, our conversations are always lively.

One morning, for instance, when I was in the midst of the seventeenth chapter of my new novel, Mini stole into the room and putting her hand into mine, said: "Father! Ramdayal the door keeper calls a crow a krow! He doesn't know anything, does he?"

Before I could explain the language differences in this country, she was on the trace of another subject. "What do you think, Father? Shola says there is an elephant in the clouds, blowing water out of his trunk, and that is why it rains!"

The child had seated herself at my feet near the table and was playing softly, drumming on her knees. I was hard at work on my seventeenth chapter, where Pratap Singh, the hero, had just caught Kanchanlata, the heroine, in his arms and was about to escape with her by the third-story window of the castle, when all

---

1 **Cabul:** (also Kabul), the capital of Afghanistan

of a sudden Mini left her play and ran to the window, crying, "A Cabuliwallah! A Cabuliwallah!" Sure enough, in the street below was a Cabuliwallah passing slowly along. He wore the loose, soiled clothing of his people and a tall turban; there was a bag on his back, and he carried boxes of grapes in his hand.

I cannot tell what my daughter's feelings were at the sight of this man, but she began to call him loudly. Ah, I thought, he will come in and my seventeenth chapter will never be finished! At this exact moment the Cabuliwallah turned and looked up at the child. When she saw this she was overcome by terror, fled to her mother's protection, and disappeared. She had a blind belief that inside the bag which the big man carried were two or three children like herself. Meanwhile, the peddler entered my doorway and greeted me with a smiling face.

So **precarious** was the position of my hero and my heroine that my first impulse was to stop and buy something, especially since Mini had called to the man. I made some small purchases, and a conversation began about Abdurrahman, the Russians, the English, and the Frontier Policy.[2]

> **precarious**
> *insecure; risky*

As he was about to leave, he asked: "And where is the little girl, sir?"

I, thinking that Mini must get rid of her false fear, had her brought out. She stood by my chair, watching the Cabuliwallah and his bag. He offered her nuts and raisins but she would not be tempted, and only clung closer to me, with all her doubts increased. This was their first meeting.

One morning, however, not many days later, as I was leaving the house I was startled to find Mini seated on a bench near the door, laughing and talking with the great Cabuliwallah at her feet. In all her life, it appeared, my small daughter had never found so patient a listener, except for her father. Already the corner of her little sari was stuffed with almonds and raisins, gifts from her visitor. "Why did you give her those?" I said, and taking out an eight-anna piece,[3] handed it to him. The man accepted the

---

2 **Abdurrahman . . . Policy:** Abdurrahman Khan, an Afghanistan ruler who came to power in 1880 after Great Britain relinquished its power over internal matters. Great Britain had been vying with Russia for control of the nation.

3 **eight-anna piece:** a former Indian coin

money without delay and slipped it into his pocket.

Alas, on my return an hour later, I found the unfortunate coin had made twice its own worth of trouble! The Cabuliwallah had given it to Mini, and her mother, seeing the bright, round object, had pounced on the child with: "Where did you get that eight-anna piece?"

"The Cabuliwallah gave it to me," said Mini cheerfully.

"The Cabuliwallah gave it to you!" cried her mother, much shocked. "Oh, Mini! How could you take it from him?"

impending
approaching; coming

Entering at this moment, I saved her from **impending** disaster and proceeded to make my own inquiries. I found that it was not the first or the second time the two had met. The Cabuliwallah had overcome the child's first terror by a **judicious** bribery of nuts and almonds, and the two were now great friends.

judicious
thoughtful; astute

They had many quaint jokes which afforded them a great deal of amusement. Seated in front of him, and looking with all her tiny dignity on his gigantic frame, Mini would ripple her face with laughter and begin, "O Cabuliwallah! Cabuliwallah! what have you got in your bag?"

He would reply in the nasal accents of a mountaineer: "An elephant!" Not much cause for merriment, perhaps, but how they both enjoyed their joke! And for me, this child's talk with a grown-up man always had in it something strangely fascinating.

"Well, little one, and when are you going to the father-in-law's house?"

Then the Cabuliwallah, not to be caught behind, would take his turn with: "Well, little one, and when are you going to the father-in-law's house?"

Now most small Bengali maidens have heard long ago about the father-in-law's house, but we, being a little modern, had kept these things from our child, and at this question Mini must have been a trifle bewildered. But she would not show it, and with instant composure replied: "Are you going there?"

Among men of the Cabuliwallah's class, however, it is well known that the words "father-in-law's house" have a double meaning. It is a euphemism for jail, the place where we are well cared for at no expense. The sturdy peddler would take my daughter's question in this sense. "Ah," he would say, shaking his fist at an invisible policeman, "I will thrash my father-in-law!" Hearing this, and picturing the poor, uncomfortable relative, Mini would go into peals of laughter, joined by her formidable friend.

These were autumn mornings, the time of year when kings of old went forth to conquest; and I, never stirring from my little corner in Calcutta, would let my mind wander over the whole world. At the very name of another country, my heart would go out to it, and at the sight of a foreigner in the streets, I would fall to weaving a network of dreams: the mountains, the glens, the forests of his distant homeland with a cottage in its setting, and the free and independent life of faraway wilds. Perhaps these scenes of travel pass in my imagination all the more vividly because I lead a vegetable existence such that a call to travel would fall upon me like a thunderbolt. In the presence of this Cabuliwallah I was immediately transported to the foot of mountains, with narrow defiles twisting in and out amongst their towering, arid peaks. I could see the string of camels bearing merchandise, and the company of turbaned merchants carrying queer old firearms and some of their spears down toward the plains. I could see—but at this point Mini's mother would intervene, **imploring** me to "beware of that man."

imploring
beseeching; entreating

Unfortunately Mini's mother is a very timid lady. Whenever she hears a noise in the street or sees people coming toward the house, she always jumps to the conclusion that they are either thieves, drunkards, snakes, tigers, malaria, cockroaches, caterpillars, or an English sailor. Even after all these years of experience, she is not able to overcome her terror. Thus she was full of doubts about the Cabuliwallah and used to beg me to keep a watchful eye on him.

I tried to gently laugh her fear away, but then she would turn on me seriously and ask solemn questions.

Were children never kidnapped?

Was it, then, not true that there was slavery in Cabul?

Was it so very absurd that this big man should be able to carry off a tiny child?

I told her that, though not impossible, it was highly

The Cabuliwallah   445

improbable. But this was not enough, and her dread persisted. As her suspicion was unfounded, however, it did not seem right to forbid the man to come to the house, and his familiarity went unchecked.

Once a year, in the middle of January, Rahmun the Cabuliwallah was in the habit of returning to his country, and as the time approached he would be very busy going from house to house collecting his debts. This year, however, he always found time to come and see Mini. It would have seemed to an outsider that there was some conspiracy between them, for when he could not come in the morning, he would appear in the evening.

Even to me it was a little startling now and then, to suddenly surprise this tall, loose-garmented man of bags in the corner of a dark room; but when Mini would run in, smiling, with her "O Cabuliwallah! Cabuliwallah!" and the two friends so far apart in age would subside into their old laughter and their old jokes, I felt reassured.

One morning, a few days before he had made up his mind to go, I was correcting my proof sheets[4] in my study. It was chilly weather. Through the window the rays of the sun touched my feet, and the slight warmth was very welcome. It was almost eight o'clock, and the early pedestrians were returning home with their heads covered. All at once I heard an uproar in the street and, looking out, saw Rahmun bound and being led away between two policemen, followed by a crowd of curious boys. There were bloodstains on the clothes of the Cabuliwallah, and one of the policemen carried a knife. Hurrying out, I stopped them and inquired what it all meant. Partly from one, partly from another, I gathered that a certain neighbor had owed the peddler something for a Rampuri shawl but had falsely denied having bought it, and that in the course of the quarrel Rahmun had struck him. Now, in the heat of his excitement, the prisoner began calling his enemy all sorts of names. Suddenly, from a verandah of my house my little Mini appeared, with her usual exclamation: "O Cabuliwallah! Cabuliwallah!" Rahmun's face lighted up as he turned to her. He had no bag under his arm today, so she could not discuss the elephant with him. She at once therefore

---

4 **proof sheets:** texts requiring editing or corrections

The Middle East & South Asia

proceeded to the next question: "Are you going to the father-in-law's house?" Rahmun laughed and said: "Just where I am going, little one!" Then seeing that the reply did not amuse the child, he held up his **fettered** hands. "Ah," he said, "I would have thrashed that old father-in-law, but my hands are bound!"

fettered
bound; shackled

On a charge of murderous assault, Rahmun was sentenced to many years of imprisonment.

◆ ◆ ◆ ◆

Time passed and he was forgotten. The accustomed work in the accustomed place was ours, and the thought of the once-free mountaineer spending his years in prison seldom occurred to us. Even my lighthearted Mini, I am ashamed to say, forgot her old friend. New companions filled her life. As she grew older she spent more of her time with girls, so much in fact that she came no more to her father's room. I was scarcely on speaking terms with her.

Many years passed. It was autumn once again and we had made arrangements for Mini's marriage; it was to take place during the Puja⁵ holidays. With the goddess Durga returning to her seasonal home in Mount Kailas, the light of our home was also to depart, leaving our house in shadows.

The morning was bright. After the rains, there was a sense of cleanness in the air, and the rays of the sun looked like pure gold, so bright that they radiated even to the sordid brick walls of our Calcutta lanes. Since early dawn, the wedding pipes had been sounding, and at each beat my own heart throbbed. The wailing tune, Bhairavi, seemed to intensify my pain at the approaching separation. My Mini was to be married tonight.

From early morning, noise and bustle pervaded the house. In the courtyard the canopy had to be slung on its bamboo poles; the tinkling chandeliers should be hung in each room and verandah; there was great hurry and excitement. I was sitting in my study, looking through the accounts, when someone entered, saluting respectfully, and stood before me. It was Rahmun the Cabuliwallah, and at first I did not recognize him. He had no bag, nor the long hair, nor the same vigor that he used to have. But he

---

5 **Puja:** a Hindu observance of certain deities or gods

smiled, and I knew him again.

"When did you come, Rahmun?" I asked him.

"Last evening," he said, "I was released from jail."

The words struck harsh upon my ears. I had never talked with anyone who had wounded his fellow man, and my heart shrank when I realized this, for I felt that the day would have been better omened if he had not turned up.

"There are ceremonies going on," I said, "and I am busy. Could you perhaps come another day?"

At once he turned to go, but as he reached the door he hesitated and said: "May I not see the little one, sir, for a moment?" It was his belief that Mini was still the same. He had pictured her running to him as she used to do, calling, "O

The Middle East & South Asia

Cabuliwallah! Cabuliwallah!" He had imagined that they would laugh and talk together, just as in the past. In fact, in memory of those former days he had brought, carefully wrapped up in paper, a few almonds and raisins and grapes, somehow obtained from a countryman—his own little fund was gone.

I said again: "There is a ceremony in the house, and you will not be able to see anyone today."

The man's face fell. He looked wistfully at me for a moment, said "Good morning," and went out.

I felt a little sorry and would have called him back but saw that he was returning of his own accord. He came close up to me, holding out his offerings, and said: "I brought these few things, sir, for the little one. Will you give them to her?"

I took them and was going to pay him, but he caught my hand and said: "You are very kind, sir! Keep me in your recollection; do not offer me money! You have a little girl; I too have one like her in my own home. I thought of my own and brought fruits to your child, not to make a profit for myself."

Saying this, he put his hand inside his big loose robe and brought out a small dirty piece of paper. With great care he unfolded this and smoothed it out with both hands on my table. It bore the impression of a little hand, not a photograph, not a drawing. The impression of an ink-smeared hand laid flat on the paper. This touch of his own little daughter had been always on his heart, as he had come year after year to Calcutta to sell his wares in the streets.

Tears came to my eyes. I forgot that he was a poor Cabuli fruitseller, while I was—but no, was I more than he? He was also a father.

That impression of the hand of his little Parbati in her distant mountain home reminded me of my own little Mini, and I immediately sent for her from the inner apartment. Many excuses were raised, but I would not listen. Clad in the red silk of her wedding day, with the sandal paste on her forehead, and adorned as a young bride, Mini came and stood bashfully before me.

The Cabuliwallah was staggered at the sight of her. There was no hope of reviving their old friendship. At last he smiled and said: "Little one, are you going to your father-in-law's house?"

But Mini now understood the meaning of the word "father-in-law," and she could not reply to him as in the past. She flushed at the question and stood before him with her bride's face looking down.

I remembered the day when the Cabuliwallah and my Mini first met, and I felt sad. When she had gone, Rahmun heaved a deep sigh and sat down on the floor. The idea had suddenly come to him that his daughter also must have grown up during this long time, and that he would have to make friends with her all over again. Surely he would not find her as he used to know her; besides, what might have happened to her in these eight years?

The marriage pipes sounded, and the mild autumn sun streamed around us. But Rahmun sat in the little Calcutta lane and saw before him the barren mountains of Afghanistan.

I took out a bank note and gave it to him, saying: "Go back to your own daughter, Rahmun, in your own country, and may the happiness of your meeting bring good fortune to my child!"

After giving this gift, I had to eliminate some of the festivities. I could not have the electric lights, not the military band, and the ladies of the house were saddened. But to me the wedding feast was brighter because of the thought that in a distant land a long-lost father met again with his only child.

Responding to the Selection

1. What do you learn about the Indian culture from the punishment given to the Cabuliwallah as well as people's reaction to it?

2. How would you characterize the offering Mini's father gives to the Cabuliwallah after the latter has been released from prison? Discuss whether something like that would ever happen in the United States.

3. How does Mini's relationship with both the Cabuliwallah and her father change by the time she is ready for marriage? Describe the change in her personality.

4. A euphemism is a phrase that substitutes for one that seems too blunt or harsh. For example, "passing away" is a euphemism for "dying." What euphemism in this story serves to unite different parts of the narrative?

Like the Sun

R. K. Narayan

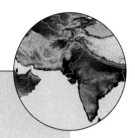

WORLD LENS
◆◆◆
INDIA

Truth, Sekhar reflected, is like the sun. I suppose no human being can ever look it straight in the face without blinking or being dazed. He realized that, morning till night, the essence of human relationships consisted in tempering truth so that it might not shock. This day he set apart as a unique day—at least one day in the year we must give and take absolute Truth whatever may happen. Otherwise life is not worth living. The day ahead seemed to him full of possibilities. He told no one of his experiment. It was a quiet resolve, a secret pact between him and eternity.

The very first test came while his wife served him his morning meal. He showed hesitation over a tidbit, which she had thought was her **culinary** masterpiece. She asked, "Why, isn't it good?" At other times he would have said, considering her feelings in the matter, "I feel full-up, that's all." But today he said, "It isn't good. I'm unable to swallow it." He saw her wince and said to himself, Can't be helped. Truth is like the sun.

His next trial was in the common room when one of his colleagues came up and said, "Did you hear of the death of so and so? Don't you think it a pity?" "No," Sekhar answered. "He was

culinary
related to the kitchen or cooking

Like the Sun   451

such a fine man—" the other began. But Sekhar cut him short with: "Far from it. He always struck me as a mean and selfish brute."

During the last period when he was teaching geography for Third Form A,[1] Sekhar received a note from the headmaster: "Please see me before you go home." Sekhar said to himself: It must be about these horrible test papers. A hundred papers in the boys' scrawls; he had shirked this work for weeks, feeling all the time as if a sword were hanging over his head.

The bell rang and the boys burst out of the class.

Sekhar paused for a moment outside the headmaster's room to button up his coat; that was another subject the headmaster always sermonized about.

He stepped in with a very polite "Good evening, sir."

The headmaster looked up at him in a very friendly manner and asked, "Are you free this evening?"

Sekhar replied, "Just some outing which I have promised the children at home—"

"Well, you can take them out another day. Come home with me now."

"Oh . . . yes, sir, certainly . . . " And then he added timidly, "Anything special, sir?"

"Yes," replied the headmaster, smiling to himself . . . "You didn't know my weakness for music?"

"Oh, yes, sir . . . "

"I've been learning and practicing secretly, and now I want you to hear me this evening. I've engaged a drummer and a violinist to accompany me—this is the first time I'm doing it full-dress and I want your opinion. I know it will be valuable."

Sekhar's taste in music was well known. He was one of the most dreaded music critics in the town. But he never anticipated his musical inclinations would lead him to this trial . . . "Rather a surprise for you, isn't it?" asked the headmaster. "I've spent a fortune on it behind closed doors . . . " They started for the headmaster's house. "God hasn't given me a child, but at least let him not deny me the consolation of music," the headmaster said, pathetically, as they walked. He incessantly chattered about

---

1 **Third Form A:** a class or grade level in an Anglo-Indian secondary school

music: how he began one day out of sheer boredom; how his teacher at first laughed at him, and then gave him hope; how his ambition in life was to forget himself in music.

At home the headmaster proved very **ingratiating**. He sat Sekhar on a red silk carpet, set before him several dishes of delicacies, and fussed over him as if he were a son-in-law of the house. He even said, "Well, you must listen with a free mind. Don't worry about these test papers." He added half humorously, "I will give you a week's time."

ingratiating
charming; flattering

. . . his ambition in life was to forget himself in music.

"Make it ten days, sir," Sekhar pleaded.

"All right, granted," the headmaster said generously. Sekhar felt really relieved now—he would attack them at the rate of ten a day and get rid of the nuisance.

The headmaster lighted incense sticks. "Just to create the right atmosphere," he explained. A drummer and a violinist, already seated on a Rangoon[2] mat, were waiting for him. The headmaster sat down between them like a professional at a concert, cleared his throat, and began an alapana,[3] and paused to ask, "Isn't it good Kalyani?" Sekhar pretended not to have heard the question. The headmaster went on to sing a full song composed by Thyagaraja and followed it with two more. All the time the headmaster was singing, Sekhar went on commenting within himself, He croaks like a dozen frogs. He is bellowing like a buffalo. Now he sounds like loose window shutters in a storm.

The incense sticks burnt low. Sekhar's head throbbed with the medley of sounds that had assailed his ear-drums for a couple of hours now. He felt half stupefied. The headmaster had gone nearly hoarse, when he paused to ask, "Shall I go on?" Sekhar replied, "Please don't, sir, I think this will do. . . . " The headmaster looked stunned. His face was beaded with perspiration. Sekhar felt the greatest pity for him. But he felt he could not help it. No judge delivering a sentence felt more pained and helpless. Sekhar noticed that the headmaster's wife peeped in

---

2 **Rangoon:** made in Rangoon, the capital of Burma

3 **alapana:** the beginning of a song in southern India

from the kitchen, with eager curiosity. The drummer and the violinist put away their burdens with an air of relief. The headmaster removed his spectacles, mopped his brow, and asked, "Now, come out with your opinion."

"Can't I give it tomorrow, sir?" Sekhar asked tentatively.

"No. I want it immediately—your frank opinion. Was it good?"

"No, sir . . . " Sekhar replied.

"Oh! . . . Is there any use continuing my lessons?"

"Absolutely none, sir . . . " Sekhar said with his voice trembling. He felt very unhappy that he could not speak more soothingly. Truth, he reflected, required as much strength to give as to receive.

Truth, he reflected, required as much strength to give as to receive.

All the way home he felt worried. He felt that his official life was not going to be smooth sailing hereafter. There were questions of **increment** and confirmation and so on, all depending upon the headmaster's goodwill. All kinds of worries seemed to be in store for him. . . . Did not Harischandra[4] lose his throne, wife, child, because he would speak nothing less than the absolute Truth whatever happened?

increment
increase; step up (as on a salary scale)

At home his wife served him with a sullen face. He knew she was still angry with him for his remark of the morning. Two casualties for today, Sekhar said to himself. If I practice it for a week, I don't think I shall have a single friend left.

He received a call from the headmaster in his classroom next day. He went up apprehensively.

"Your suggestion was useful. I have paid off the music master. No one would tell me the truth about my music all these days. Why such antics at my age! Thank you. By the way, what about those test papers?"

"You gave me ten days, sir, for correcting them."

"Oh, I've reconsidered it. I must positively have them here

---

4 **Harischandra:** (1850–1885), an Indian famous for his poetry, criticism, and reportage

tomorrow. . . . " A hundred papers in a day! That meant all night's sitting up! "Give me a couple of days, sir . . . "

"No. I must have them tomorrow morning. And remember, every paper must be thoroughly **scrutinized**."

scrutinized
examined; inspected

"Yes, sir," Sekhar said, feeling that sitting up all night with a hundred test papers was a small price to pay for the luxury of practicing Truth.

Responding to the Selection

1. Diction refers to the choice of words an author makes. Even though Indian writer R. K. Narayan writes in English, do you notice anything about the diction in "Like the Sun" that makes his voice sound "foreign"? If so, point out examples.

2. In your own words, why is truth like the sun?

3. In what other situations or areas of life is it perhaps best not to speak the truth?

4. Find some details in the story that make the narrator come alive for you. What kind of a man do you think he is?

Sweet Like a Crow
(for Helli Corea, 8 years old)

Michael Ondaatje

WORLD LENS

•••

SRI LANKA/
CANADA

Although Canada likes to claim him as one of their own, Michael Ondaatje was born in what was then called Ceylon and is now called Sri Lanka. Raised there by parents who were members of Ceylon's colonial society, Ondaatje grew to know the Sinhalese, Sri Lanka's dominant ethnic group. He wrote the following poem in response to a comment by the American writer Paul Bowles.[1]

"The Sinhalese are beyond a doubt one of the least musical people in the world. It would be quite impossible to have less sense of pitch, line or rhythm."—Paul Bowles

Your voice sounds like a scorpion being pushed
through a glass tube
like someone has just trod on a peacock
like wind howling in a coconut
like a rusty bible, like someone pulling barbed wire
across a stone courtyard, like a pig drowning,
a vattacka[2] being fried
a bone shaking hands
a frog singing at Carnegie Hall.

Like a crow swimming in milk,
like a nose being hit by a mango

---

1 **Paul Bowles:** (1910–1999), an American writer and composer who lived much of his life in Morocco

2 **vattacka:** a kind of pumpkin

The Middle East & South Asia

like the crowd at the Royal-Thomian match,
a womb full of twins, a pariah[3] dog
with a magpie in its mouth
like the midnight jet from Casablanca[4]
like Air Pakistan curry,
a typewriter on fire, like a hundred
pappadams[5] being crunched, like someone
trying to light matches in a dark room,
the clicking sound of a reef when you put your head into
    the sea,
a dolphin reciting epic poetry to a sleepy audience,
the sound of a fan when someone throws brinjals[6] at it,
like pineapples being sliced in the Pettah[7] market
like betel[8] juice hitting a butterfly in mid-air
like a whole village running naked onto the street
and tearing their sarongs, like an angry family
pushing a jeep out of the mud, like dirt on the needle,
like 8 sharks being carried on the back of a bicycle
like 3 old ladies locked in the lavatory
like the sound I heard when having an afternoon sleep
and someone walked through my room in ankle bracelets.

Responding to the Selection

1. An emigrant himself, the poet, Michael Ondaatje, is fond of exploring
   themes of national identity in his writing. How does this poem give you
   clues to the culture in Sri Lanka, the country that he grew up in before
   emigrating to Canada?

2. How does this poem illustrate the dangers in making generalizations—
   blanket statements—about a culture not one's own?

---

3 **pariah:** an outcast

4 **Casablanca:** the largest city in Morocco

5 **pappadams:** deep-fried crackers

6 **brinjals:** eggplants

7 **Pettah:** an Anglo-Indian term for a public market located outside of a fortress
  city or town

8 **betel:** a popular leaf chew in many Asian countries

The Middle East & South Asia

Discussing

1. What do you learn about the role of women in the societies described in the selections by Djebar, Rifaat, al-Idlibi, and Ayyoub? Discuss how the women cope with the conflicts they encounter.

2. Three of the selections here—"An Arab Shepherd . . .," "The Swimming Contest," and "Song of Becoming" concern the Middle East conflict. Sometimes fiction and poetry can help readers to understand the emotions behind a distant or unfamiliar conflict. In your opinion, which of these selections evokes the human side of this conflict most powerfully?

3. Are cultures only different in their details? Discuss the assumptions about men and women, class status, religion, race, and the body that you encounter in one of the selections in this unit.

4. Characters in the stories by Indian writers Desai and Tagore experience both conflict and satisfaction from interacting with people who are unlike themselves. Discuss why such a theme might be common for a writer from this part of the world, and why it might be less common for writers from the Arabic-speaking, Muslim worlds.

5. Western readers have not been as exposed to Arabic-speaking Muslim societies as they have to other cultures. What do you learn about Arabic cultures in the selections here, and what more would you like to know?

6. Setting (the time and place in which a literary work takes place) and mood (atmosphere) are important elements in many of these stories. Choose one story and describe some aspects of its setting: where it takes place; what mood is created by the details of weather, place, and time; and how this setting helps to convey the theme of the story.

Writing

7. Like the family in "Five Hours to Simla," most people have had the experience of

looking forward to a vacation and then having it go horribly wrong. Yet, these are the journeys that give us our best stories. Write about a time when a vacation went wrong, making sure to capture all of the atmospheric details that contributed to your unease, discomfort, and utter lack of enjoyment. If you learned anything about yourself or your country, include that as well.

8. Note how the poets in this unit communicate their thoughts about their cultures without resorting to statements of fact or opinion. Write a poem about something you love—your country, a person, an artistic or leisure activity—that has also made life hard for you. Instead of "telling" about your beliefs and experiences, "show" them using images and metaphors.

Speaking/Listening

9. Interview one of your parents, grandparents, or other older family members or friends to find out what knowledge they would like to pass down to you and your siblings. What values, insights, and experiences can they share with you? What worked for them, and what did not? Prepare your interview questions beforehand and tape the interview. Afterward, share any good advice with your classmates.

Hands-on Project

Music from this part of the world is generally quite different from Western music in terms of its tone, rhythm, structure, instrumentation, and uses. Choose any country from this region and research some aspect of its music, then demonstrate what you find to your class. You can bring in instruments to show them or put together a recording of a country's various styles, from popular to classical music. Also, see if there is someone in your community who could visit your class to demonstrate music from the Middle East or South Asia.

Personal Connections

After reading the selections in this unit, choose one of the following questions to write about in your journal.

1. Which characters or selections helped open your eyes to a new way of seeing the world?

2. What new understanding do you have about American culture, your family, or yourself?

3. Which differences among cultures do you think really matter? Explain.

RESEARCHING THE WORLD

General Research Subjects

The following general subjects are merely starting points for research. After choosing one that interests you, you will have to narrow your topic considerably.

Belief Systems
Celebrations and
    Ceremonies
Children and Family
Coming of Age
Courtship and Marriage
Crime and Justice
The Economy
Education

The Environment
Famous Figures
Food
Geography
Globalism
Important Events
Language
Literature and the Arts
The Media

Oppression and Exile
Popular Culture
Rural and Urban Life
Sports
Technology
Travel
Work and Leisure

Specific Research Topics

Pick from the following topics or use them as starting points for your research. Some topics can be applied to more than one country in this region; others pertain to a single country or group of people. Note that in order to be a manageable size, many of these topics will require further narrowing.

Arts/Leisure

- Middle Eastern women writers
- Arabic architecture
- Indian festivals such as *Holi, Diwali,* and *Id*
- "Bollywood," the Indian film industry
- Yoga (origins, theory, and practice)

Culture/Geography

- Muslim women and the veil
- *Suttee* and dowry deaths in India
- The sacred Ganges river
- The Hindu caste system
- Population displacement (from dams, floods, industrial accidents)

History/Politics

- Conflicts between Palestine and Israel (the 1967 War, the Intifadas)
- The Talibans in Afghanistan
- Nuclear weapons (Israel, Pakistan, India)
- Leaders (Gandhi, Nehru, Hussein)
- The conservative Muslim resurgence (Egypt, Iran, Turkey)

AUTHOR BIOGRAPHIES

Yehuda Amichai (1924–2000) Yehuda Amichai was born in Germany but moved with his family to Palestine in 1935. During World War II, he fought with the Jewish Brigade of the British Army. He became a naturalized citizen of Israel when that nation was created in 1948, then fought again in the Arab-Israeli War the same year. Though a native speaker of German, Amichai became fluent in Hebrew, the language in which he wrote his poetry and fiction. He has been called "the most widely translated Hebrew poet since King David." His books of poetry include *Songs of Jerusalem and Myself, Amen,* and *Even a Fist Was Once an Open Palm with Fingers.* The late British poet Ted Hughes admired Amichai's genius for "telling of real things he has lived and felt, in a poetry that seems the natural speech of people who speak of such things candidly, humorously, generously."

Dhu'l Nun Ayyoub (1908–1988) Dhu'l Nun Ayyoub is a leading figure among Iraqi fiction writers of the 20th century. In his stories, individuals contend with the religious and political discord in the Arabic world as well as the ongoing conflicts between tradition and modernity.

Anita Desai (1937–) Indian author Anita Desai writes novels, children's books, and short stories. Her Mother was German, so her family spoke German at home and Hindi to their friends. Desai writes in English, which she learned in school. Pointing out that India has many languages, she said, "one tends to pick up and use whatever is at hand. It makes one realize each language has its own distinct genius." Desai published her first story in a children's magazine at age nine. Many of her novels—such as *In Custody* and *Clear Light of Day*—are about women's lives. She also deals with German anti-Semitism and Western ideas about India. Desai has taught and lived in the United States. Her many literary awards include the Guardian Prize for Children's Fiction for *The Village by the Sea.*

Assia Djebar (1936–) Fatima-Zohra Imalayan is an Algerian novelist, poet, translator, and filmmaker. Her father, a teacher, sent her to school despite the fact that education was uncommon for Algerian girls. When she wrote her first novel, she began using the name Assia Djebar in case he didn't approve of her work. Djebar writes in French, although she enriches that language with the sounds and rhythms of Arabic. She explores the lives of Muslim women—their rebellion against patriarchy, their experiences of domestic violence and of war, and their problems with Islamic fundamentalism. Her writing has won literary awards, and her first film won the International Critics Prize at the 1979 Film Festival in Venice.

Ulfat al-Idlibi (1912–) Syrian author and literary critic Ulfat al-Idlibi has been called "the grandmother of modern Syrian literature." She was born to a wealthy Damascus family who saw to it that she got a better education than most women of her time and culture. After her son died in 1947, Idlibi began writing realistic short stories. With her first book, *Al-Qarar Al-Akheer* (The final decision), she began to win awards and recognition. Her other books include *Hikayet Jaddi* (The story of my grandfather). Ulfat al-Idlibi's works have been translated and published in more than ten foreign languages.

Moushegh Ishkhan (1913–) Mousegh Ishkhan has written about the era of Armenian Dispersion, the period dating back to the mid-1800s, during which Armenians have been victims of political persecution, forced exile, and genocide. His autobiographical work, *Farewell, Childhood*, tells of his family's relocation to Damascus after being chased out of Armenia by enemy armies. Ishkhan's writing encourages the preservation of Armenian identity and emphasizes the importance of serving one's native land. Loyalty to the traditions, spirituality, and values of his native culture are expressed in his prose and, perhaps most tenderly, in his poetry.

Muzaffer Izgü (1933–) A teacher who writes short stories, novels, and plays for stage and radio, Muzaffer Izgü is one of Turkey's best known humorists. When Izgü was a child, his family was very poor and their small house was cold. At a friend's suggestion, he started going to the public library to do his homework. There he also found books to read—beginning with *Treasure Island* by Robert Louis Stevenson—and decided to become a writer. Izgü writes for both children and adults and has won many awards. His short story collections include *For the Crazy Each Day Is a Holiday*.

Naguib Mahfouz (1911–) Egyptian author Naguib Mahfouz began writing at age 17. Although his earliest novels and stories were set in ancient Egypt, they often commented on modern society. In novels such as his *Cairo Trilogy*, Mahfouz wrote realistically—sometimes autobiographically—about contemporary life. His later and more mystical works often rely on allegory and symbolism to make political statements. In 1959, his novel, the *Children of Gebelawi*, was serialized in an Egyptian newspaper. This story about humanity's search for spiritual values—which includes characters resembling Adam and Eve, Moses, Jesus, and Mohammed—caused such an uproar that it wasn't published as a book until many years later. In 1988, Mahfouz was awarded the Nobel Prize in literature for creating "an Arabian narrative art that applies to all mankind." He said in an interview, "If the urge to write should ever leave me, I want that day to be my last."

R. K. Narayan (1906–2001) Indian author Rasipuram Krishnaswami Narayanswami shortened his name to Narayan at the suggestion of his English publisher. He wrote his often humorous stories, novels, and essays in English. In Narayan's most highly praised novel, *The Guide*, a former convict is mistaken for a holy man. His *Gods, Demons and Others* is a retelling of ancient tales from *The Mahabharata*, *The Ramayana*, and other Hindu epics. In it Narayan writes, "It is personality alone that remains unchanging and makes sense in any age or idiom, whether the setting is 3000 B.C. or 2000 A.D."

Michael Ondaatje (1943–) Poet, memoirist, novelist, and filmmaker Michael Ondaatje was born in Ceylon (now Sri Lanka). He moved with his mother to England in 1954 and grew up in London, then settled permanently in Canada in 1962. His work has been as varied as his life. He has written several books of poetry, including *The Cinnamon Peeler* and *Handwriting*. His novels include *In the Skin of the Lion* and *The English Patient*. The latter was made into a movie, which won nine Academy Awards in 1996. Some of his books defy categorization. For example, *The Collected Works of Billy the Kid* is made up of poems, songs, snapshots, diary entries, and other materials. One question dogs Ondaatje whenever he is at work: "How do I write this book? That's always the question. I never think ahead."

Alifa Rifaat (1930–) Born in rural Egypt, Alifa Rifaat was expected to become an obedient wife and mother. Instead of being allowed to go to a university, she was married off to her cousin. Nevertheless Rifaat continued reading and educating herself. She began writing short stories criticising the restrictions on women in her culture. In her story "Bahiyya's Eyes," she says, "The fact is there's no joy for a girl in growing up . . . " When a few of her stories were published, they were very controversial, and her husband demanded that she stop writing. In 1974, when she became a widow, Rifaat published 18 short stories she had kept hidden. She has become one of Egypt's most highly regarded authors.

Rabindranath Tagore (1861–1941) The poet, essayist, playwright, fiction writer, and composer Rabindranath Tagore is recognized as India's greatest artist of the 20th century. His poetry, including his collection *Gitanjali*, won him the Nobel Prize for literature in 1913. He was also an innovative educator, who founded an experimental school about 100 miles from Calcutta. While in his seventies, he took up visual art and produced many fine paintings. Like his friend Mohandas Gandhi, Tagore opposed British colonialism and rejected his knighthood in protest against British atrocities in India. Even so, he was deeply influenced by Western culture and wary of nationalism. A student of many cultures and religions, he considered his work "a confluence of three cultures: Hindu, Mohammedan, and British." Fittingly, both India and Bangladesh adopted songs by Tagore as their national anthems.

Benjamin Tammuz (1919–1989) In 1924, the family of young Benjamin Tammuz moved from the Ukraine to Palestine. There, Tammuz eventually became a newspaper columnist and an author of novels and short stories. His fiction was often about the relationship between Arabs and Jews. In his earliest stories, Tammuz envisioned a peaceful, utopian state where all could live in peace. Later, he wrote about the elusiveness of that dream. His novel *Orchard* is about half-brothers—one a Jew, the other an Arab. In his novel *Minotaur*—widely acclaimed by critics—Tammuz contrasted the viewpoints of his characters to give a full picture of the story's events.

Fadwa Tuqan (1917–) Born in Palestine, Fadwa Tuqan was forced to leave school at age 13 because a teen-aged boy sent her a flower. Her brother, Ibrahim Tuqan, was already a famous poet. He took her to Jerusalem to live in his house and introduced her to great works of literature. Fadwa Tuqan learned to write traditional poetry, then expanded into free verse forms. She writes about love and loss, both at a personal and a national level. Her poetry has been published in several collections—including *Alone on the Summit of the World*. Her two-part autobiography is called *A Mountainous Journey* and *The Most Difficult Journey*.

The Literature of East Asia & the Pacific Rim

Michael Harris

Professor of English, Central College, Pella, Iowa

O h, East is East, and West is West, and never the twain shall meet." With this famous line, British writer Rudyard Kipling has captured the idea that the East and West are so radically different that their people can't possibly understand one another. Indeed, one of the main themes of the literature of East Asia and the Pacific Rim is the region's relationship to the West. A primary reason for this focus is that most countries there have experienced an aggressive, sometimes imperial presence by European countries and by America.

After absorbing Western influences, Japan itself became an imperial power in the early 20th century, invading China and Korea. Its shattering defeat in World War II—symbolized by the atomic bombs on Hiroshima and Nagasaki—led Japanese writers to reassess the country's culture and tradition. Countries formerly under Japan's control also began to redefine, with the help of writers, their culture and national identity.

Modern Japanese writing retains traditional elements while also reflecting a Western influence. The traditional Japanese verse form, the *haiku*, remains popular in Japan and throughout the world. Japan's ancient tradition of fiction writing has been revived in the modern era. Influential writers address such social issues as the role of gender and the gap between rich and poor created by Japan's post-war adoption of Western capitalism.

Following World War II, the central events reflected in Chinese writing have been the civil war between Communists and

Nationalists and the Cultural Revolution (1966–1976). As with other countries in this region, such as Korea and Vietnam, Chinese resistance to the West resulted in a divided state. After Mao Tse-tung established Communist rule on the mainland, the Nationalists fled to Taiwan. During the Cultural Revolution, the work of many Chinese writers and intellectuals was discredited and destroyed by the government in a period marked by violent suppression.

Other East Asian and Pacific nations that are divided as a result of Japanese, Western, or American involvement are Korea and Vietnam. Somewhat like the civil war in China, the Korean War (1950–1953) left the country divided in two at the thirty-eighth parallel: the Communist North and the democratic South. This arbitrary boundary left families divided and relatives almost permanently cut off from one another. Vietnam also suffered from a partition between the Communist North and the U.S.-supported South, a division that lasted throughout the bloody Vietnam War until the Communist victory in 1975.

Literature from the Pacific Rim countries also bears marks of an encounter with Western powers. Australia, for example, experienced a profound change when it went from being a British colony to a separate Commonwealth country in 1901. The British settlers living in this strange, sometimes hostile Southern environment produced a literature about people making adjustments and sacrifices and searching for an identity to fit their new land. In some Australian literature, the land itself becomes a significant character. Later Australian writing often looks with irony and skepticism upon the effects of colonizing and "Americanizing" this continent that was previously occupied by generations of Aborigines. In recent years, Aborigine writers from Australia and Maoris from New Zealand have written about their people's efforts to hold onto traditional ways of life.

Although seemingly a world away from the United States, writers from East Asia and the Pacific Rim have much to tell us. Due to the rapid advances in communication and transportation, the East is not so far away anymore. We owe it to ourselves to find out about our neighbors in this vitally important part of the world.

The Literature of East Asia & the Pacific Rim

Ha Jin China

Bei Dao China

Aisin-Gioro P'u Yi China

Feng Ji-cai China

Pramoedya Ananta Toer Indonesia

Literary Map of East Asia & the Pacific Rim

EAST ASIA

Tōge Sankichi   Japan

Yukio Mishima   Japan

Fumiko Hayashi   Japan

Hwang Sun-won   Korea

Nguyen Thi Vinh   Vietnam

PACIFIC RIM

Patricia Grace   New Zealand

AUSTRALIA

Peter Porter   Australia

Judith Wright   Australia

Peter Carey   Australia

469

from *From Emperor to Citizen*

Aisin-Gioro P'u Yi

As the last Emperor of China, Aisin-Gioro P'u Yi had for a brief time exceptional power and wealth. In 1908, at age three, P'u Yi assumed his title, but the Republican Revolution four years later forced him to relinquish his throne. The young man was allowed to retain his title, money, and home in the Forbidden City, an area inside the Imperial Palace reserved for the emperor and his employees. The following excerpt from his biography, *From Emperor to Citizen*, covers this time period.

The rest of his life was not so pampered. In 1924, he and his family were forced at gunpoint to flee China. After World War II he was charged with war crimes and imprisoned in Communist China. His eventual release and "rehabilitation" led to a new career as a mechanic in a public garden until his death.

The "Articles for Favorable Treatment" stipulated that I could live temporarily in the Imperial Palace without fixing any definite time limit. Apart from three large halls that were handed over to the Republic, the rest of the Forbidden City continued to belong to the Imperial Palace. It was in this tiny world that I was to spend the most absurd childhood possible until I was driven out by the soldiers of the National Army in 1924. I call it absurd because at a time when China was called a republic and mankind had advanced into the twentieth century, I was still living the life of an emperor, breathing the dust of the nineteenth century.

Whenever I think of my childhood, my head fills with a yellow mist. The glazed tiles were yellow, my sedan chair was yellow, my chair cushions were yellow, the linings of my hats and clothes were yellow, the girdle round my waist was yellow, the dishes and bowls from which I ate and drank, the padded cover of the rice-gruel saucepan, the material in which my books were wrapped, the window curtains, the bridle of my horse . . . everything was yellow. This color, the so-called "brilliant yellow," was used exclusively by the imperial household and made me feel from my earliest years that I was unique and had a "heavenly" nature different from that of everybody else.

When I was ten, my grandmother and mother started to come and visit me on the orders of the High Consorts,[1] and they brought my brother Pu Chieh and my first sister to play with me for a few days. Their first visit started off very drearily: I and my grandmother sat on the *kang*,[2] and she watched me playing dominoes while my brother and sister stood below us very properly, gazing at me with a fixed stare like attendants on duty in a *yamen*.[3] Later it occurred to me to take them along to the part of the palace in which I lived, where I asked Pu Chieh, "What games do you play at home?"

"Pu Chieh can play hide-and-seek," said my brother, who was a year younger than I, in a very respectful way.

"So you play hide-and-seek too? It's a jolly good game." I was very excited. I had played it with the eunuchs[4] but never with children younger than myself. So we started to play hide-and-seek, and in the excitement of the game, my brother and sister forgot their inhibitions. We deliberately let down the blinds to make the room very dark. My sister, who was two years younger than I, was at the same time enraptured and terrified, and as my brother and I kept giving her frights, we got so carried away that we were laughing and shouting. When we were exhausted, we climbed up onto the *kang* to get our breath back, and I told them to think of some new game. Pu Chieh was thoughtful for a while, then started to gaze at me wordlessly, a silly smile on his face.

"What are you grinning at?"

He went on grinning.

---

1 **High Consorts:** widows of previous emperors

2 *kang:* a brick platform used for sleeping

3 *yamen:* office of a Chinese public official

4 **eunuchs:** castrated men, sometimes in charge of a harem or other duties in a palace

"Tell me! Tell me!" I urged him impatiently, thinking that he must certainly have thought out some new game. To my surprise he came out with, "I thought, oh, Pu Chieh thought that Your Majesty would be different from ordinary people. The emperors on the stage have long beards . . . ." As he spoke, he pretended to be stroking his beard.

This gesture was his undoing. As he raised his hand, I noticed that the lining of his sleeve was a very familiar color. My face blackened.

"Pu Chieh, are you allowed to wear that color?"

"But . . . bu . . . but isn't it apricot?"

"Nonsense! It's imperial brilliant yellow."

"Yes, sire, yes, sire . . . ." Pu Chieh stood away from me, his arms hanging respectfully by his sides. My sister slipped over to stand with him, frightened to the point of tears.

"It's brilliant yellow. You have no business to be wearing it."

"Yes, sire."

With his "yes, sire" my brother reverted to being my subject. The sound "yes, sire" died out long ago, and it seems very funny when one thinks of it today. But I got used to it from early childhood, and if people did not use the words when replying to me, I would not stand for it. It was the same with kneeling and kowtowing.

From my infancy I was accustomed to having people kowtow to me, particularly people over ten times my own age. They included old officials of the Ching Dynasty[5] and the elders of my own clan, men in the court robes of the Ching Dynasty and officials of the Republic in Western dress.

Another strange thing which seemed quite normal at the time was the daily **pomp**.

pomp
splendor; show of magnificence

retinue
following; entourage

Every time I went to my schoolroom to study, or visited the High Consorts to pay my respects, or went for a stroll in the garden, I was always followed by a large **retinue**. Every trip I made to the Summer Palace must have cost thousands of Mexican dollars: the Republic's police had to be asked to line the roads to protect me, and I was accompanied by a motorcade consisting of dozens of vehicles.

---

5 **Ching Dynasty:** (1644–1912), the most recent dynasty in China's history

Whenever I went for a stroll in the garden, a procession had to be organized. In front went a eunuch from the Administrative Bureau whose function was roughly that of a motor horn: he walked twenty or thirty yards ahead of the rest of the party intoning the sound "chir . . . chir . . . " as a warning to anyone who might be in the vicinity to go away at once. Next came two chief eunuchs, advancing crabwise on either side of the path; ten paces behind them came the center of the procession—the Empress Dowager[6] or myself. If I was being carried in a chair, there would be two junior eunuchs walking beside me to attend to my wants at any moment; if I was walking, they would be supporting me. Next came a eunuch with a large silk canopy followed by a large group of eunuchs of whom some were empty-handed and others were holding all sorts of things: a seat in case I wanted to rest, change of clothing, umbrellas and parasols. After these eunuchs of the imperial presence came eunuchs of the imperial tea bureau with boxes of various kinds of cakes and delicacies and, of course, jugs of hot water and a tea service; they were followed by eunuchs of the imperial **dispensary** bearing cases of medicine and first-aid equipment suspended from carrying poles. The medicines carried always included potions prepared from lampwick sedge, chrysanthemums, the roots of reeds, bamboo leaves, and bamboo skins; in summer there were always Essence of Betony Pills for Rectifying the Vapor, Six Harmony Pills for Stabilizing the Center, Gold coated, Heat-dispersing Cinnabar, Fragrant Herb Pills, Omnipurpose Bars, colic medicine and anti-plague powder; and throughout all four seasons there would be the Three Immortals Beverage to aid the digestion, as well as many other medicaments. At the end of the procession came the eunuchs who carried commodes and chamber pots. If I was walking, a sedan chair, open or covered according to the season, would bring up the rear. This **motley** procession of several dozen people would proceed in perfect silence and order.

But I would often throw it into confusion. When I was young, I liked to run around when I was in high sprits as just any child does. At first they would all scuttle along after me puffing and

dispensary
medicine store; place where medicines are stored and distributed

motley
varied; miscellaneous

---

6 **Empress Dowager:** the widow of the deceased emperor

panting with their procession reduced to chaos. When I grew a little older and knew how to give orders, I would tell them to stand and wait for me; then, apart from the junior eunuchs of the imperial presence who came with me, they would all stand there waiting in silence with their loads. After I had finished running around, they would form up again behind me. When I learned to ride a bicycle and ordered the removal of all the upright wooden thresholds in the palace so that I could ride around without obstruction, the procession was no longer able to follow me, and so it had to be temporarily abolished. But when I went to pay my respects to the High Consorts or to my schoolroom, I still had to have something of a retinue, and without it I would have felt rather odd. When I heard people telling the story of the last emperor of the Ming Dynasty who had only one eunuch left with him at the end, I felt very uncomfortable.

The type of extravagant display that wasted the most effort, money and material was meals. There were special terms to refer to the emperor's eating, and it was absolutely forbidden to fail to use them correctly. Food was called not "food" but "viands"; eating was called "consuming viands"; serving the meal was "transmitting the viands"; and the kitchen was the "imperial viands room." When it was time to eat (and the times of the meals were not set but were whenever the emperor felt like eating), I would give the command "Transmit the viands!" The junior eunuchs of the presence would then repeat "Transmit the viands" to the eunuchs standing in the main hall of the palace in which I lived, and they would pass it on to the eunuchs standing on duty outside the hall; these would in turn call it out to the eunuchs of the "imperial viands room" waiting in the Western Avenue of the Forbidden City. Thus my order went straight to the kitchens, and before its echoes had died away a procession rather of the sort that used to take a bride's trousseau[7] to her groom's house had already issued from the "viands room." It was made up of an imposing column of several dozen neatly dressed eunuchs hurrying to the Mind Nurture Palace with seven tables of various sizes and scores of red-lacquered boxes painted with

---

7 **trousseau:** a bride's belongings, including clothing, accessories, and household items

East Asia & the Pacific Rim

golden dragons. When they reached the main hall, they handed their burdens over to young eunuchs wearing white sleeves, who laid out the meal in an eastern room of the palace.

Usually there were two tables of main dishes with another one of chafing dishes added in winter; there were three tables with cakes, rice and porridge, respectively; and there was another small table of salted vegetables. All the crockery was imperial yellow porcelain with dragon designs and the words "Ten thousand long lives without limit" painted on it. In winter I ate from silver dishes placed on top of porcelain bowls of hot water. Every dish or bowl had a strip of silver on it as a precaution against poison, and for the same reason all the food was tasted by a eunuch before it was brought in. This was called "appraising the viands." When everything had been tasted and laid out, and before I took my place, a young eunuch would call out "Remove the covers." This was the signal for four or five other junior eunuchs to take the silver lids off all the food dishes, put them in a large box and carry them out. I then began to "use the viands."

And what was the food laid out "ten cubits square"?[8] The empress dowager Lung Yu would have about a hundred main dishes on six tables, an extravagance inherited from the empress dowager Tzu Hsi. I had about thirty. But these dishes which were brought in with such ceremonial were only for show. The reason

The empress dowager Lung Yu would have about a hundred main dishes on six tables . . .

why the food could be served almost as soon as I gave the word was that it had been prepared several hours or even a whole day in advance and was being kept warm over the kitchen stoves. The cooks knew that at least since the time of Kuang Hsu, the emperor had not eaten this food. The food I ate was sent over by the Empress Dowager, and after her death, by the High Consorts. She and each of the High Consorts had kitchens of their own staffed by highly skilled chefs who produced twenty or more really delicious dishes for every meal. This was the food that was put in front of me, while that prepared by the imperial kitchens was set

---

8 **ten cubits square:** each side measuring sixteen to eighteen feet

some distance away as it was only there for the sake of appearances.

To show how they loved and cared for me, the High Consorts also sent a responsible eunuch to report on how I had "consumed viands." This too was a pure formality. No matter what I had really eaten, the eunuch would go to the quarters of the High Consorts, kneel before them and say:

"Your slave reports to his masters: the Lord of Ten Thousand Years consumed one bowl of old rice viands (or white rice viands), one steamed breadroll (or a griddle cake) and a bowl of congee. He consumed it with relish."

At Chinese New Year and other festivals and on the birthdays of the High Consorts, my kitchen sent a spread of food to the Consorts as a mark of my filial[9] piety. This food could be described as expensive and showy without being good, and was neither nutritious nor tasty.

According to the record of one month of the second year of my reign, the empress dowager Lung Yu, the four High Consorts and myself used up 3,960 catties of meat (over two tons) and 388 chickens and ducks every month, of which 810 catties and 240 chickens and ducks were for me, a four-year-old child. In addition there was a monthly allocation for the numerous people in the palace who served us: members of the grand council, imperial bodyguards, tutors, Hanlin academicians, painters, men who drew the outlines of characters for others to fill in, important eunuchs, *shaman*[10] magicians who came every day to sacrifice to the spirits, and many others. Including the Dowager, the Consorts and myself, the monthly consumption of pork was 14,642 catties at a cost of 2,342.72 taels[11] of silver. On top of this there were the extra dishes we had every day, which often cost several times as much again. In the month in question there were 31,844 catties of extra meat, 814 catties of extra pork fat and 4,786 extra chickens and ducks, to say nothing of the fish, shrimps and eggs. All these extras cost 11,641.07 taels, and with miscellaneous items added, the total expenditure came to 14,794.19 taels. It is

---

9 **filial:** befitting a son or daughter

10 ***shaman:*** a high priest

11 **taels:** Chinese units of money

obvious that all this money (except what was embezzled) was wasted in order to display the grandeur of the emperor. This figure, moreover, does not include the cost of the cakes, fruit, sweets and drinks that were constantly being devoured.

Just as food was cooked in huge quantities but not eaten, so was a vast amount of clothing made which was never worn. I cannot now remember much about this, but I do know that while the Dowager and the High Consorts had fixed yearly allocations, there were no limits for the emperor, for whom clothes were constantly made throughout the year. I do not know what exactly was made, but everything I wore was always new. I have before me an account from an unspecified year headed "List of materials actually used in making clothes for His Majesty's use from the sixth day of the eleventh month." According to this list the following garments were made for me that month: eleven fur jackets, six fur inner and outer gowns, two fur waistcoats, and thirty padded waistcoats and pairs of trousers. Leaving aside the cost of the main materials and of the labor, the bill for such minor items as the edgings, pockets, buttons and

MANCHU EMPEROR HSUAN
TUNG AS A YOUNG BOY
1917

from *From Emperor to Citizen*

thread came to 2,137.6335 silver dollars.

My changes of clothing were all laid down in regulations and were the responsibility of the eunuchs of the clothing storerooms. Even my everyday gowns came in twenty-eight different styles, from the one in black and white inlaid fur that I started wearing on the nineteenth of the first lunar month to the sable one I changed into on the first day of the eleventh month. Needless to say, my clothes were far more complicated on festivals and ceremonial occasions.

To manage all this extravagant pomp there was, of course, a suitable proliferation of offices and personnel. The Household Department, which administered the domestic affairs of the emperor, had under its control seven bureaus and forty-eight offices. The seven bureaus—the storage bureau, the guard bureau, the protocol, the counting house, the stock-raising bureau, the disciplinary bureau and the construction bureau—all had storerooms, workshops and so on under them. The storage bureau, for example, was for stores for silver, fur, porcelain, satin, clothes and tea. According to a list of officials dating from 1909, the personnel of the Household Department numbered 1,023 (excluding the Palace Guard, the eunuchs and the servants known as "sulas"); in the early years of the Republic, this number was reduced to something over 600, and at the time I left the Imperial Palace there were still more than 300. It is not hard to imagine an organization as large as this with so many people in it, but the triviality of some of its functions was almost unthinkable. One of the forty-eight offices, for example, was the As You Wish Lodge (Ju Yi Kuan). Its only purpose was to paint pictures and do calligraphy for the Empress Dowager and the High Consorts; if the Dowager wanted to paint something, the As You Wish Lodge would outline a design for her so that all she had to do was to fill in the colors and write a title on it. The calligraphy for large tablets was sketched out by the experts of the Great Diligence Hall or else done by the Hanlin academicians. Nearly all late Ching inscriptions that purport to be the brushwork of a dowager or an emperor were produced in this way.

The buildings all around me and the furniture of the palace were all a part of my indoctrination. Apart from the golden-glazed tiles that were exclusively for the use of the emperor, the very height of the buildings was an imperial **prerogative** that served to teach me from an early age that not only was everything under heaven the emperor's land but even the sky above my head belonged to nobody else. Every piece of furniture was "direct method" teaching material for me. It was said that the emperor Chien Lung once laid it down that nothing in the palace, not even a blade of grass, must be lost. To put this principle into practice, he put some blades of grass on a table in the palace and gave orders that they were to be counted every day to see that not a single one of them was missing. This was called "taking the grass as a standard." Even in my time these thirty-six withered blades of grass were still preserved in a cloisonné[12] canister in the Mind Nurture Palace. This grass filled me with unbounded admiration for my ancestor and unbridled hatred for the Revolution of 1911.

There is no longer any way of calculating exactly the enormous cost of the daily life of an emperor, but a record called "A comparison between the expenditure of the seventh year of Hsuan Tung (1915) and the past three years" compiled by the Household Department shows that expenditure in 1915 topped 2,790,000 taels and that, while it dropped in each of the following three years, it was always over 1,890,000 taels. Thus it was that with the **connivance** of the Republican authorities we continued our **prodigious** waste of the sweat and blood of the people in order to maintain our former pomp and continue our parasitic way of life.

Some of the rules in the palace were originally not simply for the sake of show. The system by which all the food dishes had strips of silver on them and the food was tasted before the emperor ate it and the large-scale security precautions [were taken] whenever he went out was basically to protect him against any attempt on his life. It was said that the reason why emperors had no outside privies was that one emperor had been set upon by an assassin when going out to relieve himself. These stories and all the display had the same effect on me: they made me believe that I was a very important and august[13] person, a man apart who ruled and owned the universe.

prerogative
right; special privilege

connivance
complicity; secret cooperation

prodigious
tremendous; monstrous

---

12 **cloisonné:** decorative enamel
13 **august:** majestically dignified

Responding to the Selection

1. Which details of the young emperor's wealth most amaze, puzzle, and disturb you? Point them out.

2. Why is euphemistic language used to refer to the young emperor's meals and eating procedure?

3. "Just as food was cooked in huge quantities but not eaten, so was a vast amount of clothing made which was never worn." What do you think is the point of all this waste?

4. A popular television show in the United States was called "Lifestyles of the Rich and Famous" (maybe you have even watched it). Discuss why it is that so many people are fascinated by the trappings of wealth and royalty. Do you think this interest is healthy?

5. P'u Yi's autobiography, from which this excerpt is taken, was published in 1960 with the "help" of a government editor. Some readers believe the former emperor was forced by the Mao government to criticize the dynastic system. How true does P'u Yi's tone and attitude ring to you? Explain what you do or do not find convincing.

An Ancient Temple

Bei Dao

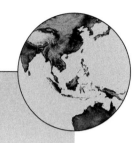

As a child of the Cultural Revolution, Bei Dao was anxious to convey the truth about the troubled social and political climate in China. "An Ancient Temple" was included in the 1982 Meng Long Shi ("cloud/mist poems") anthology, a collection that helped to fuel the student demonstration at Tiananmen Square in 1989. Although the term "Meng Long Shi" was originally meant as an insult to Bei Dao and his contemporaries, implying that their poetry was unclear, the authors soon adopted it as their slogan, claiming that it represented the work of stifled writers before them.

WORLD LENS
◆◆◆
CHINA

The long ago songs of a bell
weaved this spider web; in the column's crevices,
grown outward, one sees annual rings there for the counting.
No memories are here; stones
that merely scattered the echoes in this mountain valley,
have no memories.
That little path, even, by-passed it;
its dragons and strange birds are gone.
They took with them the silent bells that hung from the eaves.
They took the unrecorded legends of the place, too.
The words on the walls are all worn clean and torn.
Maybe if it caught on fire
one could read the words on the inside.
See the annual growths of the wild grasses,
so indifferent.
They don't care if they submit to any master,
to the shoes of the old monks,
or to the winds, either.
Out front the sky is held up by a broken stone tablet.
Still, led by the gaze of some living person,

the tortoise may revive and
come out carrying his heavy secret,
crawl right out there on the temple's threshold.

Translated by Gordon T. Osing and De-An Wu Swihart

Responding to the Selection

1. What do you believe is the poem's theme, or main idea?

2. What do you think is the poet's attitude toward history and time, and their transformation of this sacred place?

3. Do you believe the translator has done a good job? Cite some examples of language in the poem that is striking and memorable.

4. Without knowing anything about Buddhism, the religion practiced widely in ancient China, what items of description give you some notion of what practitioners found important or symbolic?

5. Knowing what you do about Chinese history in the 20th century, what other possible reasons exist for the disrepair and disuse of this temple?

The Tall Woman and Her Short Husband

Feng Ji-cai

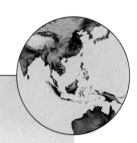

This short story by Chinese writer Feng Ji-cai is a reminder of the regimental history of China. When the Cultural Revolution took place in the mid-1960s, the Communist party was strengthened, leading to stricter conformity in lifestyle, beliefs, and practices. The following story shows the rigidity of Chinese society. Anyone skirting party dictates or social conventions was subject to ridicule, slander, and even imprisonment.

WORLD LENS

◆◆◆

CHINA

1

Say you have a small tree in your yard and are used to its smooth trunk. If one day it turns twisted and gnarled it strikes you as awkward. As time goes by, however, you grow to like it, as if that was how this tree should always have been. Were it suddenly to straighten out again you would feel indescribably put out. A trunk as dull and boring as a stick! In fact it would simply have reverted to its original form, so why should you worry?

Is this force of habit? Well, don't underestimate "habit." It runs through everything done under the sun. It is not a law to be strictly observed, yet flouting it is simply asking for trouble. Don't complain though if it proves so binding that sometimes, unconsciously, you conform to it. For instance, do you presume to throw your weight about before your superiors? Do you air your views recklessly in front of your seniors? When a group photograph is taken, can you shove celebrities aside to stand swaggering and chortling in the middle? You can't, of course you can't. Or again, would you choose a wife ten years older than you, heftier than you or a head taller than you? Don't be in a rush to answer. Here's an instance of such a couple.

2

She was seventeen centimetres taller than he.

One point seven five metres in height, she towered above most of her sex like a crane over chickens. Her husband, a bare 1.58 metres, had been nicknamed Shorty at college. He came up to her earlobes but actually looked two heads shorter.

And take their appearances. She seemed dried up and scrawny with a face like an unvarnished ping-pong bat. Her features would pass, but they were small and insignificant as if carved in shallow relief. She was flat-chested, had a ramrod back and buttocks as scraggy as a scrubbing board. Her husband on the other hand seemed a rubber rolypoly: well-fleshed, solid and radiant. Everything about him—his calves, insteps, lips, nose and fingers—were like pudgy little meatballs. He had soft skin and a fine complexion shining with excess fat and ruddy because of all the red blood in his veins. His eyes were like two high-voltage little light bulbs, while his wife's were like glazed marbles. The two of them just did not match, and formed a marked contrast. But they were inseparable.

One day some of their neighbours were having a family reunion. After drinking his fill the grandfather put a tall, thin empty wine bottle on the table next to a squat tin of pork.

"Who do these remind you of?" he asked. Before anyone could guess he gave the answer. "That tall woman downstairs and that short husband of hers."

Everyone burst out laughing and went on laughing through the meal.

What had brought such a pair together?

This was a mystery to the dozens of households living in Unity Mansions. Ever since this couple moved in, the old residents had eyed them curiously. Some registered a question mark in their minds, while others put their curiosity into words. Tongues started wagging, especially in wet weather when the two of them went out and it was always Mrs. Tall who held the umbrella. If anything dropped to the ground, though, it was simpler for Mr.

CHINESE PROPAGANDA POSTER FROM THE CULTURAL REVOLUTION 1967

Short to pick it up. Some old ladies at a loose end would gesticulate, finding this comic, and splutter with laughter. This set a bad example for the children who would burst out laughing at sight of the pair and hoot, "Long carrying-pole; big, low stool!" The husband and wife pretended not to hear and kept their

The Tall Woman and Her Short Husband

tempers, paying no attention. Maybe for this reason their relations with their neighbours remained rather cool. The few less **officious** ones simply nodded a greeting when they met. This made it hard for those really intrigued by them to find out more about them. For instance, how did they hit it off? Why had they married? Which gave way to the other? They could only speculate.

officious
intrusive; meddlesome

This was an old-fashioned block of flats with large sunny rooms and wide, dark corridors. It stood in a big courtyard with a small gatehouse. The man who lived there was a tailor, a decent fellow. His wife, who brimmed over with energy, liked to call on her neighbours and gossip. Most of all she liked to **ferret** out their secrets. She knew exactly how husbands and wives got on, why sisters-in-law quarrelled, who was lazy, who hard-working, and how much everyone earned. If she was unclear about anything she would leave no stone unturned to get at the truth. The thirst for knowledge makes even the ignorant wise. In this respect she was outstanding. She analyzed conversations, watched expressions, and could even tell what people were secretly thinking. Simply by using her nose, she knew which household was eating meat or fish, and from that could deduce their income. For some reason or other, ever since the sixties each housing estate had chosen someone like this as a "neighbourhood activist," giving legal status to these nosey-parkers so that their officiousness could have full play. It seems the Creator will never waste any talent.

ferret
seek; pry

Though the tailor's wife was **indefatigable** she failed to discover how this **incongruous** couple who passed daily before her eyes had come to marry. She found this most frustrating; it posed a formidable challenge. On the basis of her experience, however, and by racking her brains she finally came up with a **plausible** explanation: either husband or wife must have some physiological deficiency. Otherwise no one would marry someone a whole head taller or shorter. Her grounds for this reasoning were that after three years of marriage they still had no children. The residents of Unity Mansions were all convinced by this brilliant hypothesis.

indefatigable
tireless; inexhaustible

incongruous
incompatible; odd

plausible
believable; likely

But facts are merciless. The tailor's wife was **debunked** and lost face when Mrs. Tall appeared in the family way. Her womb

debunked
disproved; deflated

could be seen swelling from day to day, for being relatively far from the ground it was all too evident. Regardless of their amazement, misgivings or embarrassment, she gave birth to a fine baby. When the sun was hot or it rained and the couple went out, Mrs. Tall would carry the baby while Mr. Short held the umbrella. He plodded along comically on his plump legs, the umbrella held high, keeping just behind his wife. And the neighbours remained as intrigued as at the start of this ill-assorted, inseparable couple. They went on making plausible **conjectures**, but could find no confirmation for any of them.

The tailor's wife said, "They must have something to hide, those two. Why else should they keep to themselves? Well, it's bound to come to light some day, just wait and see."

One evening, sure enough, she heard the sound of breaking glass in their flat. On the pretext of collecting money for sweeping the yard she rushed to knock on their door, sure that their long hidden feud had come to a head and avid to watch the confrontation between them. The door opened. Mrs. Tall asked her in with a smile. Mr. Short was smiling too at a smashed plate on the floor—that was all the tailor's wife saw. She hastily collected the money and left to puzzle over what had happened. A plate had been smashed, yet instead of quarrelling they had treated it as a joke. How very strange!

Later the tailor's wife became the residents' representative for Unity Mansions. When she helped the police check up on living permits, she at last found the answer to this puzzle. A reliable and irrefutable answer. The tall woman and her short husband both worked in the Research Institute of the Ministry of Chemical Industry. He was chief engineer, with a salary of over 180 yuan! She was an ordinary laboratory technician earning less than sixty yuan, and her father was a hard-working low-paid postman. So that explained why she had married a man so much shorter. For status, money and an easy life. Right! The tailor's wife lost no time in passing on this priceless information to all the bored old ladies in Unity Mansions. Judging others by themselves, they believed her. At last this riddle was solved. They saw the light. Rich Mr. Short was congenitally deficient while poor Mrs. Tall was a money-grabber on the make. When they discussed the good

conjectures
guesses; suppositions

luck of this tall woman who looked like a horse, they often voiced resentment—especially the tailor's wife.

3

Sometimes good luck turns into bad.

In 1966, disaster struck China.[1] Great changes came into the lives of all the residents in Unity Mansions, which was like a **microcosm** of the whole country. Mr. Short as chief engineer was the first to suffer. His flat was raided, his furniture moved out, he was struggled against and confined in his institute. And worse was to come. He was accused of smuggling out the results of his research to write up at home in the evenings, with a view to fleeing the country to join a wealthy relative abroad. This preposterous charge of passing on scientific secrets to foreign capitalists was widely believed. In that period of lunacy people took leave of their senses and cruelly made up groundless accusations in order to find some Hitler in their midst. The institute kept a stranglehold on its chief engineer. He was threatened, beaten up, put under all kinds of pressure; his wife was ordered to hand over that manuscript which no one had ever seen. But all was to no effect. Someone proposed holding a struggle meeting against them both in the courtyard of Unity Mansions. As everyone dreads losing face in front of relatives and friends, this would put more pressure on them. Since all else had failed, it was at least worth trying. Never before had Unity Mansions been the scene of such excitement.

In the afternoon the institute sent people to fix up ropes between two trees in the yard, on which to hang a poster with the name of Mr. Short on it—crossed out. Inside and outside the yard they pasted up threatening slogans, and on the wall put eighteen more posters listing the engineer's "crimes." As the meeting was to be held after supper, an electrician was sent to fix up four big 500-watt bulbs. By now the tailor's wife, promoted to be the chairman of the neighbourhood's Public Security Committee, was a powerful person, full of self-importance, and much fatter than before. She had been busy all day bossing the other women

microcosm
little world; miniature representation

---

1 **In . . . China:** 1966 was the beginning of the Cultural Revolution led by Communist leader Mao Tse-tung.

East Asia & the Pacific Rim

about, helping to put up slogans and make tea for the revolutionaries from the institute. The wiring for the lights had been fixed up from her gatehouse as if she were celebrating a wedding!

After supper, the tailor's wife assembled all the residents in the yard, lit up as brilliantly as a sportsground at night. Their shadows, magnified ten-fold, were thrown on the wall of the building. These shadows stayed stock-still, not even the children daring to play about. The tailor's wife led a group also wearing red armbands, in those days most awe-inspiring, to guard the gate and keep outsiders out. Presently a crowd from the institute, wearing armbands and shouting slogans, marched in the tall woman and her short husband. He had a placard hung round his neck, she had none. The two of them were marched in front of the platform, and stood there side by side with lowered heads.

The tailor's wife darted forward. "This wretch is too short for the revolutionary masses at the back to see," she cried. "I'll soon fix that." She dashed into the gatehouse, her fat shoulders heaving, to fetch a soapbox which she turned upside down. Mr. Short standing on this was the same height as his wife. But at this point little attention was paid to the relative heights of this couple facing disaster.

The meeting followed the customary procedure. After slogans had been shouted, passionate accusations were made, punctuated by more slogans. The pressure built up. First Mrs. Tall was ordered to come clean, to produce that "manuscript." Questions and denunciations were fired at her, hysterical screams, angry shouts and threatening growls. But she simply shook her head gravely and sincerely. What use was sincerity? To believe in her would have made the whole business a farce.

No matter what bullies sprang forward to shake their fists at her, or what tricky questions were asked to try to trap her, she simply shook her head. The members of the institute were at a loss, afraid that if this went on the struggle meeting would fizzle out and end up a fiasco.

The tailor's wife had listened with mounting exasperation. Being illiterate she took no interest in the "manuscript" they wanted, and felt these research workers were too soft-spoken. All of a sudden she ran to the platform. Raising her right arm with its red armband she pointed accusingly at Mrs. Tall.

"Say!" she screeched. "Why did you marry him?"

"Say!" she screeched. "Why did you marry him?"

The members of the institute were staggered by this unexpected question. What connection had it with their investigation?

Mrs. Tall was staggered too. This wasn't the sort of question asked these days. She looked up with surprise on her thin face which showed the ravages of the last few months.

"So you don't dare answer, eh?" The tailor's wife raised her voice. "I'll answer for you! You married this scoundrel, didn't you, for his money? If he hadn't had money who'd want such a short fellow!" She sounded rather smug, as if she alone had seen through Mrs. Tall.

Mrs. Tall neither nodded nor shook her head. She had seen through the tailor's wife too. Her eyes glinted with derision and contempt.

"All right, you won't admit it. This wretch is done for now, he's a broken reed. Oh, I know what you're thinking." The tailor's wife slapped her chest and brandished one hand gloatingly. Some other women chimed in.

flummoxed
confounded; confused

The members of the institute were **flummoxed**. A question like this was best ignored. But though these women had strayed far from the subject, they had also livened up the meeting. So the institute members let them take the field. The women yelled:

"How much has he paid you? What has he bought you? What has he bought you? Own up!"

"Two hundred a month isn't enough for you, is it? You have to go abroad!"

"Is Deng Tuo[2] behind you?"

That day you made a long-distance call to Beijing, were you ringing up the Three Family Village[3]?

---

2 **Deng Tuo:** historian and author who criticized Mao for his policies during the Cultural Revolution

3 **Three Family Village:** three writers of a newspaper column deemed subversive during the Cultural Revolution

East Asia & the Pacific Rim

The success of a meeting depends on the enthusiasm worked up. The institute members who had convened this meeting saw that the time was ripe now to shout a few more slogans and conclude it. They then searched Mrs. Tall's flat, **prizing** up floorboards and stripping off wallpaper. When they discovered nothing, they marched her husband away, leaving her behind.

Mrs. Tall stayed in all the next day but went out alone after dark, unaware that though the light in the gatehouse was out the tailor's wife was watching her from the window. She trailed her out of the gate and past two crossroads till Mrs. Tall stopped to knock softly on a gate. The tailor's wife ducked behind a telegraph pole and waited, holding her breath, as if to pounce on a rabbit when it popped out of its burrow.

The gate creaked open. An old woman led out a child.

"All over, is it?" she asked.

Mrs. Tall's answer was inaudible.

"He's had his supper and a sleep," the old woman said. "Take him home quickly now."

The tailor's wife realized that this was the woman who minded their little boy. Her excitement died down as Mrs. Tall turned back to lead her son home. All was silence apart from the sound of their footsteps. The tailor's wife stood motionless behind the telegraph pole till they had gone, then scurried home herself.

The next morning when Mrs. Tall led her son out, her eyes were red. No one would speak to her, but they all saw her red, swollen eyes. Those who had denounced her the previous day had a strange feeling of guilt. They turned away so as not to meet her eyes.

4

After the struggle meeting Mr. Short was not allowed home again. The tailor's wife, who was in the know, said he had been imprisoned as an active counter-revolutionary. That made Mrs. Tall the lowest of the low, naturally unfit to live in a roomy flat. She was forced to change places with the tailor's wife and moved into the little gatehouse. This didn't worry her, as it meant she could avoid the other residents who snubbed her. But they could look through her window and see her all alone there. Where she had sent her son, they didn't know, for he only came home for a few days at a time. Ostracized by all, she looked older than a woman in her thirties.

"Mark my words," the tailor's wife said, "she can only keep this up for at most a year. Then if Shorty doesn't get out she'll have to remarry. If I were her I'd get a divorce and remarry. Even if he's let out his name will be mud, and he won't have any money."

A year went by. Mr. Short still didn't come back and Mrs. Tall kept to herself. In silence she went to work, came back, lit her stove and went out with a big shabby shopping basket. Day after day she did this, the whole year round . . . But one day in autumn Mr. Short reappeared—thinly clad, his head shaved, and his whole appearance changed. He seemed to have shrunk and his skin no longer gleamed with health. He went straight to his old flat. Its new master, the honest tailor, directed him to the gatehouse. Mrs. Tall was squatting in the doorway chopping firewood. At the sound of his voice she sprang up to stare at him. After two years' separation both were appalled by the change in the other. One was wrinkled, the other haggard; one looked taller than before, the other shorter. After gazing at each other they hastily turned away, and Mrs. Tall ran inside. When finally she came out again he had picked up the axe and squatted down to chop firewood, until two big boxes of wood had been chopped into kindling, as if he feared some new disaster might befall them at any moment. After that they were inseparable again, going to work together and coming back together just as before. The neighbours, finding them unchanged, gradually lost interest in them and ignored them.

One morning Mrs. Tall had an accident. Her husband rushed frantically out and came back with an ambulance to fetch her. For days the gatehouse was empty and dark at night. After three weeks Mr. Short returned with a stranger. They were carrying her on a stretcher. She was confined to her room. He went to work as usual, hurrying back at dusk to light the stove and go out with the shopping basket. This was the same basket she had used every day. In his hand it looked even bigger and nearly reached the ground.

When the weather turned warmer Mrs. Tall came out. After so

long in bed her face was deathly white, and she swayed from side to side. She held a cane in her right hand and kept her elbow bent in front of her. Her half-paralysed left leg made walking difficult. She had obviously had a stroke. Every morning and every evening Mr. Short helped her twice round the yard, painfully and slowly. By hunching up his shoulders he was able to grip her crooked arm in both hands. It was hard for him, but he smiled to encourage her. As she couldn't raise her left foot, he tied a rope round it and pulled this up when she wanted to take a step forward. This was a pathetic yet impressive sight, and the neighbours were touched by it. Now when they met the couple they nodded cordially to them.

5

Mrs. Tall's luck had run out: she was not to linger long by the side of the short husband who had loved her so dearly. Death and life were equally cruel to her. Life had struck her down and now death carried her off. Mr. Short was left all alone.

But after her death fortune smiled on him again. He was rehabilitated, his confiscated possessions were returned, and he received all his back pay. Only his flat, occupied by the tailor's wife, was not given back to him. The neighbours watched to see what he would do. It was said that some of his colleagues had proposed finding him another wife, but he had declined their offers.

"I know the kind of woman he wants," said the tailor's wife. "Just leave it to me!"

Having passed her **zenith** she had become more subdued. Stripped of her power she had to wear a smile. With a photograph of a pretty girl in her pocket she went to the gatehouse to find Mr. Short. The girl in the picture was her niece.

zenith
peak; high point

She sat in the gatehouse sizing up its furnishing as she proposed this match to rich Mr. Short. Smiling all over her face she held forth with gusto until suddenly she realized that he had not said a word, his face was black, and behind him hung a picture of him and Mrs. Tall on their wedding day. Then she beat a retreat without venturing to produce the photograph of her niece.

Since then several years have passed. Mr. Short is still a widower, but on Sundays he fetches his son home to keep him company. At the sight of his squat, lonely figure, his neighbours recall all that he has been through and have come to understand why he goes on living alone. When it rains and he takes an umbrella to go to work, out of force of habit perhaps he still holds it high. Then they have the strange sensation that there is a big empty space under that umbrella, a vacuum that nothing on earth can fill.

Translated by Gladys Yang

Responding to the Selection

1. There are many similes—comparisons using *like* or *as*—used to describe the characters in this story. Point out a simile that you especially like for its humor, wordplay, or the way it characterizes a person.

2. What critical event took place in China in 1966? Using information provided in this book and elsewhere, describe the impact this had on ordinary Chinese citizens, and so, the characters in this fictional story.

3. Why does it bother people if a couple doesn't fit the norm?

4. Which elements of the story (the plot, characters, or relationships) could only have happened in this setting and which elements are universal?

5. There are a couple of references to "losing face" in this story. Find out the cultural significance in China of "losing face" and compare it to the significance of losing face in this country.

Saboteur[1]

Ha Jin

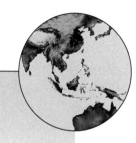

The social and political climate in China just after the Cultural Revolution (1966–1969) was unpredictable and repressive. The dust was still settling from the invigoration of the Communist Party, and many common citizens were mistreated by those who had recently risen to power. Ha Jin focuses his attention on this period in his story, "Saboteur." Now a resident of the United States, Ha Jin writes in English and has won many prestigious awards for his fiction.

WORLD LENS

♦♦♦

CHINA

Mr. Chiu and his bride were having lunch in the square before Muji Train Station. On the table between them were two bottles of soda spewing out brown foam and two paper boxes of rice and sautéed cucumber and pork. "Let's eat," he said to her, and broke the connected ends of the chopsticks. He picked up a slice of streaky pork and put it into his mouth. As he was chewing, a few crinkles appeared on his thin jaw.

To his right, at another table, two railroad policemen were drinking tea and laughing; it seemed that the stout, middle-aged man was telling a joke to his young comrade, who was tall and of athletic build. Now and again they would steal a glance at Mr. Chiu's table.

The air smelled of rotten melon. A few flies kept buzzing above the couple's lunch. Hundreds of people were rushing around to get on the platform or to catch buses to downtown. Food and fruit vendors were crying for customers in lazy voices. About a dozen young women, representing the local hotels, held up placards which displayed the daily prices and words as large as

---

1 **saboteur:** one who practices sabotage, or the deliberate destruction of another's property or plans

a palm, like FREE MEALS, AIR-CONDITIONING, and ON THE RIVER. In the center of the square stood a concrete statue of Chairman Mao,[2] at whose feet peasants were napping, their backs on the warm granite and their faces toward the sunny sky. A flock of pigeons perched on the Chairman's raised hand and forearm.

The rice and cucumber tasted good, and Mr. Chiu was eating unhurriedly. His **sallow** face showed exhaustion. He was glad that the honeymoon was finally over and that he and his bride were heading back for Harbin. During the two weeks' vacation, he had been worried about his liver, because three months ago he had suffered from acute hepatitis; he was afraid he might have a relapse. But he had had no severe symptoms, despite his liver being still big and tender. On the whole he was pleased with his health, which could endure even the strain of a honeymoon; indeed, he was on the course of recovery. He looked at his bride, who took off her wire glasses, kneading the root of her nose with her fingertips. Beads of sweat coated her pale cheeks.

"Are you all right, sweetheart?" he asked.

"I have a headache. I didn't sleep well last night."

"Take an aspirin, will you?"

"It's not that serious. Tomorrow is Sunday and I can sleep in. Don't worry."

As they were talking, the stout policeman at the next table stood up and threw a bowl of tea in their direction. Both Mr. Chiu's and his bride's sandals were wet instantly.

"Hooligan!" she said in a low voice.

Mr. Chiu got to his feet and said out loud, "Comrade Policeman, why did you do this?" He stretched out his right foot to show the wet sandal.

"Do what?" the stout man asked huskily, glaring at Mr. Chiu while the young fellow was whistling.

"See, you dumped tea on our feet."

"You're lying. You wet your shoes yourself."

"Comrade Policeman, your duty is to keep order, but you purposely tortured us common citizens. Why violate the law you are supposed to enforce?" As Mr. Chiu was speaking, dozens of

sallow
yellowish; sickly

---

2 **Chairman Mao:** Mao Tse-tung, Communist party leader responsible for the Cultural Revolution (1966–1969)

East Asia & the Pacific Rim

people began gathering around.

With a wave of his hand, the man said to the young fellow, "Let's get hold of him!"

They grabbed Mr. Chiu and clamped handcuffs around his wrists. He cried, "You can't do this to me. This is utterly unreasonable."

"Shut up!" The man pulled out his pistol. "You can use your tongue at our headquarters."

The young fellow added, "You're a saboteur, you know that? You're disrupting public order."

The bride was too petrified to say anything coherent. She was a recent college graduate, had majored in fine arts, and had never seen the police make an arrest. All she could say was, "Oh, please, please!"

The policemen were pulling Mr. Chiu, but he refused to go with them, holding the corner of the table and shouting, "We have a train to catch. We already bought the tickets."

The stout man punched him in the chest. "Shut up. Let your ticket expire." With the pistol butt he chopped Mr. Chiu's hands, which at once released the table. Together the two men were dragging him away to the police station.

Realizing he had to go with them, Mr. Chiu turned his head and shouted to his bride, "Don't wait for me here. Take the train. If I'm not back by tomorrow morning, send someone over to get me out."

She nodded, covering her sobbing mouth with her palm.

◆ ◆ ◆ ◆ ◆

After removing his belt, they locked Mr. Chiu into a cell in the back of the Railroad Police Station. The single window in the room was blocked by six steel bars; it faced a spacious yard, in which stood a few pines. Beyond the trees, two swings hung from an iron frame, swaying gently in the breeze. Somewhere in the building a cleaver[3] was chopping rhythmically. There must be a kitchen upstairs, Mr. Chiu thought.

He was too exhausted to worry about what they would do to him, so he lay down on the narrow bed and shut his eyes. He

---

3 **cleaver:** a sharp knife used to butcher animal carcasses

propagating
spreading; broadcasting

wasn't afraid. The Cultural Revolution was over already, and recently the Party had been **propagating** the idea that all citizens were equal before the law. The police ought to be a law-abiding model for common people. As long as he remained coolheaded and reasoned with them, they probably wouldn't harm him.

Late in the afternoon he was taken to the Interrogation Bureau on the second floor. On his way there, in the stairwell, he ran into the middle-aged policeman who had manhandled him. The man grinned, rolling his bulgy eyes and pointing his fingers at him as if firing a pistol. Egg of a tortoise! Mr. Chiu cursed mentally.

The moment he sat down in the office, he burped, his palm shielding his mouth. In front of him, across a long desk, sat the chief of the bureau and a donkey-faced man. On the glass desktop was a folder containing information on his case. He felt it bizarre that in just a matter of hours they had accumulated a small pile of writing about him. On second thought he began to wonder whether they had kept a file on him all the time. How could this have happened? He lived and worked in Harbin, more than three hundred miles away, and this was his first time in Muji City.

The chief of the bureau was a thin, bald man who looked serene and intelligent. His slim hands handled the written pages in the folder in the manner of a lecturing scholar. To Mr. Chiu's left sat a young scribe, with a clipboard on his knee and a black fountain pen in his hand.

"Your name?" the chief asked, apparently reading out the question from a form.

"Chiu Maguang."

"Age?"

"Thirty-four."

"Profession?"

"Lecturer."

"Work unit?"

"Harbin University."

"Political status?"

"Communist Party member."

The chief put down the paper and began to speak. "Your crime is sabotage, although it hasn't induced serious consequences yet.

Because you are a Party member, you should be punished more. You have failed to be a model for the masses and you—"

"Excuse me, sir," Mr. Chiu cut him off.

"What?"

"I didn't do anything. Your men are the saboteurs of our social order. They threw hot tea on my feet and on my wife's feet. Logically speaking, you should criticize them, if not punish them."

"That statement is groundless. You have no witness. Why should I believe you?" the chief said matter-of-factly.

"This is my evidence." He raised his right hand. "Your man hit my fingers with a pistol."

"That doesn't prove how your feet got wet. Besides, you could have hurt your fingers yourself."

"But I am telling the truth!" Anger flared up in Mr. Chiu. "Your police station owes me an apology. My train ticket has expired, my new leather sandals are ruined, and I am late for a conference in the provincial capital. You must compensate me for the damage and losses. Don't mistake me for a common citizen who would tremble when you sneeze. I'm a scholar, a philosopher, and an expert in dialectical materialism.[4] If necessary, we will argue about this in The Northeastern Daily, or we will go to the highest People's Court in Beijing. Tell me, what's your name?" He got carried away with his **harangue**, which was by no means trivial and had worked to his advantage on numerous occasions.

harangue
lecture; tirade

"Stop bluffing us," the donkey-faced man broke in. "We have seen a lot of your kind. We can easily prove you are guilty. Here are some of the statements given by eyewitnesses." He pushed a few sheets of paper toward Mr. Chiu.

Mr. Chiu was dazed to see the different handwritings, which all stated that he had shouted in the square to attract attention and refused to obey the police. One of the witnesses had identified herself as a purchasing agent from a shipyard in Shanghai. Something stirred in Mr. Chiu's stomach, a pain rising to his rib. He gave out a faint moan.

"Now you have to admit you are guilty," the chief said.

---

4 **dialectical materialism:** A Marxian theory emphasizing that reality is dynamic rather than static and that economic systems greatly affect political and cultural developments.

"Although it's a serious crime, we won't punish you severely, provided you write out a self-criticism and promise that you won't disrupt the public order again. In other words, your release will depend on your attitude toward this crime."

"You're daydreaming," Mr. Chiu cried. "I won't write a word, because I'm innocent. I demand that you provide me with a letter of apology so I can explain to my university why I'm late."

Both the interrogators smiled contemptuously. "Well, we've never done that," said the chief, taking a puff at his cigarette.

"Then make this a precedent."

"That's unnecessary. We are pretty certain that you will comply with our wishes." The chief blew a column of smoke toward Mr. Chiu's face.

At the tilt of the chief's head, two guards stepped forward and grabbed the criminal by the arms. Mr. Chiu meanwhile went on saying, "I shall report you to the Provincial Administration. You'll have to pay for this! You are worse than the Japanese military police."

They dragged him out of the room.

◆ ◆ ◆ ◆ ◆

After dinner, which consisted of a bowl of millet porridge, a corn bun, and a piece of pickled turnip, Mr. Chiu began to have a fever, shaking with a chill and sweating profusely. He knew that the fire of anger had gotten into his liver and that he was probably having a relapse. No medicine was available, because his briefcase had been left with his bride. At home it would have been time for him to sit in front of their color TV, drinking jasmine tea and watching the evening news. It was so lonesome in here. The orange bulb above the single bed was the only source of light, which enabled the guards to keep him under surveillance at night. A moment ago he had asked them for a newspaper or a magazine to read, but they turned him down.

Through the small opening on the door noises came in. It seemed that the police on duty were playing cards or chess in a nearby office; shouts and laughter could be heard now and then. Meanwhile, an accordion kept coughing from a remote corner in the building. Looking at the ballpoint and the letter paper left for him by the guards when they took him back from the Interrogation Bureau, Mr. Chiu remembered the old saying, "When a scholar runs into soldiers, the more he argues, the muddier his point becomes." How ridiculous this whole thing was. He ruffled his thick hair with his fingers.

He felt miserable, massaging his stomach continually. To tell the truth, he was more upset than frightened, because he would have to catch up with his work once he was back home—a paper that was due at the printers next week, and two dozen books he ought to read for the course he was going to teach in the fall.

A human shadow flitted across the opening. Mr. Chiu rushed to the door and shouted through the hole, "Comrade Guard, Comrade Guard!"

"What do you want?" a voice rasped.

"I want you to inform your leaders that I'm very sick. I have heart disease and hepatitis. I may die here if you keep me like this without medication."

"No leader is on duty on the weekend. You have to wait till Monday."

"What? You mean I'll stay in here tomorrow?"

"Yes."

"Your station will be held responsible if anything happens to me."

"We know that. Take it easy, you won't die."

It seemed illogical that Mr. Chiu slept quite well that night, though the light above his head had been on all the time and the straw mattress was hard and infested with fleas. He was afraid of ticks, mosquitoes, cockroaches—any kind of insect but fleas and bedbugs. Once, in the countryside, where his school's faculty and staff had helped the peasants harvest crops for a week, his colleagues had joked about his flesh, which they said must have tasted nonhuman to fleas. Except for him, they were all afflicted with hundreds of bites.

More amazing now, he didn't miss his bride a lot. He even enjoyed sleeping alone, perhaps because the honeymoon had tired him out and he needed more rest.

The backyard was quiet on Sunday morning. Pale sunlight streamed through the pine branches. A few sparrows were jumping on the ground, catching caterpillars and ladybugs. Holding the steel bars, Mr. Chiu inhaled the morning air, which smelled meaty. There must have been an eatery or a cooked-meat stand nearby. He reminded himself that he should take this detention with ease. A sentence that Chairman Mao had written to a hospitalized friend rose in his mind: "Since you are already in here, you may as well stay and make the best of it."

His desire for peace of mind originated in his fear that his hepatitis might get worse. He tried to remain unperturbed. However, he was sure that his liver was swelling up, since the fever still persisted. For a whole day he lay in bed, thinking about his paper on the nature of contradictions. Time and again he was overwhelmed by anger, cursing aloud, "A bunch of thugs!" He swore that once he was out, he would write an article about this experience. He had better find out some of the policemen's names.

It turned out to be a restful day for the most part; he was certain that his university would sent somebody to his rescue. All he should do now was remain calm and wait patiently. Sooner or later the police would have to release him, although they had no idea that he might refuse to leave unless they wrote him an apology. Damn those hoodlums, they had ordered more than they could eat!

When he woke up on Monday morning, it was already light. Somewhere a man was moaning; the sound came from the backyard. After a long yawn, and kicking off the tattered blanket, Mr. Chiu climbed out of bed and went to the window. In the middle of the yard, a young man was fastened to a pine, his wrists handcuffed around the trunk from behind. He was wriggling and swearing loudly, but there was no sight of anyone else in the yard. He looked familiar to Mr. Chiu.

Mr. Chiu squinted his eyes to see who it was. To his astonishment, he recognized the man, who was Fenjin, a recent graduate from the Law Department at Harbin University. Two years ago Mr. Chiu had taught a course in Marxist materialism, in which Fenjin had enrolled. Now, how on earth had this young devil landed here?

Then it dawned on him that Fenjin must have been sent over

by his bride. What a stupid woman! A bookworm, who only knew how to read foreign novels! He had expected that she would contact the school's Security Section, which would for sure send a cadre[5] here. Fenjin held no official position; he merely worked in a private law firm that had just two lawyers; in fact, they had little business except for some detective work for men and women who suspected their spouses of having extramarital affairs. Mr. Chiu was overcome with a wave of nausea.

Should he call out to let his student know he was nearby? He decided not to, because he didn't know what had happened. Fenjin must have quarreled with the police to incur such a punishment. Yet this could never have occurred if Fenjin hadn't come to his rescue. So no matter what, Mr. Chiu had to do something. But what could he do?

It was going to be a scorcher. He could see purple steam shimmering and rising from the ground among the pines. Poor devil, he thought, as he raised a bowl of corn glue to his mouth, sipped, and took a bite of a piece of salted celery.

When a guard came to collect the bowl and the chopsticks, Mr. Chiu asked him what had happened to the man in the backyard. "He called our boss 'bandit,'" the guard said. "He claimed he was a lawyer or something. An arrogant son of a rabbit."

Now it was obvious to Mr. Chiu that he had to do something to help his rescuer. Before he could figure out a way, a scream broke out in the backyard. He rushed to the window and saw a tall policeman standing before Fenjin, an iron bucket on the ground. It was the same young fellow who had arrested Mr. Chiu in the square two days before. The man pinched Fenjin's nose, then raised his hand, which stayed in the air for a few seconds, then slapped the lawyer across the face. As Fenjin was groaning, the man lifted up the bucket and poured water on his head.

"This will keep you from getting sunstroke, boy. I'll give you some more every hour," the man said loudly.

Fenjin kept his eyes shut, yet his wry face showed that he was struggling to hold back from cursing the policeman, or, more likely, that he was sobbing in silence. He sneezed, then raised his face and shouted, "Let me go take a piss."

---

5 **cadre:** a group of revolutionary leaders

"Oh yeah?" the man bawled. "Pee in your pants."

Still Mr. Chiu didn't make any noise, gripping the steel bars with both hands, his fingers white. The policeman turned and glanced at the cell's window; his pistol, partly holstered, glittered in the sun. With a snort he spat his cigarette butt to the ground and stamped it into the dust.

Then the door opened and the guards motioned Mr. Chiu to

come out. Again they took him upstairs to the Interrogation Bureau.

The same men were in the office, though this time the scribe was sitting there empty-handed. At the sight of Mr. Chiu the chief said, "Ah, here you are. Please be seated."

After Mr. Chiu sat down, the chief waved a white silk fan and said to him, "You may have seen your lawyer. He's a young man without manners, so our director had him taught a crash course in the backyard."

"It's illegal to do that. Aren't you afraid to appear in a newspaper?"

"No, we are not, not even on TV. What else can you do? We are not afraid of any story you make up. We call it fiction. What we do care about is that you cooperate with us. That is to say, you must admit your crime."

"What if I refuse to cooperate?"

"Then your lawyer will continue his education in the sunshine."

A swoon swayed Mr. Chiu, and he held the arms of the chair to steady himself. A numb pain stung him in the upper stomach and nauseated him, and his head was throbbing. He was sure that the hepatitis was finally attacking him. Anger was flaming up in his chest; his throat was tight and clogged.

The chief resumed, "As a matter of fact, you don't even have to write out your self-criticism. We have your crime described clearly here. All we need is your signature."

Holding back his rage, Mr. Chiu said, "Let me look at that."

With a smirk the donkey-faced man handed him a sheet, which carried these words:

I hereby admit that on July 13 I disrupted public order at Muji Train Station, and that I refused to listen to reason when the railroad police issued their warning. Thus I myself am responsible for my arrest. After two days' detention, I have realized the **reactionary** nature of my crime. From now on, I shall continue to educate myself with all my effort and shall never commit this kind of crime again.

reactionary
*not progressive; opposed
to change*

A voice started screaming in Mr. Chiu's ears, "Lie, lie!" But he shook his head and forced the voice away. He asked the chief, "If I sign this, will you release both my lawyer and me?"

"Of course, we'll do that." The chief was drumming his fingers on the blue folder—their file on him.

Mr. Chiu signed his name and put his thumbprint under his signature.

"Now you are free to go," the chief said with a smile, and handed him a piece of paper to wipe his thumb with.

Mr. Chiu was so sick that he couldn't stand up from the chair at first try. Then he doubled his effort and rose to his feet. He staggered out of the building to meet his lawyer in the backyard, having forgotten to ask for his belt back. In his chest he felt as though there were a bomb. If he were able to, he would have razed the entire police station and eliminated all their families. Though he knew he could do nothing like that, he made up his mind to do something.

♦ ♦ ♦ ♦

"I'm sorry about this torture, Fenjin," Mr. Chiu said when they met.

"It doesn't matter. They are savages." The lawyer brushed a patch of dirt off his jacket with trembling fingers. Water was still dribbling from the bottoms of his trouser legs.

"Let's go now," the teacher said.

The moment they came out of the police station, Mr. Chiu caught sight of a tea stand. He grabbed Fenjin's arm and walked over to the old woman at the table. "Two bowls of black tea," he said and handed her a one-yuan note.

After the first bowl, they each had another one. Then they set out for the train station. But before they walked fifty yards, Mr. Chiu insisted on eating a bowl of tree-ear soup at a food stand. Fenjin agreed. He told his teacher, "You mustn't treat me like a guest."

"No, I want to eat something myself."

As if dying of hunger, Mr. Chiu dragged his lawyer from restaurant to restaurant near the police station, but at each place he ordered no more than two bowls of food. Fenjin wondered why his teacher wouldn't stay at one place and eat his fill.

Mr. Chiu bought noodles, wonton, eight-grain porridge, and chicken soup, respectively, at four restaurants. While eating, he kept saying through his teeth, "If only I could kill all the bastards!" At the last place he merely took a few sips of the soup without tasting the chicken cubes and mushrooms.

Fenjin was baffled by his teacher, who looked ferocious and muttered to himself mysteriously, and whose jaundiced[6] face was covered with dark puckers. For the first time Fenjin thought of Mr. Chiu as an ugly man.

◆ ◆ ◆ ◆ ◆

Within a month over eight hundred people contracted acute hepatitis in Muji. Six died of the disease, including two children. Nobody knew how the epidemic had started.

Responding to the Selection

1. Is there any reason you can surmise that makes the police want to harass Mr. Chiu and his wife?

2. What does this story tell us about the nature of police and citizen relations in China at the time of the story (right after the Cultural Revolution)? Try to chart the progression of attitudes Mr. Chiu experiences toward the police throughout the story.

3. Do you think what has happened to Mr. Chiu justifies what he does at the end? Explain your answer, remembering to take into account the possibility that this is not the only time he has had to deal with unwanted interference in his life by public officials.

4. Consider the aftermath of the September 11, 2001 tragedy and the worldwide hunt for terrorists. Would you consider Mr. Chiu a terrorist? Explain your answer.

5. What do you make of the old saying Mr. Chiu remembers in prison: "When a scholar runs into soldiers, the more he argues, the muddier his point becomes"?

---

6 **jaundiced:** affected with jaundice, a disease that makes skin look yellow

Cranes

Hwang Sun-won

WORLD LENS

◆◆◆

KOREA

In 1953, the civil war in Korea was coming to an end. Author Hwang Sun-won and his family were displaced during the three-year struggle, living in both Soviet-occupied North Korea and the American-occupied South. The setting in "Cranes"—Korea's Thirty-eighth Parallel, the dividing line between North and South Korea—is a scene of ongoing conflict and a symbol for the divisions that have disrupted families, friends, and communities since the border agreement.

Hwang Sun-won is considered one of Korea's finest short story writers and is one of the first contemporary Korean writers to be translated into English.

The northern village at the border of the Thirty-eighth Parallel was snugly settled under the high, bright autumn sky.

One white gourd lay against another on the dirt floor of an empty farmhouse. The occasional village elders first put out their bamboo pipes before passing by, and the children, too, turned aside some distance off. Their faces were ridden with fear.

The village as a whole showed few traces of destruction from the war, but it did not seem like the same village Song-sam had known as a boy.

At the foot of a chestnut grove on the hill behind the village he stopped and climbed a chestnut tree. Somewhere far back in his mind he heard the old man with a wen[1] shout, "You bad boy, you're climbing up my chestnut tree again!"

The old man must have passed away, for among the few village elders Song-sam had met, the old man was not to be found. Holding the trunk of the tree, Song-sam gazed at the blue sky for

---

1 **wen:** a harmless tumor, often on the head

a while. Some chestnuts fell to the ground as the dry clusters opened of their own accord.

◆◆◆◆◆

In front of the farmhouse that had been turned into a public peace-police office, a young man stood, tied up. He seemed to be a stranger, so Song-sam approached him to have a close look. He was taken aback; it was none other than his boyhood playmate, Tok-chae.

Song-sam asked the police officer who had come with him from Chontae what it was all about. The prisoner was vice-chairman of the Farmers' Communist League and had just been flushed out of his hideout in his own house, Song-sam learned.

Song-sam sat down on the dirt floor and lit a cigarette.

Tok-chae was to be escorted to Chongdan by one of the peace policemen.

After a time, Song-sam lit a new cigarette from the first and stood up.

"I'll take the fellow with me."

Tok-chae, his face averted, refused to look at Song-sam. They left the village.

Song-sam kept on smoking, but the tobacco had no taste. He just kept drawing in the smoke and blowing it out. Then suddenly he thought that Tok-chae, too, must want a puff. He thought of the days when they used to share dried gourd leaves behind walls, hidden from the adults. But today, how could he offer a cigarette to a fellow like this?

"So how many have you killed?"

Once, when they were small, he went with Tok-chae to steal some chestnuts from the grandpa[2] with the wen. It was Song-sam's turn to go up the tree. Suddenly there came shouts from the old man. He slipped and fell to the ground. Song-sam got chestnut needles all over his bottom, but he kept on running. It was only when they reached a safe place where the old man could not overtake them that he turned his bottom to Tok-chae. Plucking out those needles hurt so much that he could not keep

---

2 **grandpa:** elderly man

tears from welling up in his eyes. Tok-chae produced a fistful of chestnuts from his pocket and thrust them into Song-sam's . . . Song-sam threw away the cigarette he had just lit. Then he made up his mind not to light another while he was escorting Tok-chae.

◆ ◆ ◆ ◆ ◆

They reached the hill pass, the hill where he and Tok-chae used to cut fodder for the cows until Song-sam had had to move near Chontae, south of the Thirty-eighth Parallel, two years before the liberation.[3]

---

3 **liberation:** In 1945, Japan surrendered to allied forces, ending World War II and Japan's control of Korea.

East Asia & the Pacific Rim

Song-sam felt a sudden surge of anger in spite of himself and shouted, "So how many have you killed?"

For the first time, Tok-chae cast a quick glance at him and then turned away.

"How many did you kill, you?" he asked again.

Tok-chae turned toward him once again and glared. The glare grew intense and his mouth twitched.

"So you managed to kill many, eh?" Song-sam felt his heart becoming clear from within, as if an obstruction had been removed. "If you were vice-chairman of the Communist League, why didn't you run? You must have been lying low with a secret mission."

Tok-chae did not answer.

"Speak up, what was your mission?"

Tok-chae kept walking. Tok-chae is hiding something, Song-sam thought. He wanted to take a good look at him, but Tok-chae would not turn his averted face.

Fingering the revolver at his side, Song-sam went on: "No excuse is necessary. You are sure to be shot anyway. Why don't you tell the truth, here and now?"

"I'm not going to make any excuses. They made me vice-chairman of the league because I was one of the poorest and I was a hard-working farmer. If that constitutes a crime worthy of death, so be it. I am still what I used to be—the only thing I'm good at is digging in the soil." After a short pause, he added, "My old man is bedridden at home. He's been ill almost half a year." Tok-chae's father was a widower, a hard-working poor farmer who lived only for his son. Seven years ago his back had given out and his skin had become diseased.

"You married?"

"Yes," replied Tok-chae after a while.

"To whom?"

"Shorty."

"To Shorty?" How interesting! A woman so small and plump that she knew the earth's vastness but not the sky's altitude. Such a cold fish! He and Tok-chae used to tease her and make her cry. And Tok-chae had married that girl.

"How many kids?"

"The first is arriving this fall, she says."

Song-sam had difficulty swallowing a laugh about to explode in spite of himself. Although he had asked how many kids Tok-chae had, he could not help wanting to burst into laughter at the image of her sitting down, with a large stomach, one span around. But he realized this was no time to laugh or joke over such matters.

"Anyway, it's strange you did not run away."

"I tried to escape. They said that once the South invaded, no man would be spared. So men between seventeen and forty were forcibly taken to the North. I thought of evacuating, even if I had to carry my father on my back. But father said no. How could the farmers leave the land behind when the crops were ready for harvest? He grew old on that farm depending on me as the prop and mainstay of the family. I wanted to be with him in his last moments so that I could close his eyes with my own hand. Besides, where can farmers like us go, who know only living on the land?"

♦ ♦ ♦ ♦ ♦

Last June Song-sam had had to take refuge. At night he had broken the news privately to his father. But his father had said the same thing! Where can a farmer go, leaving all the chores behind? So Song-sam left alone. Roaming about the strange streets and villages in the South, Song-sam had been haunted by thoughts of his old parents and the young children, left with all the chores. Fortunately, his family was safe then, as now.

They crossed the ridge of a hill. This time Song-sam walked with his face averted. The autumn sun was hot on his forehead. This was an ideal day for the harvest, he thought.

♦ ♦ ♦ ♦ ♦

When they reached the foot of the hill, Song-sam hesitatingly stopped. In the middle of a field he spied a group of cranes that looked like men in white clothes bending over. This used to be the neutralized zone[4] along the Thirty-eighth Parallel. The cranes

---

4 **neutralized zone:** an area between North and South Korea that is not controlled by anyone militarily

were still living here, as before, while the people were all gone.

Once, when Song-sam and Tok-chae were about twelve, they had set a trap here, without the knowledge of the adults, and had caught a crane, a Tanjong crane.[5] They had roped the crane, even its wings, and had paid daily visits, patting its neck and riding on its back. Then one day they overheard the neighbors whispering. Someone had come from Seoul with a permit from the governor-general's office[6] to catch cranes as specimens or something. Then and there the two boys dashed off to the field. That they would be found out and punished was no longer a weighty concern; all they worried about was the fate of their crane. Without a moment's delay, still out of breath from running, they untied the crane's feet and wings. But the bird could hardly walk. It must have been worn out from being bound.

. . . all they worried about was the fate of their crane.

The two held it up in the air. Then, all of a sudden, a shot was fired. The crane fluttered its wings a couple of times and came down again.

It was shot, they thought. But the next moment, as another crane from a nearby bush fluttered its wings, the boys' crane stretched its long neck with a whoop and disappeared into the sky. For a long time the two boys could not take their eyes away from the blue sky into which their crane had soared.

"Hey, why don't we stop here for a crane hunt?" Song-sam spoke up suddenly.

Tok-chae was puzzled, struck dumb.

"I'll make a trap with this rope; you flush a crane over here."

Having untied Tok-chae's hands, Song-sam had already started crawling among the weeks.

Tok-chae's face turned white. "You are sure to be shot anyway"—these words flashed through his mind. Pretty soon a bullet would fly from where Song-sam has gone, he thought.

Some paces away, Song-sam quickly turned toward him.

---

5 **Tanjong crane:** a large, long-legged North Korean bird

6 **governor-general's office:** office of Korea's chief executive, appointed when Japan was in control of Korea

"Hey, how come you're standing there like you're dumb? Go flush the crane!"

Only then did Tok-chae catch on. He started crawling among the weeds.

A couple of Tanjong cranes soared high into the clear blue autumn sky, fluttering their huge wings.

Translated by Peter H. Lee

Responding to the Selection

1. The main character in this story suffers a conflict of the heart. Describe the inner and outer sources of Song-sam's conflict.

2. How would you respond if you were Song-sam? Say whether you think he acts appropriately and whether childhood ties can be more important than patriotic ties.

3. Name some of the acts of courage in this story.

4. What do you learn from this story about the human costs of dividing countries whose people were once united by history, culture, family, and social ties?

Thoughts of Hanoi

Nguyen Thi Vinh

During the Vietnam War (1954–1975), Hanoi, then the capital of North Vietnam, was heavily bombed. During the lengthy and brutal Vietnam conflict, an estimated 2–3 million people were killed. Communist forces in the North eventually prevailed over the South, and Hanoi became the capital of the united territories.

WORLD LENS

♦♦♦

VIETNAM

The night is deep and chill
as in early autumn. Pitchblack,
it thickens after each lightning flash.
I dream of Hanoi:
Co-ngu Road
ten years of separation
the way back sliced by a frontier of hatred.
I want to bury the past
to burn the future
still I yearn
still I fear
those endless nights
waiting for dawn.

Brother,
how is Hang Dao now?
How is Ngoc Son temple?
Do the trains still run
each day from Hanoi
to the neighboring towns?
To Bac-ninh, Cam-giang, Yen-bai,
the small villages, islands
of brown thatch in a lush green sea?

The girls
bright eyes
ruddy cheeks
four-piece dresses
raven-bill scarves[1]
sowing harvesting
spinning weaving
all year round,
the boys
ploughing
transplanting
in the fields
in their shops
running across
the meadow at evening
to fly kites
and sing alternating songs.

Stainless blue sky,
jubilant voices of children
stumbling through the alphabet,
village graybeards strolling to the temple,
grandmothers basking in twilight sun,
chewing betel leaves
while the children run—

Brother,
how is all that now?
Or is it obsolete?
Are you like me,
reliving the past,
imagining the future?
Do you count me as a friend
or am I the enemy in your eyes?
Brother, I am afraid

---

1 **raven-bill scarves:** head scarves folded into triangles, like the bill of a bird

East Asia & the Pacific Rim

that one day I'll be with the March-North Army[2]
meeting you on your way to the South.
I might be the one to shoot you then
or you me
but please
not with hatred.

For don't you remember how it was,
you and I in school together,
plotting our lives together?
Those roots go deep!

Brother, we are men,
conscious of more
than material needs.
How can this happen to us
my friend
my foe?

Translated by Nguyen Ngoc Bich

Responding to the Selection

1. Who is the speaker addressing and under what circumstances?

2. What is the tone of this poem? Give details that support your answer.

3. This poem has a lot of description, something which can feel slow and static to a reader if it is not done well. See if you can find any elements in the poem that contribute to its energy.

4. Imagine you are separated from your brother or sister in a violent civil war such as the Vietnamese conflict. Write down some of the details that you might use to remind your sibling of your shared upbringing and community.

---

2 **March-North Army:** the South Vietnamese army marching into North Vietnam

Tokyo

Fumiko Hayashi

WORLD LENS

•••

JAPAN

One of Japan's most popular and critically acclaimed female writers, Fumiko Hayashi came up from poverty to achieve wealth and fame by the time she died. She was familiar with life on the streets—the subject of the following story—from holding a variety of menial jobs that often left her hungry and homeless. Much of her work depicts poor people, usually women, imbued with a relentless spirit and hope for better times. "Tokyo" is one of her most highly regarded short stories.

It was a bitter, windy afternoon. As Ryo hurried down the street with her rucksack, she kept to the side where the pale sun shone down over the roofs of the office buildings. Every now and then she looked about curiously—at a building, at a parked car—at one of those innumerable bomb sites[1] scattered through downtown Tokyo.

Glancing over a boarding, Ryo saw a huge pile of rusty iron, and next to it a cabin with a glass door. A fire was burning within, and the warm sound of the crackling wood reached where she was standing. In front of the cabin stood a man in overalls with a red kerchief about his head. There was something pleasant about this tall fellow, and Ryo screwed up her courage to call out, "Tea for sale! Would you like some tea, please?"

"Tea?" said the man.

"Tea," said Ryo with a nervous smile. "It's Shizuoka tea."[2]

She stepped in through an opening in the boarding and, unfastening the straps of her rucksack, put it down by the cabin. Inside she could see a fire burning in an iron stove; from a bar

---

1 **bomb sites:** places where bombs were dropped during World War II
2 **Shizuoka tea:** tea from the Honshu region of Japan

above hung a brass kettle with a wisp of steam rising from the spout.

"Excuse me," said Ryo, "but would you mind if I came in and warmed myself by your stove a few minutes? It's freezing out, and I've been walking for miles."

"Of course you can come in," said the man. "Close the door and get warm."

He pointed towards the stool, which was his only article of furniture, and sat down on a packing case in the corner. Ryo hesitated a moment. Then she dragged her rucksack into the cabin and, crouching by the stove, held up her hands to the fire.

"You'll be more comfortable on that stool," said the man, glancing at her attractive face, flushed in the sudden warmth, and at her shabby attire.

"Surely this isn't what you usually do—hawk tea from door to door?"

"Oh yes, it's how I make my living," Ryo said. "I was told that this was a good neighborhood, but I've been walking around here since early morning and have only managed to sell one packet of tea. I'm about ready to go home now, but I thought I'd have my lunch somewhere on the way."

"Well, you're perfectly welcome to stay here and eat your lunch," said the man. "And don't worry about not having sold your tea," he added, smiling. "It's all a matter of luck, you know! You'll probably have a good day tomorrow."

The kettle came to a boil with a whistling sound. As he unhooked it from the bar, Ryo had a chance to look about her. She took in the boarded ceiling black with soot, the blackboard by the window, the shelf for family gods on which stood a potted sakaki tree. The man took a limp-looking packet from the table, and unwrapping it, disclosed a piece of cod. A few minutes later the smell of baking fish permeated the cabin.

"Come on," said the man. "Sit down and have your meal."

Ryo took her lunch box out of the rucksack and seated herself on the stool.

"Selling things is never much fun, is it?" remarked the man, turning the cod over on the grill. "Tell me, how much do you get for a hundred grams of that tea?"

"I should get thirty-five yen to make any sort of profit. The people who send me the stuff often mix in bad tea, so I'm lucky if I can get thirty yen."

In Ryo's lunch box were two small fish covered with some boiled barley and a few bean-paste pickles. She began eating.

"Where do you live?" the man asked her.

"In the Shitaya district. Actually, I don't know one part of Tokyo from another! I've only been here a few weeks and a friend's putting me up until I find something better."

The cod was ready now. He cut it in two and gave Ryo half, adding potatoes and rice from a platter. Ryo smiled and bowed slightly in thanks, then took out a bag of tea from her rucksack and poured some into a paper handkerchief.

"Do put this into the kettle," she said, holding it out to him.

He shook his head and smiled, showing his white teeth.

"Good Lord, no! It's far too expensive."

Quickly Ryo removed the lid and poured the tea in before he could stop her. Laughing, the man went to fetch a teacup and a mug from the shelf.

"What about your husband?" he asked, while ranging them on the packing case. "You're married, aren't you?"

"Oh yes, I am. My husband's still in Siberia.[3] That's why I have to work like this."

Ryo's thoughts flew to her husband, from whom she had not heard for six years; by now he had come to seem so remote that it required an effort to remember his looks, or the once-familiar sound of his voice. She woke up each morning with a feeling of emptiness and desolation. At times it seemed to Ryo that her husband had frozen into a ghost in that subarctic Siberia—a ghost, or a thin white pillar, or just a breath of frosty air. Nowadays no one any longer mentioned the war and she was almost embarrassed to let people know that her husband was still a prisoner.

"It's funny," the man said. "The fact is, I was in Siberia myself! I spent three years chopping wood near the Amur River—I only managed to get sent home last year. Well, it's all in a matter of luck! It's tough on your husband. But it's just as tough on you."

---

3 **Siberia:** region of the former Soviet Union, where prisoners of war were held

"So you've really been **repatriated** from Siberia! You don't seem any the worse for it," Ryo said.

"Well, I don't know about that!" the man shrugged his shoulders. "Anyway, as you see, I'm still alive."

Ryo closed her lunch box, and as she did so, she studied him. There was a simplicity and directness about this man that made her want to talk openly in a way that she found difficult with more educated people.

"Got any kids?" he said.

"Yes, a boy of six. He should be at school, but I've had difficulty getting him registered here in Tokyo. These officials certainly know how to make life complicated for people!"

The man untied his kerchief, wiped the cup and the mug with it, and poured out the steaming tea.

"It's good stuff this!" he said, sipping noisily.

"Do you like it? It's not the best quality, you know: only two hundred and ten yen a kilo wholesale. But you're right—it's quite good."

The wind had grown stronger while they were talking; it whistled over the tin roof of the cabin. Ryo glanced out of the window, steeling herself for her long walk home.

"I'll have some of your tea—seven hundred and fifty grams," the man told her, extracting two crumbled hundred-yen notes from the pocket of his overalls.

"Don't be silly," said Ryo. "You can have it for nothing."

"Oh no, that won't do. Business is business!" He forced the money into her hand. "Well, if you're ever in this part of the world again, come in and have another chat."

"I should like to," said Ryo, glancing around the tiny cabin. "But you don't live here, do you?"

"Oh, but I do! I look after that iron out there and help load the trucks. I'm here most of the day."

He opened a door under the shelf, disclosing a sort of cubbyhole containing a bed neatly made up. Ryo noticed a colored postcard of the Fifty Bells of Yamada tacked to the back of the door.

"My, you've fixed it up nicely," she said smiling. "You're really quite snug here, aren't you?"

She wondered how old he could be.

repatriated
sent back; returned to one's home country

2

From that day on, Ryo came regularly to the Yotsugi district to sell tea; each time she visited the cabin on the bomb site. She learned that the man's name was Tsuruishi Yoshio. Almost invariably he had some small delicacy waiting for her to put in her lunch box— a pickled plum, a piece of beef, a sardine. Her business began to improve and she acquired a few regular customers in the neighborhood.

A week after their first meeting, she brought along her boy, Ryukichi. Tsuruishi chatted with the child for a while and then took him out for a walk. When they returned, Ryukichi was carrying a large caramel cake.

"He's got a good appetite, this youngster of yours," said Tsuruishi, patting the boy's close-cropped head.

Ryo wondered vaguely whether her new friend was married; in fact she found herself wondering about various aspects of his life. She was now twenty-nine, and she realized with a start that this was the first time she had been seriously interested in any man but her husband. Tsuruishi's easy, carefree temperament somehow appealed to her, though she took great care not to let him guess that.

A little later Tsuruishi suggested taking Ryo and Ryukichi to see Asakusa[4] on his next free day. They met in front of the information booth in Ueno Station, Tsuruishi wearing an ancient gray suit that looked far too tight, Ryo clad in a blue dress of kimono material and a light-brown coat. In spite of her cheap clothes, she had about her something youthful and elegant as she stood there in the crowded station. Beside the tall, heavy Tsuruishi, she looked like a schoolgirl off on a holiday. In her shopping bag lay their lunch: bread, oranges, and seaweed stuffed with rice.

"Well, let's hope it doesn't rain," said Tsuruishi, putting his arm lightly round Ryo's waist as he steered her through the crowd.

They took the subway to Asakusa Station, then walked from the Matsuya Department Store to the Niten Shinto Gate past hundreds of tiny stalls. The Asakusa district was quite different from what Ryo had imagined. She was amazed when Tsuruishi

---

4 **Asakusa:** a shopping district in Tokyo

pointed to a small red-lacquered temple and told her that this was the home of the famous Asakusa Goddess of Mercy. In the distance she could hear the plaintive wail of a trumpet and a saxophone emerging from some loud-speaker; it mingled strangely with the sound of the wind whistling through the branches of the ancient sakaki trees.

They made their way through the old-clothes market, and came to a row of food-stalls squeezed tightly against each other beside the Asakusa Pond; here the air was **redolent** with the smell of burning oil. Tsuruishi went to one of the stalls and bought Ryukichi a stick of yellow candy-floss. The boy nibbled at it, as the three of them walked down a narrow street plastered with American-style billboards advertising restaurants, movies, revues. It was less than a month since Ryo had first noticed Tsuruishi by his cabin, yet she felt as much at ease with him as if she had known him all her life.

> **redolent**
> *smelling; scented*

"Well, it's started raining after all," he said, holding out his hand. Ryo looked up, to see scattered drops of rain falling from the gray sky. So their precious excursion would be ruined, she thought.

"We'd better go in there," said Tsuruishi, pointing to one of the shops, outside which hung a garish lantern with characters announcing the "Merry Teahouse." They took seats at a table underneath a ceiling decorated with artificial cherry blossoms. The place had a strangely unhomelike atmosphere, but they were determined to make the best of it and ordered a pot of tea; Ryo distributed her stuffed seaweed, bread, and oranges. It was not long before the meal was finished and by then it had started raining in earnest.

"We'd better wait till it lets up a bit," suggested Tsuruishi. "Then I'll take you home."

Ryo wondered if he was referring to her place or his. She was staying in the cramped apartment of a friend from her home town and did not even have a room to call her own; rather than go there, she would have preferred returning to Tsuruishi's cabin, but that too was scarcely large enough to hold three people. Taking out her purse, she counted her money under the table. The seven hundred yen should be enough to get shelter for a few hours at an inn.

"D'you know what I'd really like?" she said. "I'd like us to go to a movie and then find some inn and have a dish of food before saying good-bye to each other. But I suppose that's all rather expensive!"

"Yes, I suppose it is," said Tsuruishi, laughing. "Come on! We'll do it all the same."

Taking his overcoat off the peg, he threw it over Ryukichi's head, and ran through the downpour to a movie theatre. Of course there were no seats! Standing watching the film, the little boy went sound asleep, leaning against Tsuruishi. The air in the theatre seemed to get thicker and hotter every moment; on the roof they could hear the rain beating down.

It was getting dark as they left the theatre and hurried through the rain, which pelted down with the swishing sound of banana leaves in a high wind. At last they found a small inn where the landlord led them to a carpeted room at the end of a drafty passage. Ryo took off her wet socks. The boy sat down in a corner and promptly went back to sleep

"Here, he can use this as a pillow," said Tsuruishi, picking up an old cushion from a chair and putting it under Ryukichi's head.

From an overflowing gutter above the window the water poured in a steady stream onto the courtyard. It sounded like a waterfall in some faraway mountain village.

Tsuruishi took out a handkerchief and began wiping Ryo's wet hair. A feeling of happiness coursed through her as she looked up at him. It was as if the rain had begun to wash away all the loneliness which had been gathering within her year after year.

She went to see if they could get some food and in the corridor met a maid in Western clothes carrying a tea tray. After Ryo had ordered two bowls of spaghetti, she and Tsuruishi sat down to drink their tea, facing each other across an empty brazier. Later Tsuruishi came and sat on the floor beside Ryo. Leaning their backs against the wall they gazed out at the darkening, rainy sky.

"How old are you, Ryo?" Tsuruishi asked her. "I should guess twenty-five."

Ryo laughed. "I'm afraid not, Tsuru, I'm already an old woman! I'm twenty-eight."

"Oh, so you're a year older than me."

"My goodness, you're young!" said Ryo. "I thought you must be at least thirty."

She looked straight at him, into his dark, gentle eyes with their bushy brows. He seemed to be blushing slightly. Then he bent forward and took off his wet socks.

The rain continued unabated. Presently the maid came with some cold spaghetti and soup. Ryo woke the boy and gave him a plate of soup; he was half asleep as he sipped it.

"Look, Ryo," Tsuruishi said, "we might as well all stay the night at this inn. You can't go home in this rain, can you?"

"No," said Ryo. "No, I suppose not."

Tsuruishi left the room and returned with a load of quilted bedrolls which he spread on the floor. At once the whole room seemed to be full of bedding. Ryo tucked up her son in one of the rolls, the boy sleeping soundly as she did so. Then she turned out the light, undressed, and lay down. She could hear Tsuruishi settling down at the other end of the room.

"I suppose the people in this inn think we're married," said Tsuruishi after a while.

"Yes, I suppose so. It's not very nice of us to fool them!"

She spoke in jest, but now that she lay undressed in her bedroll, she felt for the first time vaguely disturbed and guilty. Her husband for some reason seemed much closer than he had for years. But of course she was only here because of the rain, she reminded herself . . . And gradually her thoughts began to wander pleasantly afield, and she dozed off.

When she awoke it was still dark. She could hear Tsuruishi whispering her name from his corner, and she sat up with a start.

"Ryo, Ryo, can I come and talk to you for a while?"

"No, Tsuru," she said, "I don't think you should."

On the roof the rain was still pattering down, but the force of the storm was over; only a trickle was dropping from the gutter into the yard. Under the sound of the rain she thought she could hear Tsuruishi sigh softly.

"Look Tsuru," she said after a pause. "I've never asked you before, but are you married?"

"No. Not now," Tsuruishi said.

"You used to be?"

"Yes. I used to be. When I got back from the army, I found that my wife was living with another man."

"Were you—angry?"

"Angry? Yes, I suppose I was. Still, there wasn't much I could do about it. She'd left me, and that was that."

They were silent again.

"What shall we talk about?" Ryo asked.

Tsuruishi laughed. "Well, there really doesn't seem to be anything special to talk about. That spaghetti wasn't very good, was it?"

"No, one certainly couldn't call it good. And they charged us a hundred yen each for it!"

"It would be nice if you and Ryukichi had your own room to live in, wouldn't it?" Tsuruishi remarked.

"Oh yes, it would be marvelous! You don't think we might find a room near you? I'd really like to live near you, Tsuru, you know."

"It's pretty hard to find rooms these days, especially downtown. But I'll keep a lookout and let you know . . . You're such a wonderful person, Ryo!"

"Me?" said Ryo laughing. "Don't be silly!"

"Yes, yes, you're wonderful! . . . really wonderful!"

Ryo lay back on the floor. Suddenly she wanted to throw her arms around Tsuruishi, to feel his body close to hers. She did not dare speak for fear that her voice might betray her; her breath came almost painfully; her whole body tingled. Outside the window an early morning truck clattered past.

"Where are your parents, Tsuru?" she asked after a while.

"In the country near Fukuoka."

"But you have a sister in Tokyo?"

"Yes. She's all alone, like you, with two kids to take care of. She's got a sewing machine and makes Western-style clothes. Her husband was killed several years ago in the war in China. War, always war!"

Outside the window Ryo could make out the first glimmer of dawn. So their night together was almost over, she thought unhappily. In a way she wished that Tsuruishi hadn't given up so easily, and yet she was convinced that it was best like this. If he had been a man she hardly knew, or for whom she felt nothing, she might have given herself to him with no afterthought. With Tsuruishi it would have been different—quite different.

"Ryo, I can't get to sleep." His voice reached her again. "I'm wide awake, you know. I suppose I'm not used to this sort of thing."

"What sort of thing?"

"Why—sleeping in the same room with a girl."

"Oh Tsuru, don't tell me that you don't have girl friends occasionally!"

"Only professional girl friends."

Ryo laughed. "Men have it easy! In some ways, at least. . . ."

She heard Tsuruishi moving about. Suddenly he was beside her, bending over her. Ryo did not move, not even when she felt his arms around her, his face against hers. In the dark her eyes were wide open, and before them bright lights seemed to be flashing. His hot lips were pressed to her cheek.

"Ryo . . . Ryo."

"It's wrong you know," she murmured. "Wrong to my husband. . . ."

But almost at once she regretted the words. As Tsuruishi bent over her, she could make out the silhouette of his face against the lightening sky. Bowed forward like that, he seemed to be offering **obeisance** to some god. Ryo hesitated for a moment. Then she threw her warm arms about his neck.

obeisance
homage; gesture of respect

3

Two days later Ryo set out happily with her boy to visit Tsuruishi. When she reached the bomb site, she was surprised not to see him before his cabin, his red kerchief tied about his head. Ryukichi ran ahead to find out if he were home and came back in a moment.

"There are strangers there, Mamma!"

Seized with panic, Ryo hurried over to the cabin and peered in. Two workmen were busy piling up Tsuruishi's effects in a corner.

"What is it, ma'am?" one of them said, turning his head.

"I'm looking for Tsuruishi."

"Oh, don't you know? Tsuruishi died yesterday."

"Died," she said. She wanted to say something more but no words would come.

She had noticed a small candle burning on the shelf for family gods, and now she was aware of its somber meaning.

"Yes," went on the man, "he was killed about eight o'clock last night. He went in a truck with one of the men to deliver some iron bars in Omiya, and on their way back the truck overturned on a narrow bridge. He and the driver were both killed. His sister went to Omiya today with one of the company officials to see about the cremation."

Ryo stared vacantly before her. Vacantly she watched the two men piling up Tsuruishi's belongings. Beside the candle on the shelf she caught sight of the two bags of tea he had bought from her that first day—could it be only two weeks ago? One of them was folded over halfway down; the other was still unopened.

"You were a friend of his, ma'am, I imagine? He was a fine fellow, Tsuru! Funny to think that he needn't have gone to Omiya at all. The driver wasn't feeling well and Tsuru said he'd go along to Omiya to help him unload. Crazy, isn't it—after getting through the war and Siberia and all the rest of it, to be killed like that!"

One of the men took down the postcard of the Fifty Bells of Yamada and blew the dust off it. Ryo stood looking at Tsuruishi's belongings piled on the floor—the kettle, the frying pan, the rubber boots. When her eyes reached the blackboard, she noticed for the first time a message scratched awkwardly in red chalk: 'Ryo—I waited for you till two o'clock. Back this evening."

Automatically she bowed to the two men and swung the rucksack on her back. She felt numb as she left the cabin, holding Ryukichi by the hand, but as they passed the bomb site, the burning tears welled into her eyes.

"Did that man die, Mamma?"

"Yes, he died," Ryo said.

"Why did he die?"

"He fell into a river."

The tears were running down her cheeks now; they poured out uncontrollably as she hurried through the downtown streets. They came to an arched bridge over the Sumida River, crossed it, and walked along the bank in the direction of Hakuho.

"Don't worry if you get pregnant," Tsuruishi had told her that morning in Asakusa, "I'll look after you whatever happens, Ryo!" And later on, just before they parted, he had said, "I haven't got much money, but you must let me help you a bit. I can give you two thousand yen a month out of my salary." He had taken Ryukichi to a shop that specialized in foreign goods and bought him a baseball cap with his name written on it. Then the three of them had walked gaily along the streetcar lines, skirting the enormous puddles left by the rain. When they came to a milk bar, Tsuruishi had taken them in and ordered them each a big glass of milk . . . .

"I'll look after you whatever happens, Ryo!"

Now an icy wind seemed to have blown up from the dark river. A flock of waterfowl stood on the opposite bank, looking frozen and miserable. Barges moved slowly up and down the river.

"Mamma, I want a sketchbook. You said I could have a sketchbook."

"Later," answered Ryo, "I'll get you one later."

"But Mamma, we just passed a stall with hundreds of sketchbooks. I'm hungry, Mamma. Can't we have something to eat?"

"Later. A little later!"

They were passing a long row of barrack-like buildings. They must be private houses, she thought. The people who lived there probably all had rooms of their own. From one of the windows a bedroll had been hung out to air and inside a woman could be seen tidying the room.

"Tea for sale!" called out Ryo softly. "Best quality Shizuoka tea!"

There was no reply and Ryo repeated her call a little louder.

"I don't want any," said the woman. She pulled in the bedroll and shut the window with a bang.

Ryo went from house to house down the row calling her ware, but nobody wanted any tea. Ryukichi followed behind, muttering that he was hungry and tired. Ryo's rucksack cut painfully into her shoulders, and occasionally she had to stop to adjust the straps. Yet in a way she almost welcomed the physical pain.

4

The next day she went downtown by herself, leaving Ryukichi at home. When she came to the bomb site she noticed that a fire was burning inside the cabin. She ran to the door and walked in. By Tsuruishi's stove sat an old man in a short workman's overcoat, feeding the flames with firewood. The room was full of smoke and it was billowing out of the window.

"What do you want?" said the old man, looking round.

"I've come to sell some Shizuoka tea."

"Shizuoka tea? I've got plenty of good tea right here."

Ryo turned without a word and hurried off. She had thought of asking for the address of Tsuruishi's sister and of going to burn a stick of incense in his memory, but suddenly this seemed quite pointless. She walked back to the river, which reflected the late afternoon sun, and sat down by a pile of broken concrete. The body of a dead kitten was lying upside down a few yards away. As her thoughts went to Tsuruishi, she wondered vaguely whether it would have been better never to have met him. No, no, certainly not that! She could never regret knowing him, nor anything that had happened with him. Nor did she regret having come to Tokyo. When she had arrived, a month or so before, she had planned to return to the country if her business was unsuccessful, but now she knew that she would be staying on here in Tokyo— yes, probably right here in downtown Tokyo where Tsuruishi had lived.

She got up, swung the rucksack on her back, and walked away from the river. As she strolled along a side street, she noticed a hut which seemed to consist of old boards nailed haphazardly together. Going to the door, she called out, "Tea for sale! Would anyone like some tea?" The door opened and in the entrance appeared a woman dressed far more poorly than Ryo herself.

"How much does it cost?" asked the woman. And, then, seeing the rucksack, she added, "Come in and rest a while, if you like. I'll see how much money we've got left. We may have enough for some tea."

Ryo went in and put down her rucksack. In the small room

four sewing women were sitting on the floor around and oil stove, working on a mass of shirts and socks. They were women like herself, thought Ryo, as she watched their busy needles moving in and out of the material. A feeling of warmth came over her.

Translated by Ivan Morris

Responding to the Selection

1. What do you think is the theme of this story? Explain your answer using clues from the text.

2. The author of this story, Fumiko Hayashi, was poor and lived on the street herself before becoming the most popular female writer in Japan. What attitudes and details of Tokyo street life seem authentic to you?

3. Although this story is about poverty and thwarted hopes, there are many instances of beauty. Find one or two and discuss why the author chooses to include such details in this portrait of Tokyo's post-war poor.

4. What setting details indicate behavior and ideas that are very different from what you are used to here in the United States?

5. Think about all of the characters in this story and their actions and dialogue. What values are held by these survivors of World War II?

Swaddling Clothes

Yukio Mishima

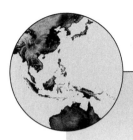

WORLD LENS

◆◆◆

JAPAN

Controversial and acclaimed writer Yukio Mishima wrote fiction that is sexually frank as well as emotionally and psychologically astute. His writing critiques contemporary Japan, which Mishima—an ultraconservative and fervent nationalist—believed was losing its way in the years after World War II. He is famous for committing suicide in the samurai (warrior) manner to protest a weakened Japanese military.

H e was always busy, Toshiko's husband. Even tonight he had to dash off to an appointment, leaving her to go home alone by taxi. But what else could a woman expect when she married an actor—an attractive one? No doubt she had been foolish to hope that he would spend the evening with her. And yet he must have known how she dreaded going back to their house, unhomely with its Western-style furniture and with the bloodstains still showing on the floor.

Toshiko had been oversensitive since girlhood: that was her nature. As the result of constant worrying she never put on weight, and now, an adult woman, she looked more like a transparent picture than a creature of flesh and blood. Her delicacy of spirit was evident to her most casual acquaintance.

Earlier that evening, when she had joined her husband at a night club, she had been shocked to find him entertaining friends with an account of "the incident." Sitting there in his American-style suit, puffing at a cigarette, he had seemed to her almost a stranger.

flamboyantly
wildly; showily

"It's a fantastic story," he was saying, gesturing **flamboyantly** as if in an attempt to outweigh the attractions of the dance band. "Here this new nurse for our baby arrives from the employment agency, and the very first thing I notice about her is her stomach.

It's enormous—as if she had a pillow stuck under her kimono![1]
No wonder, I thought, for I soon saw that she could eat more
than the rest of us put together. She polished off the contents of
our rice bin like that . . . ." He snapped his fingers. "'Gastric
dilation'—that's how she explained her girth and her appetite.
Well, the day before yesterday we heard groans and moans
coming from the nursery. We rushed in and found her squatting
on the floor, holding her stomach in her two hands, and moaning
like a cow. Next to her our baby lay in his cot, scared out of his wits
and crying at the top of his lungs. A pretty scene, I can tell you!"

"So the cat was out of the bag?" suggested one of their friends,
a film actor like Toshiko's husband.

"Indeed it was! And it gave me the shock of my life. You see,
I'd completely swallowed that story about 'gastric dilation.' Well,
I didn't waste any time. I rescued our good rug from the floor and
spread a blanket for her to lie on. The whole time the girl was
yelling like a stuck pig. By the time the doctor from the maternity
clinic arrived, the baby had already been born. But our sitting
room was a pretty shambles!"

"Oh, that I'm sure of!" said another of their friends, and the
whole company burst into laughter.

Toshiko was dumbfounded to hear her husband discussing
the horrifying happening as though it were no more than an
amusing incident which they chanced to have witnessed. She shut
her eyes for a moment and all at once she saw the newborn baby
lying before her: on the parquet[2] floor the infant lay, and his frail
body was wrapped in bloodstained newspapers.

Toshiko was sure that the doctor had done the whole thing
out of spite. As if to emphasize his scorn for this mother who had
given birth to a bastard under such sordid conditions, he had told
his assistant to wrap the baby in some loose newspapers, rather
than proper swaddling. This callous treatment of the newborn
child had offended Toshiko. Overcoming her disgust at the entire
scene, she had fetched a brand-new piece of flannel from her
cupboard and, having swaddled the baby in it, had lain him
carefully in an armchair.

---

1 **kimono:** a traditional Japanese robe

2 **parquet:** a patterned wood surface

brayed
played loudly or harshly

poignantly
painfully; touchingly

This all had taken place in the evening after her husband had left the house. Toshiko had told him nothing of it, fearing that he would think her oversoft, oversentimental; yet the scene had engraved itself deeply in her mind. Tonight she sat silently thinking back on it, while the jazz orchestra **brayed** and her husband chatted cheerfully with his friends. She knew that she would never forget the sight of the baby, wrapped in stained newspapers and lying on the floor—it was a scene fit for a butchershop. Toshiko, whose own life had been spent in solid comfort, **poignantly** felt the wretchedness of the illegitimate baby.

I am the only person to have witnessed its shame, the thought occurred to her. The mother never saw her child lying there in its newspaper wrappings, and the baby itself of course didn't know. I alone shall have to preserve that terrible scene in my memory. When the baby grows up and wants to find out about his birth, there will be no one to tell him, so long as I preserve the silence. How strange that I should have this feeling of guilt! After all, it

was I who took him up from the floor, swathed him properly in flannel, and laid him down to sleep in the armchair.

They left the night club and Toshiko stepped into the taxi that her husband had called for her. "Take this lady to Ushigomé," he told the driver and shut the door from the outside. Toshiko gazed through the window at her husband's smiling face and noticed his strong, white teeth. Then she leaned back in the seat, oppressed by the knowledge that their life together was in some way too easy, too painless. It would have been difficult for her to put her thoughts into words. Through the rear window of the taxi she took a last look at her husband. He was striding along the street toward his Nash car, and soon the back of his rather garish tweed coat had blended with the figures of the passers-by.

The taxi drove off, passed down a street dotted with bars and then by a theatre, in front of which the throngs of people jostled each other on the pavement. Although the performance had only just ended, the lights had already been turned out and in the half dark outside it was depressingly obvious that the cherry blossoms decorating the front of the theatre were merely scraps of white paper.

Even if that baby should grow up in ignorance of the secret of his birth, he can never become a respectable citizen, reflected Toshiko, pursuing the same train of thoughts. Those soiled newspaper swaddling clothes will be the symbol of his entire life. But why should I keep worrying about him so much? Is it because I feel uneasy about the future of my own child? Say twenty years from now, when our boy will have grown up into a fine, carefully educated young man, one day by a quirk of fate he meets the other boy, who then will also have turned twenty. And say that the other boy, who has been sinned against, savagely stabs him with a knife . . . .

It was a warm, overcast April night, but thoughts of the future made Toshiko feel cold and miserable. She shivered on the back seat of the car.

No, when the time comes I shall take my son's place, she told herself suddenly. Twenty years from now I shall be forty-three. I shall go to that young man and tell him straight out about everything—about his newspaper swaddling clothes, and about how I went and wrapped him in flannel.

The taxi ran along the dark wide road that was bordered by the park and by the Imperial Palace moat. In the distance Toshiko noticed the pinpricks of light which came from the blocks of tall office buildings.

desolate
bleak; cheerless

Twenty years from now that wretched child will be in utter misery. He will be living a **desolate**, hopeless, poverty-stricken existence—a lonely rat. What else could happen to a baby who has had such a birth? He'll be wandering through the streets by himself, cursing his father, loathing his mother.

No doubt Toshiko derived a certain satisfaction from her somber thoughts: she tortured herself with them without cease. The taxi approached Hanzomon and drove past the compound of the British Embassy. At that point the famous rows of cherry trees were spread out before Toshiko in all their purity. On the spur of the moment she decided to go and view the blossoms by herself in the dark night. It was a strange decision for a timid and unadventurous young woman, but then she was in a strange state of mind and she dreaded the return home. That evening all sorts of unsettling fancies had burst open in her mind.

She crossed the wide street—a slim, solitary figure in the darkness. As a rule when she walked in the traffic Toshiko used to cling fearfully to her companion, but tonight she darted alone between the cars and a moment later had reached the long narrow park that borders the Palace moat. Chidorigafuchi, it is called—the Abyss of the Thousand Birds.

Tonight the whole park had become a grove of blossoming cherry trees. Under the calm cloudy sky the blossoms formed a mass of solid whiteness. The paper lanterns that hung from wires between the trees had been put out; in their place electric light bulbs, red, yellow, and green, shone dully beneath the blossoms. It was well past ten o'clock and most of the flower-viewers had gone home. As the occasional passers-by strolled through the park, they would automatically kick aside the empty bottles or crush the waste paper beneath their feet.

Newspapers, thought Toshiko, her mind going back once again to those happenings. Bloodstained newspapers. If a man were ever to hear of that piteous birth and know that it was he who had lain there, it would ruin his entire life. To think that I, a perfect stranger, should from now on have to keep such a secret— the secret of a man's whole existence . . . .

Lost in these thoughts, Toshiko walked on through the park. Most of the people still remaining there were quiet couples; no one paid her any attention. She noticed two people sitting on a stone bench beside the moat, not looking at the blossoms, but gazing silently at the water. Pitch black it was, and swathed in heavy shadows. Beyond the moat the somber forest of the Imperial Palace blocked her view. The trees reached up, to form a solid dark mass against the night sky. Toshiko walked slowly along the path beneath the blossoms hanging heavily overhead.

On a stone bench, slightly apart from the others, she noticed a pale object—not, as she had at first imagined, a pile of cherry blossoms, nor a garment forgotten by one of the visitors to the park. Only when she came closer did she see that it was a human form lying on the bench. Was it, she wondered, one of those miserable drunks often to be seen sleeping in public places? Obviously not, for the body had been systematically covered with newspapers, and it was the whiteness of those papers that had attracted Toshiko's attention. Standing by the bench, she gazed down at the sleeping figure.

It was a man in a brown jersey who lay there, curled up on layers of newspapers, other newspapers covering him. No doubt this had become his normal night residence now that spring had arrived. Toshiko gazed down at the man's dirty, unkempt hair, which in places had become hopelessly matted. As she observed the sleeping figure wrapped in its newspapers, she was inevitably reminded of the baby who had lain on the floor in its wretched swaddling clothes. The shoulder of the man's jersey rose and fell in the darkness in time with his heavy breathing.

It seemed to Toshiko that all her fears and premonitions had suddenly taken concrete form. In the darkness the man's pale forehead stood out, and it was a young forehead, though carved with the wrinkles of long poverty and hardship. His khaki trousers had been slightly pulled up; on his sockless feet he wore a pair of battered gym shoes. She could not see his face and suddenly had an overmastering desire to get one glimpse of it.

She walked to the head of the bench and looked down. The man's head was half buried in his arms, but Toshiko could see that he was surprisingly young. She noticed the thick eyebrows and the fine bridge of his nose. His slightly open mouth was alive with youth.

But Toshiko had approached too close. In the silent night the newspaper bedding rustled, and abruptly the man opened his eyes. Seeing the young woman standing directly beside him, he raised himself with a jerk, and his eyes lit up. A second later a powerful hand reached out and seized Toshiko by her slender wrist.

She did not feel in the least afraid and made no effort to free herself. In a flash the thought had struck her. Ah, so the twenty years have already gone by! The forest of the Imperial Palace was pitch dark and utterly silent.

Translated by Ivan Morris

Responding to the Selection

1. Name some of the internal and external conflicts Toshiko faces in this story. In your opinion, how equipped is she to cope with such conflicts?

2. Using only information from the first four paragraphs, describe the husband and wife in this story. Do their later actions conform to your first impressions?

3. What are some of the things you learn from "Swaddling Clothes" about gender roles and expectations at the time of the story? You might want to do some research to see how much, if at all, things have changed since its publication in 1966.

4. Were you prepared for the story's ending? Explain why or why not.

5. Are there any conceptions you had about Japan prior to reading this story that have changed as a result of reading it? Explain.

The Shadow

Tōge Sankichi

WORLD LENS
◆ ◆ ◆
JAPAN

Cheap movie theaters, saloons, fly-by-night markets,
burned, rebuilt, standing, crumbling, spreading like the itch—
the new Hiroshima,
head shiny with hair oil,
barefaced in its resurgence;
already visible all over the place,
in growing numbers, billboards in English;
one of these: "Historic A-Bomb Site."

Enclosed by a painted fence
on a corner of the bank steps,
stained onto the grain of the dark red stone:
a quiet pattern.

That morning
a flash tens of thousands of degrees hot
burned it all of a sudden onto the thick slab of granite:
someone's trunk.

Burned onto the step, cracked and watery red,
the mark of the blood that flowed as intestines melted to mush:
a shadow.

◆◆

Ah! If you are from Hiroshima
and on that morning,
amid indescribable flash and heat and smoke,
were buffeted in the whirlpool of the glare of the flames, the
    shadow of the cloud,
crawled about dragging skin that was peeling off,
so transformed that even your wife and children
would not have known you,
this shadow
is etched in tragic memory
and will never fade.

Right beside the street where the people of the city come and go,
well-meaning but utterly indifferent,
assaulted by the sun, attacked by the rain, covered over by dust,
growing fainter year by year: this shadow.

The bank with the "Historic Site" sign at the foot of its steps
dumped out into the street pieces of stone and glass, burned gritty,
completed a major reconstruction,
and set the whole enormous building sparkling in the evening sun.
In the vacant lot diagonally across,
drawing a crowd: a quack in the garb of a mountain ascetic.

Indifferent, the authorities say: "If we don't protect it with glass or
      something,
it will fade away," but do nothing.
Today, too,
foreign sailors amble up in their white leggings,
come to a stop with a click of their heels,
and, each having taken a snapshot, go off;
the shoeshine boy who followed them here
peers over the fence, wonders why all the fuss,
and goes on his way.

Translated by Richard H. Minear

Responding to the Selection

1. How would you describe the poet's attitude to "the new Hiroshima"?

2. What, if anything, in this poem surprises you?

3. How does it enhance the poem to personify the city of Hiroshima?

4. Why does the poet mention the "quack in the garb of a mountain ascetic"?

5. *Should* we allow the shadow to fade?

Inem

Pramoedya Ananta Toer

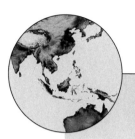

WORLD LENS

♦♦♦

INDONESIA

Celebrated Indonesian writer Prameodya Ananta Toer was imprisoned for nearly 16 years under suspicion of being a communist. Most of that time he was restricted from reading and writing, and so he composed his fiction in his mind. His prison mates collaborated in helping him to recall and write his books, giving him their extra provisions of paper and food and shouldering his portion of physical labor. His most famous writing to come out of this time is The Buru Quartet, a series of novels that covers the conflicts with the Dutch before Indonesia achieved independence in 1949.

Inem was one of the girls I knew. She was eight years old—two years older than me. She was no different from the others. And if there was a difference, it was that she was one of the prettier little girls in our neighborhood. People liked to look at her. She was polite, unspoiled, deft, and hard-working—qualities which quickly spread her fame even into other neighborhoods as a girl who would make a good daughter-in-law.

And once when she was heating water in the kitchen, she said to me, "Gus[1] Muk, I'm going to be married."

"You're fooling!" I said.

"No, the proposal came a week ago. Mama and Papa and all the relatives have accepted the proposal."

"What fun to be a bride!" I exclaimed happily.

"Yes, it'll be fun, I know it will! They'll buy me all sorts of nice clothes. I'll be dressed up in a bride's outfit, with flowers in my hair, and they'll make me up with powder and mascara. Oh, I'll like that!"

♦♦♦♦♦

---

1 **Gus:** a title of respect used by servants for their employers

East Asia & the Pacific Rim

And it was true. One afternoon her mother called on mine. At that time Inem was living with us as a servant. Her daily tasks were to help with the cooking and to watch over me and my younger brothers and sisters as we played.

Inem's mother made a living by doing batik[2] work. That was what the women in our neighborhood did when they were not working in the rice fields. Some put batik designs on sarongs,[3] while others worked on head cloths. The poorer ones preferred to do head cloths; since it did not take so long to finish a head cloth, they received payment for it sooner. And Inem's mother supported her family by putting batik designs on head cloths. She got the cloth and the wax from her employer, the Idjo Store. For every two head cloths that she finished, she was paid one and a half cents. On the average, a woman could do eight to eleven head cloths a day.

Inem's father kept gamecocks. All he did, day after day, was to wager his bird in cockfights. If he lost, the victor would take his cock. And in addition he would have to pay two and a half rupiahs, or at the very least seventy-five cents. When he was not gambling on cockfights, he would play cards with his neighbors for a cent a hand.

Sometimes Inem's father would be away from home for a month or half a month, wandering around on foot. His return would signify that he was bringing home some money.

Mother once told me that Inem's father's main occupation had been robbing people in the teak forest between our town, Blora, and the coastal town of Rembang. I was then in the first grade, and heard many stories of robbers, bandits, thieves, and murderers. As a result of those stories and what Mother told me, I came to be terrified of Inem's father.

Everybody knew that Inem's father was a criminal, but no one could prove it and no one dared complain to the police. Consequently he was never arrested by the police. Furthermore, almost all of Inem's mother's relatives were policemen. There was even one with the rank of agent first class. Inem's father himself had once been a policeman but had been discharged for taking bribes.

---

2 **batik:** a type of design using wax to control where fabric is dyed

3 **sarongs:** long strips of fabric worn loosely as skirts or dresses

Mother also told me that in the old days Inem's father had been an important criminal. As a way of countering an outbreak of crime that was getting out of hand, the Netherlands Indies government had appointed him a policeman, so that he could round up his former associates. He never robbed any more after that, but in our area he continued to be a focus of suspicion.

When Inem's mother called on my mother, Inem was heating water in the kitchen. I tagged along after Inem's mother. The visitor, Mother, and I sat on a low, red couch.

"Ma'am," said Inem's mother, "I've come to ask for Inem to come back home."

"Why do you want Inem back? Isn't it better for her to be here? You don't have any of her expenses, and here she can learn how to cook."

"Yes, ma'am, but I plan for her to get married after the coming harvest."

"What?" exclaimed Mother, startled. "She's going to be married?"

"Yes, ma'am. She's old enough to be married now—she's eight years old," said Inem's mother.

At this my mother laughed. And her visitor was surprised to see Mother laugh.

"Why, a girl of eight is still a child!" said Mother.

"We're not upper-class people, ma'am. I think she's already a year too old. You know Asih? She married her daughter when she was two years younger than mine."

Mother tried to dissuade the woman. But Inem's mother had another argument. Finally the visitor spoke again: "I feel lucky that someone wants her. If we let a proposal go by this time, maybe there will never be another one. And how humiliating it would be to have a daughter turn into an old maid! And it just might be that if she gets married she'll be able to help out with the household expenses."

Mother did not reply. Then she looked at me and said, "Go get the betel set and the spittoon."[4]

So I went to fetch the box of betel-chewing ingredients and the brass spittoon.

---

4 **spittoon:** a spit receptacle

"And what does your husband say?"

"Oh, he agrees. What's more, Markaban is the son of a well-to-do man—his only child. Markaban has already begun to help his father trade cattle in Rembang, Tjepu, Medang, Pati, Ngawen, and also here in Blora," said Inem's mother.

This information seemed to cheer Mother up, although I could not understand why. Then she called Inem, who was at work in the kitchen. Inem came in. And Mother asked, "Inem, do you want to get married?"

Inem bowed her head. She was very respectful toward Mother. I never once heard her oppose her. Indeed, it is rare to find people who are powerless opposing anything that others say to them.

I saw then that Inem was beaming. She often looked like that; give her something that pleased her even a little and she would beam. But she was not accustomed to saying "thank you." In the society of the simple people of our neighborhood, the words "thank you" were still unfamiliar. It was only through the glow radiating from their faces that gratitude found expression.

"Yes, ma'am," said Inem so softly as to be almost inaudible.

Then Inem's mother and mine chewed some betel. Mother herself did not like to chew betel all the time. She did it only when she had a woman visitor. Every few moments she would spit into the brass spittoon.

When Inem had gone back to the kitchen Mother said, "It's not right to make children marry."

These words surprised Inem's mother. But she did not say anything nor did her eyes show any interest.

"I was eighteen when I got married," said Mother.

Inem's mother's surprise vanished. She was no longer surprised now, but she still did not say anything.

"It's not right to make children marry," repeated Mother.

And Inem's mother was surprised again.

"Their children will be stunted."

Inem's mother's surprise vanished once more.

"Yes, ma'am." Then she said placidly, "My mother was also eight when she got married."

Mother paid no attention and continued, "Not only will they be stunted, but their health will be affected too."

"Yes, ma'am, but ours is a long-lived family. My mother is still alive, though she's over fifty-nine. And my grandmother is still alive too. I think she must be seventy-four. She's still vigorous and strong enough to pound corn in the mortar."

Still ignoring her, Mother went on, "Especially if the husband is also a child."

"Yes, ma'am, but Markaban is seventeen."

"Seventeen! My husband was thirty when he married me."

Inem's mother was silent. She never stopped shifting the wad of tobacco leaves that was stuck between her lips. One moment she would move the tobacco to the right, a moment later to the left, and the next moment she would roll it up and scrub her coal-black teeth with it.

Now Mother had no more arguments with which to oppose her visitor's intention. She said, "Well, if you've made up your mind to marry Inem off, I only hope that she gets a good husband who can take care of her. And I hope she gets someone who is **compatible**."

Inem's mother left, still shifting the tobacco about in her mouth.

"I hope nothing bad happens to that child."

"Why would anything bad happen to her?" I asked.

"Never mind, Muk, it's nothing." Then Mother changed the subject. "If the situation of their family improves, we won't lose any more of our chickens."

"Is somebody stealing our chickens, Mama?" I asked.

"No, Muk, never mind," Mother said slowly. "Such a little child! Only eight years old. What a pity it is. But they need money. And the only way to get it is to marry off their daughter."

Then Mother went to the garden behind the house to get some string beans for supper.

Fifteen days after this visit, Inem's mother came again to fetch her daughter. She seemed greatly pleased that Inem made no objection to being taken away. And when Inem was about to leave our house, never to be a member of our family again, she spoke to me in the kitchen doorway, "Well, good bye, Gus Muk. I'm going home, Gus Muk," she said very softly.

She always spoke softly. Speaking softly was one of the

compatible
agreeable; like-minded

customary ways of showing politeness in our small-town society. She went off as joyfully as a child who expects to be given a new blouse.

◆ ◆ ◆ ◆ ◆

From that moment, Inem no longer lived in our house. I felt very deeply the loss of my constant companion. From that moment also, it was no longer Inem who took me to the bathing cubicle at night to wash my feet before going to bed, but my adoptive older sister.

Sometimes I felt an intense longing to see Inem. Not infrequently, when I had got into bed, I would recall the moment when her mother drew her by the hand and the two of them left our house. Inem's house was in back of ours, separated only by a wooden fence.

She had been gone a month. I often went to her house to play with her, and Mother always got angry when she found out that I had been there. She would always say, "What can you learn at Inem's house that's of any use?"

And I would never reply. Mother always had a good reason for scolding me. Everything she said built a thick wall that was impenetrable to excuses. Therefore my best course was to be silent. And as the clinching argument in her lecture, she was almost certain to repeat the sentences that she uttered so often: "What's the point to your playing with her? Aren't there lots of other children you can ask to play with you? What's more, she's a woman who's going to be married soon."

But I kept on sneaking over to her house anyway. It is surprising sometimes how a prohibition seems to exist solely in order to be violated. And when I disobeyed I felt that what I did was pleasurable. For children such as I at that time—oh, how many prohibitions and restrictions were heaped on our heads! Yes, it was as though the whole world was watching us, bent on forbidding whatever we did and whatever we wanted. Inevitably we children felt that this world was really intended only for adults.

◆ ◆ ◆ ◆ ◆

Then the day of the wedding arrived.

For five days before the ceremony, Inem's family was busy in the kitchen, cooking food and preparing various delicacies. This made me visit her house all the more frequently.

The day before the wedding, Inem was dressed in all her finery. Mother sent me there with five kilos of rice and twenty-five cents as a neighborly contribution. And that afternoon we children crowded around and stared at her in admiration. The hair over her forehead and temples and her eyebrows had been carefully trimmed with a razor and thickened with mascara. Her little bun of hair had been built up with a switch and adorned with the paper flowers with springs for stalks that we call sunduk mentul. Her clothes were made of satin. Her sarong was an expensive one made in Solo. These things had all been rented from a Chinaman in the Chinese quarter near the town square. The gold rings and bracelets were all rented too.

The house was decorated with constructions of banyan leaves and young coconut fronds. On each wall there were crossed tricolor flags encircled by palm leaves. All the house pillars were similarly decorated with tricolor bunting.

Mother herself went and helped with the preparations. But not for long. Mother rarely did this sort of thing except for her closest neighbors. She stayed less than an hour. And it was then too that the things sent by Inem's husband-to-be arrived: a load of cakes and candies, a male goat, a quantity of rice, a packet of salt, a sack of husked coconuts, and half a sack of granulated sugar.

It was just after the harvest. Rice was cheap. And when rice was cheap all other foodstuffs were cheap too. That was why the period after the harvest was a favorite time for celebrations. And for that reason Inem's family had found it impossible to contract for a puppet performance. The puppet masters had already been engaged by other families in various neighborhoods. The puppet theater was the most popular form of entertainment in our area. In our town there were three types of puppet performance: the *wajan purwa* or shadow play, which recounted stories from the *Mahabharata* and the *Ramayana*, as well as other stories similar in theme; the *wajang krutjil*, in which wooden puppets in human shape acted out stories of Arabia, Persia, India, and China, as well as tales of Madjapahit times; and the *wajang golek*, which employed wooden dolls. But this last was not very popular.

Because there were no puppet masters available, Inem's family engaged a troupe of dancing girls. At first this created a dispute. Inem's relatives on her mother's side were religious scholars and teachers. But Inem's father would not back down. The dance troupe came, with its gamelan[5] orchestra, and put on a tajuban.[6]

Usually, in our area, a tajuban was attended by the men who wanted to dance with the girls and by little children who only wanted to watch—little children whose knowledge of sexual matters did not go beyond kissing. The grown boys did not like to watch; it embarrassed them. This was even more the case with the women—none of them attended at all. And a tajuban in our area—in order to inflame sexual passions—was always accompanied by alcoholic beverages: arrack, beer, whisky, or gin.

The tajuban lasted for two days and nights. We children took great delight in the spectacle of men and women dancing and kissing one another and every now and then clinking their glasses and drinking liquor as they danced and shouted, "Huse!"

And though Mother forbade me to watch, I went anyway on the sly.

"Why do you insist on going where those wicked people are? Look at your religious teacher: he doesn't go to watch, even though he is Inem's father's brother-in-law. You must have noticed that yourself."

Our religious teacher also had a house in back of ours, to the right of Inem's house. Subsequently the teacher's failure to attend became a topic that was sure to enliven a conversation. From it there arose two remarks that itched on the tip of everyone's tongue: that the teacher was certainly a pious man, and that Inem's father was undoubtedly a **reprobate**.

reprobate
villain; scoundrel

Mother reinforced her scolding with words that I did not understand at the time: "Do you know something? They are people who have no respect for women," she said in a piercing voice.

And when the bridegroom came to be formally presented to

---

5 **gamelan:** a group of traditional Indonesian instruments and vocalists

6 **tajuban:** a party of drinking and dancing used to celebrate rites-of-passage

the bride, Inem, who had been sitting on the **nuptial** seat, was led forth. The bridegroom had reached the veranda. Inem squatted and made obeisance to her future husband, and then washed his feet with flower water from a brass pot. Then the couple were tied together and conducted side by side to the nuptial seat. At that time the onlookers could be heard saying, "One child becomes two. One child becomes two. One child becomes two."

And the women who were watching beamed as though they were to be the recipients of the happiness to come.

At that very moment I noticed that Inem was crying so much that her make-up was spoiled, and tears were trickling down her face. At home I asked Mother, "Why was the bride crying, Mama?"

"When a bride cries, it's because she is thinking of her long-departed ancestors. Their spirits also attend the ceremony. And they are happy that their descendant has been safely married," replied Mother.

I never gave any thought to those words of hers. Later I found out why Inem had been crying. She had to urinate, but was afraid to tell anyone.

◆ ◆ ◆ ◆ ◆

The celebration ended uneventfully. There were no more guests coming with contributions. The house resumed its everyday appearance, and by the time the moneylenders came to collect, Inem's father had left Blora. After the wedding, Inem's mother and Inem herself went on doing batik work—day and night. And if someone went to their house at three o'clock in the morning, he would be likely to find them still working. Puffs of smoke would be rising between them from the crucible in which the wax was melted. In addition to that, quarreling was often heard in that house.

And once, when I was sleeping with Mother in her bed, a loud scream awakened me: "I won't! I won't!"

It was still night then. The screams were repeated again and again, accompanied by the sound of blows and pounding on a door. I know that the screams came from Inem's mouth. I recognized her voice.

nuptial
marital; conjugal

"Mama, why is Inem screaming?" I asked.

"They're fighting. I hope nothing bad happens to that little girl," she said. But she gave no explanation.

"Why would anything bad happen to her, Mama?" I asked insistently.

Mother did not reply to my question. And then, when the screaming and shouting were over, we went back to sleep. Such screams were almost sure to be heard every night. Screams and screams. And every time I heard them, I would ask my mother about them. Mother would never give a satisfactory answer. Sometimes she merely sighed, "What a pity, such a little child!"

One day Inem came to our house. She went straight in to find my mother. Her face was pale, bloodless. Before saying anything, she set the tone of the occasion by crying—crying in a respectful way.

"Why are you crying, Inem? Have you been fighting again?" Mother asked.

"Ma'am," said Inem between her sobs, "I hope that you will be willing to take me back here as before."

"But you're married, aren't you Inem?"

And Inem cried some more. Through her tears she said, "I can't stand it, ma'am."

"Why, Inem? Don't you like your husband?" asked Mother.

"Ma'am, please take pity on me. Every night all he wants to do is wrestle, ma'am."

"Can't you say to him, 'Please, dear, don't be like that'?"

"I'm afraid, ma'am. I'm afraid of him. He's so big. And when he wrestles he squeezes me so hard that I can't breathe. You'll take me back, won't you, ma'am?" she pleaded.

"If you didn't have a husband, Inem, of course I'd take you back. But you have a husband . . ."

And Inem cried again when she heard what Mother said. "Ma'am, I don't want to have a husband."

"You may not want to, but the fact is that you do, Inem. Maybe eventually your husband will change for the better, and the two of you will be able to live happily. You wanted to get married, didn't you?" said Mother.

"Yes, ma'am . . . but, but . . ."

"Inem, regardless of anything else, a woman must serve her husband faithfully. If you aren't a good wife to your husband, your ancestors will curse you," said Mother.

Inem began crying harder. And because of her crying she was unable to say anything.

"Now, Inem, promise me that you will always prepare your husband's meals. When you have an idle moment, you should pray to God to keep him safe. You must promise to wash his clothes, and you must massage him when he is tired from his work. You must rub his back vigorously when he catches cold."

Inem still made no reply. Only her tears continued to fall.

"Well, now, you go home, and from this moment on be a good wife to him. No matter whether he is good or bad, you must serve him faithfully, because after all he is your husband."

Inem, who was sitting on the floor, did not stir.

"Get up and go home to your husband. You . . . if you just up and quit your husband the consequences will not be good for you, either now or in the future," Mother added.

"Yes, ma'am," Inem said submissively. Slowly she rose and walked home.

"How sad, she's so little," said Mother.

"Mama, does Daddy ever wrestle you?" I asked.

Mother looked searchingly into my eyes. Then her scrutiny relaxed. She smiled. "No," she said. "Your father is the best person in the whole world, Muk."

Then Mother went to the kitchen to get the hoe, and she worked in the garden with me.

◆◆◆◆◆

A year passed imperceptibly. On a certain occasion Inem came again. In the course of a year she had grown much bigger. It was quite apparent that she was mature, although only nine years old. As usual, she went directly to where Mother was and sat on the floor with her head bowed. She said, "Ma'am, now I don't have a husband any more."

"What?"

"Now I don't have a husband any more."

"You're divorced?" asked Mother.

"Yes, Ma'am."

"Why did you separate from him?"

She did not reply.

"Did you fail to be a good wife to him?"

"I think I was always a good wife to him, ma'am."

"Did you massage him when he came home tired from work?" asked Mother probingly.

"Yes, ma'am, I did everything you advised me to."

"Well, then, why did you separate?"

"Ma'am, he often beat me."

"Beat you? He beat a little child like you?"

"I did everything I could to be a good wife, ma'am. And when he beat me and I was in pain—was that part of being a good wife, ma'am?" she asked, in genuine perplexity.

Mother was silent. Her eyes scrutinized Inem. "He beat you," Mother whispered then.

"Yes, ma'am—he beat me just the way Mama and Papa do."

"Maybe you failed in some way after all in your duty to him. A husband would never have the heart to beat a wife who was really and truly a good wife to him."

Inem did not reply. She changed the subject: "Would you be willing to take me back, ma'am?"

There was no hesitation in Mother's reply. She said firmly, "Inem, you're a divorced woman now. There are lots of grown boys here. It wouldn't look right to people, would it?"

"But they wouldn't beat me," said the divorcée.

"No. That isn't what I mean. It just doesn't look right for a divorced woman as young as you to be in a place where there are lots of men."

"Is it because there's something wrong with me, Ma'am?"

"No, Inem, it's a question of propriety."

"Propriety, ma'am? It's for the sake of propriety that I can't stay here?"

"Yes, that's the way it is, Inem."

The divorcée did not say anything more. She remained sitting on the floor, and seemed to have no intention of leaving the place where she was sitting. Mother went up to her and patted her shoulder consolingly. "Now, Inem . . . the best thing is for you to help your parents earn a living. I really regret that I can't take you back here."

Two tears formed in the corners of the little woman's eyes. She got up. Listlessly she moved her feet, leaving our house to return to her parents' house. And from then on she was seldom seen outside her house.

And thereafter, the nine-year-old divorcée—since she was nothing but a burden to her family—could be beaten by anyone who wanted to: her mother, her brothers, her uncles, her neighbors, her aunts. Yet Inem never again came to our house.

Her screams of pain were often heard. When she moaned, I covered my ears with my hands. And Mother continued to uphold the respectability of her home.

Translated by Rufus S. Hendron

Responding to the Selection

1. Why won't the narrator's mother help Inem by rehiring her? Think about the possible consequences if she does so.

2. In every culture, there are certain rights that are respected and values that are upheld. What do you learn about the rights and values promoted in the Indonesian society of this story?

3. At one point, the narrator notes: "Indeed, it is rare to find people who are powerless opposing anything that others say to them." How does this apply to the characters in this story (Inem, her mother, the narrator, the narrator's mother, the villagers)?

4. Using lists, see if you can distinguish details of true poverty from details of typical small-town life in Indonesia.

5. Why does no one intervene to save Inem? Predict what may happen to her.

Eve to Her Daughters

Judith Wright

AUSTRALIA

It was not I who began it.
Turned out into draughty caves,
hungry so often, having to work for our bread,
hearing the children whining,
I was nevertheless not unhappy.
Where Adam went I was fairly contented to go.
I adapted myself to the punishment: it was my life.

But Adam, you know . . . !
He kept on brooding over the insult,
over the trick They had played on us, over the scolding.
He had discovered a flaw in himself
and he had to make up for it.
Outside Eden the earth was imperfect,
the seasons changed, the game was fleet-footed,
he had to work for our living, and he didn't like it.
He even complained of my cooking
(it was hard to compete with Heaven).

So, he set to work.
The earth must be made a new Eden
with central heating, domesticated animals,
mechanical harvesters, combustion engines,
escalators, refrigerators,
and modern means of communication
and multiplied opportunities for safe investment
and higher education for Abel and Cain
and the rest of the family.
You can see how his pride has been hurt.

In the process he had to unravel everything,
because he believed that mechanism
was the whole secret—he was always mechanical-minded.
He got to the very inside of the whole machine
exclaiming as he went, So this is how it works!
And now that I know how it works, why, I must have invented it.
As for God and the Other, they cannot be demonstrated,
and what cannot be demonstrated
doesn't exist.
You see, he had always been jealous.

Yes, he got to the center
where nothing at all can be demonstrated.
And clearly he doesn't exist; but he refuses
to accept the conclusion.
You see, he was always an egotist.

BARK PAINTING DEPICTING THE ABORIGINE EQUIVALENTS TO ADAM, EVE, AND THE SERPENT

Eve to Her Daughters

It was warmer than this in the cave;
there was none of this fallout.
I would suggest, for the sake of the children,
that it's time you took over.

But you are my daughters, you inherit my own faults
    of character;
you are submissive, following Adam
even beyond existence.
Faults of character have their own logic
and it always works out.
I observed this with Abel and Cain.

Perhaps the whole elaborate fable
right from the beginning
is meant to demonstrate this; perhaps it's the whole secret.
Perhaps nothing exists but our faults?

But it's useless to make
such a suggestion to Adam.
He has turned himself into God,
who is faultless, and doesn't exist.

Responding to the Selection

1. Eve has a different interpretation of the traditional Creation story found in the Bible. In what important ways is her version different?

2. Do you think anyone could be offended by this poem? Explain.

3. How does Eve characterize Adam in this poem?

4. Why has Adam's pride been hurt, and what are the consequences?

5. Remember that Eve was often blamed for the Biblical "first" couple's expulsion from Eden. In what possible way would this color her "response" to Adam and the position she has been put in?

American Dreams

Peter Carey

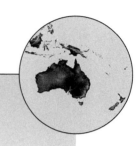

Australian author Peter Carey is notable for fiction that contains elements of the bizarre, black humor, and satire. His short fiction is said to give "a wryly inventive perspective on a modern world obsessed with materialism and with competitive values." By including surreal elements, he forces readers to make judgments without their usual reference points. "American Dreams" is a double-edged satire about the growing influence of America as well as Americans' fantasies about the rest of the world.

WORLD LENS

•••

AUSTRALIA

No one can, to this day, remember what it was we did to offend him. Dyer the butcher remembers a day when he gave him the wrong meat and another day when he served someone else first by mistake. Often when Dyer gets drunk he recalls this day and curses himself for his foolishness. But no one seriously believes that it was Dyer who offended him.

But one of us did something. We slighted him terribly in some way, this small meek man with the rimless glasses and neat suit who used to smile so nicely at us all. We thought, I suppose, he was a bit of a fool and sometimes he was so quiet and grey that we ignored him, forgetting he was there at all.

When I was a boy I often stole apples from the trees at his house up in Mason's Lane. He often saw me. No, that's not correct. Let me say I often sensed that he saw me. I sensed him peering out from behind the lace curtains of his house. And I was not the only one. Many of us came to take his apples, alone and in groups, and it is possible that he chose to exact payment for all these apples in his own peculiar way.

Yet I am sure it wasn't the apples.

What has happened is that we all, all eight hundred of us, have come to remember small **transgressions** against Mr. Gleason

transgressions
offenses; wrongs

who once lived amongst us.

My father, who has never borne malice against a single living creature, still believes that Gleason meant to do us well, that he loved the town more than any of us. My father says we have treated the town badly in our minds. We have used it, this little valley, as nothing more than a stopping place. Somewhere on the way to somewhere else. Even those of us who have been here many years have never taken the town seriously. Oh yes, the place is pretty. The hills are green and the woods thick. The stream is full of fish. But it is not where we would rather be.

For years we have watched the films at the Roxy and dreamed, if not of America, then at least of our capital city. For our own town, my father says, we have nothing but contempt. We have treated it badly, like a whore. We have cut down the giant shady trees in the main street to make doors of the school house and seats for the football pavilion. We have left big holes all over the countryside from which we have taken brown coal and given back nothing.

The commercial travellers who buy fish and chips at George the Greek's care for us more than we do, because we all have dreams of the big city, of wealth, of modern houses, of big motor cars: American Dreams, my father has called them.

Although my father ran a petrol station he was also an inventor. He sat in his office all day drawing strange pieces of equipment on the back of delivery dockets. Every spare piece of paper in the house was covered with these little drawings and my mother would always be very careful about throwing away any piece of paper no matter how small. She would look on both sides of any piece of paper very carefully and always preserved any that had so much as a pencil mark.

I think it was because of this that my father felt that he understood Gleason. He never said as much, but he inferred that he understood Gleason because he, too, was concerned with similar problems. My father was working on plans for a giant gravel crusher, but occasionally he would become distracted and become interested in something else.

There was, for instance, the time when Dyer the butcher bought a new bicycle with gears, and for a while my father talked of nothing else but the gears. Often I would see him across the road squatting down beside Dyer's bicycle as if he were talking to it.

We all rode bicycles because we didn't have the money for anything better. My father did have an old Chev truck, but he rarely used it and it occurs to me now that it might have had some mechanical problem that was impossible to solve, or perhaps it was just that he was saving it, not wishing to wear it out all at once. Normally, he went everywhere on his bicycle and, when I was younger, he carried me on the cross bar, both of us dismounting to trudge up the hills that led into and out of the main street. It was a common sight in our town to see people pushing bicycles. They were as much a burden as a means of transport.

Gleason also had his bicycle and every lunchtime he pushed and pedalled it home from the shire[1] offices to his little weatherboard house out at Mason's Lane. It was a three-mile ride and people said that he went home for lunch because he was fussy and wouldn't eat either his wife's sandwiches or the hot meal available at Mrs. Lessing's café.

But while Gleason pedalled and pushed his bicycle to and from the shire offices everything in our town proceeded as normal. It was only when he retired that things began to go wrong.

Because it was then that Mr. Gleason started supervising the building of the wall around the two-acre plot up on Bald Hill. He paid too much for this land. He bought it from Johnny Weeks, who now, I am sure, believes the whole episode was his fault, firstly for cheating Gleason, secondly for selling him the land at all. But Gleason hired some Chinese and set to work to build his wall. It was then that we knew that we'd offended him. My father rode all the way out to Bald Hill and tried to talk Mr. Gleason out of his wall. He said there was no need for us to build walls. That no one wished to spy on Mr. Gleason or whatever he wished to do on Bald Hill. He said no one was in the least bit interested in Mr. Gleason. Mr. Gleason, neat in a new sportscoat, polished his glasses and smiled vaguely at his feet. Bicycling back, my father thought that he had gone too far. Of course we had an interest in

---

1 **shire:** an area similar to a county

Mr. Gleason. He pedalled back and asked him to attend a dance that was to be held on the next Friday, but Mr. Gleason said he didn't dance.

"Oh well," my father said, "any time, just drop over."

Mr. Gleason went back to supervising his family of Chinese labourers on his wall.

Bald Hill towered high above the town and from my father's small filling station you could sit and watch the wall going up. It was an interesting sight. I watched it for two years, while I waited for customers who rarely came. After school and on Saturdays I had all the time in the world to watch the agonizing progress of Mr. Gleason's wall. It was as painful as a clock. Sometimes I could see the Chinese labourers running at a jog-trot carrying bricks on long wooden planks. The hill was bare, and on this bareness Mr. Gleason was, for some reason, building a wall.

In the beginning people thought it peculiar that someone would build such a big wall on Bald Hill. The only thing to recommend Bald Hill was the view of the town, and Mr. Gleason was building a wall that denied that view. The top soil was thin and bare clay showed through in places. Nothing would ever grow there. Everyone assumed that Gleason had simply gone mad and after the initial interest they accepted his madness as they accepted his wall and as they accepted Bald Hill itself.

Occasionally someone would pull in for petrol at my father's filling station and ask about the wall and my father would shrug and I would see, once more, the strangeness of it.

"A house?" the stranger would ask. "Up on that hill?"

"No," my father would say, "chap named Gleason is building a wall."

And the strangers would want to know why, and my father would shrug and look up at Bald Hill once more. "Damned if I know," he'd say.

Gleason still lived in his old house at Mason's Lane. It was a plain weatherboard house with a rose garden at the front, a vegetable garden down the side, and an orchard at the back.

At night we kids would sometimes ride out to Bald Hill on our bicycles. It was an agonizing, muscle-twitching ride, the worst part of which was a steep, unmade road up which we finally pushed our bikes, our lungs rasping in the night air. When we arrived we found nothing but walls. Once we broke down some of the brickwork and another time we threw stones at the tents where the Chinese labourers slept. Thus we expressed our frustration at this inexplicable thing.

The wall must have been finished on the day before my twelfth birthday. I remember going on a picnic birthday party up to Eleven Mile Creek and we lit a fire and cooked chops at a bend in the river from where it was possible to see the walls on Bald Hill. I remember standing with a hot chop in my hand and someone saying, "Look, they're leaving!"

We stood on the creek bed and watched the Chinese labourers walking their bicycles slowly down the hill. Someone said they were going to build a chimney up at the mine at A.1 and certainly there is a large brick chimney there now, so I suppose they built it.

When the word spread that the walls were finished most of the town went up to look. They walked around the four walls which were as interesting as any other brick walls. They stood in front of the big wooden gates and tried to peer through, but all they could see was a small blind wall that had obviously been constructed for this special purpose. The walls themselves were ten feet high and topped with broken glass and barbed wire. When it became obvious that we were not going to discover the contents of the enclosure, we all gave up and went home.

Mr. Gleason had long since stopped coming into town. His wife came instead, wheeling a pram down from Mason's Lane to Main Street and filling it with groceries and meat (they never bought vegetables, they grew their own) and wheeling it back to Mason's Lane. Sometimes you would see her standing with the pram halfway up the Gell Street hill. Just standing there, catching her breath. No one asked her about the wall. They knew she wasn't responsible for the wall and they felt sorry for her, having to bear the burden of the pram and her husband's madness. Even when she began to visit Dixon's hardware and buy plaster of paris and tins of paint and waterproofing compound, no one asked her what these things were for. She had a way of averting her eyes that indicated her terror of questions. Old Dixon carried the plaster of paris and the tins of paint out to her pram for her and watched her push them away. "Poor woman," he said, "poor bloody woman."

From the filling station where I sat dreaming in the sun, or from the enclosed office where I gazed mournfully at the rain, I would see, occasionally, Gleason entering or leaving his walled compound, a tiny figure way up on Bald Hill. And I'd think "Gleason," but not much more.

Occasionally strangers drove up there to see what was going on, often egged on by locals who told them it was a Chinese temple or some other silly thing. Once a group of Italians had a picnic outside the walls and took photographs of each other standing in front of the closed door. God knows what they thought it was.

But for five years between my twelfth and seventeenth birthdays there was nothing to interest me in Gleason's walls. Those years seem lost to me now and I can remember very little of them. I developed a crush on Susy Markin and followed her back from the swimming pool on my bicycle. I sat behind her in the pictures and wandered past her house. Then her parents moved to another town and I sat in the sun and waited for them to come back.

We became very keen on modernization. When coloured paints became available the whole town went berserk and brightly coloured houses blossomed overnight. But the paints were not of good quality and quickly faded and peeled, so that the town looked like a garden of dead flowers. Thinking of those years, the only real thing I recall is the soft hiss of bicycle tyres on the main street. When I think of it now it seems very peaceful, but I remember then that the sound induced in me a feeling of melancholy, a feeling somehow mixed with the early afternoons when the sun went down behind Bald Hill and the town felt as sad as an empty dance hall on a Sunday afternoon.

And then, during my seventeenth year, Mr. Gleason died. We found out when we saw Mrs. Gleason's pram parked out in front of Phonsey Joy's Funeral Parlour. It looked very sad, that pram, standing by itself in the windswept street. We came and looked at the pram and felt sad for Mrs. Gleason. She hadn't had much of a life.

Phonsey Joy carried old Mr. Gleason out to the cemetery by the Parwan Railway Station and Mrs. Gleason rode behind in a taxi. People watched the old hearse go by and thought, "Gleason," but not much else.

And then, less than a month after Gleason had been buried out at the lonely cemetery by the Parwan Railway Station, the Chinese labourers came back. We saw them push their bicycles up the hill. I stood with my father and Phonsey Joy and wondered what was going on.

And then I saw Mrs. Gleason trudging up the hill. I nearly didn't recognize her, because she didn't have her pram. She carried a black umbrella and walked slowly up Bald Hill and it wasn't until she stopped for breath and leant forward that I recognized her.

"It's Mrs. Gleason," I said, "with the Chinese."

But it wasn't until the next morning that it became obvious what was happening. People lined the main street in the way they do for a big funeral but, instead of gazing towards the Grant Street corner, they all looked up at Bald Hill.

All that day and all the next people gathered to watch the destruction of the walls. They saw the Chinese labourers darting to and fro, but it wasn't until they knocked down a large section of the wall facing the town that we realized there really was something inside. It was impossible to see what it was, but there was something there. People stood and wondered and pointed out Mrs. Gleason to each other as she went to and fro supervising the work.

And finally, in ones and twos, on bicycles and on foot, the whole town moved up to Bald Hill. Mr. Dyer closed up his butcher shop and my father got out the old Chev truck and we finally arrived up at Bald Hill with twenty people on board. They crowded into the back tray and hung on to the running boards and my father grimly steered his way through the crowds of bicycles and parked just where the dirt track gets really steep. We trudged up this last steep track, never for a moment suspecting what we would find at the top.

It was very quiet up there. The Chinese labourers worked diligently, removing the third and fourth walls and cleaning the bricks which they stacked neatly in big piles. Mrs. Gleason said nothing either. She stood in the only remaining corner of the walls and looked defiantly at the townspeople who stood open-mouthed where another corner had been.

And between us and Mrs. Gleason was the most incredibly beautiful thing I had ever seen in my life. For one moment I didn't recognize it. I stood openmouthed, and breathed the surprising beauty of it. And then I realized it was our town. The buildings were two feet high and they were a little rough but very correct. I saw Mr. Dyer nudge my father and whisper that Gleason had got the faded "U" in the BUTCHER sign of his shop.

I think at that moment everyone was overcome with a feeling of simple joy. I can't remember ever having felt so uplifted and happy. It was perhaps a childish emotion but I looked up at my father and saw a smile of such warmth spread across his face that I knew he felt just as I did. Later he told me that he thought Gleason had built the model of our town just for this moment, to let us see the beauty of our own town, to make us proud of ourselves and to stop the American Dreams we were so prone to. For the rest, my father said, was not Gleason's plan and he could not have foreseen the things that happened afterwards.

I have come to think that this view of my father's is a little sentimental and also, perhaps, insulting to Gleason. I personally believe that he knew everything that would happen. One day the proof of my theory may be discovered. Certainly there are in existence some personal papers, and I firmly believe that these papers will show that Gleason knew exactly what would happen.

We had been so overcome by the model of the town that we hadn't noticed what was the most remarkable thing of all. Not only had Gleason built the houses and the shops of our town, he had also peopled it. As we tip-toed into the town we suddenly found ourselves. "Look," I said to Mr. Dyer, "there you are."

And there he was, standing in front of his shop in his apron. As I bent down to examine the tiny figure I was staggered by the look on its face. The modeling was crude, the paintwork was sloppy, and the face a little too white, but the expression was absolutely perfect: those pursed, quizzical lips and the eyebrows lifted high. It was Mr. Dyer and no one else on earth.

And there beside Mr. Dyer was my father, squatting on the footpath and gazing lovingly at Mr. Dyer's bicycle's gears, his face marked with grease and hope.

And there was I, back at the filling station, leaning against a petrol pump in an American pose and talking to Brian Sparrow who was amusing me with his clownish antics.

Phonsey Joy standing beside his hearse. Mr. Dixon sitting inside his hardware store. Everyone I knew was there in that tiny town. If they were not in the streets or in their backyards they were inside their houses, and it didn't take very long to discover that you could lift off the roofs and peer inside.

We tip-toed around the streets peeping into each other's windows, lifting off each other's roofs, admiring each other's gardens, and, while we did it, Mrs. Gleason slipped silently away down the hill towards Mason's Lane. She spoke to nobody and nobody spoke to her.

I confess that I was the one who took the roof from Cavanagh's house. So I was the one who found Mrs. Cavanagh in bed with young Craigie Evans.

I stood there for a long time, hardly knowing what I was seeing. I stared at the pair of them for a long, long time. And when I finally knew what I was seeing I felt such an incredible mixture of jealousy and guilt and wonder that I didn't know what to do with the roof.

Eventually it was Phonsey Joy who took the roof from my hands and placed it carefully back on the house, much, I imagine, as he would have placed the lid on a coffin. By then other people had seen what I had seen and the word passed around very quickly.

And then we all stood around in little groups and regarded the model town with what could only have been fear. If Gleason knew about Mrs. Cavanagh and Craigie Evans (and no one else had), what other things might he know? Those who hadn't seen themselves yet in the town began to look a little nervous and were unsure of whether to look for themselves or not. We gazed silently at the roofs and felt mistrustful and guilty.

We all walked down the hill then, very quietly, the way people walk away from a funeral, listening only to the crunch of the gravel under our feet while the women had trouble with their high-heeled shoes.

The next day a special meeting of the shire council passed a motion calling on Mrs. Gleason to destroy the model town on the grounds that it contravened building regulations.

It is unfortunate that this order wasn't carried out before the city newspapers found out. Before another day had gone by the government had stepped in.

The model town and its model occupants were to be preserved. The minister for tourism came in a large black car and made a speech to us in the football pavilion. We sat on the high, tiered seats eating potato chips while he stood against the fence and talked to us. We couldn't hear him very well, but we heard enough. He called the model town a work of art and we stared at him grimly. He said it would be an invaluable tourist attraction. He said tourists would come from everywhere to see the model town. We would be famous. Our businesses would flourish. There would be work for guides and interpreters and caretakers and taxi drivers and people selling soft drinks and ice creams.

The Americans would come, he said. They would visit our town in buses and in cars and on the train. They would take photographs and bring wallets bulging with dollars. American dollars.

We looked at the minister mistrustfully, wondering if he knew about Mrs. Cavanagh, and he must have seen the look because he said that certain controversial items would be removed, had already been removed. We shifted in our seats, like you do when a particularly tense part of a film has come to its climax, and then we relaxed and listened to what the minister had to say. And we all began, once more, to dream our American Dreams.

We saw our big smooth cars cruising through cities with bright lights. We entered expensive night clubs and danced till dawn. We made love to women like Kim Novak and men like Rock Hudson. We drank cocktails. We gazed lazily into refrigerators filled with food and prepared ourselves lavish midnight snacks which we ate while we watched huge television sets on which we would be able to see American movies free of charge and forever.

The minister, like someone from our American Dreams,

reentered his large black car and cruised slowly from our humble sportsground, and the newspaper men arrived and swarmed over the pavilion with their cameras and notebooks. They took photographs of us and photographs of the models up on Bald Hill. And the next day we were all over the

We gazed lazily into refrigerators filled with food and prepared ourselves lavish midnight snacks which we ate while we watched huge television sets on which we would be able to see American movies free of charge and forever.

newspapers. The photographs of the model people side by side with photographs of the real people. And our names and ages and what we did were all printed there in black and white.

They interviewed Mrs. Gleason but she said nothing of interest. She said the model town had been her husband's hobby.

We all felt good now. It was very pleasant to have your photograph in the paper. And, once more, we changed our opinion of Gleason. The shire council held another meeting and named the dirt track up Bald Hill "Gleason Avenue." Then we all went home and waited for the Americans we had been promised.

It didn't take long for them to come, although at the time it seemed an eternity, and we spent six long months doing nothing more with our lives than waiting for the Americans.

Well, they did come. And let me tell you how it has all worked out for us.

The Americans arrive every day in buses and cars and sometimes the younger ones come on the train. There is now a small airstrip out near the Parwan cemetery and they also arrive there, in small aeroplanes. Phonsey Joy drives them to the cemetery where they look at Gleason's grave and then up to Bald Hill and then down to the town. He is doing very well from it all. It is good to see someone doing well from it. Phonsey is becoming a big man in town and is on the shire council.

On Bald Hill there are half a dozen telescopes through which the Americans can spy on the town and reassure themselves that it is the same down there as it is on Bald Hill. Herb Gravney sells them ice creams and soft drinks and extra film for their cameras. He is another one who is doing well. He bought the whole model from Mrs. Gleason and charges five American dollars admission. Herb is on the council now too. He's doing very well for himself. He sells them the film so they can take photographs of the houses and the model people and so they can come down to the town with their special maps and hunt out the real people.

To tell the truth most of us are pretty sick of the game. They come looking for my father and ask him to stare at the gears of Dyer's bicycle. I watch my father cross the street slowly, his head hung low. He doesn't greet the Americans any more. He doesn't ask them questions about colour television or Washington, D.C. He kneels on the footpath in front of Dyer's bike. They stand around him. Often they remember the model incorrectly and try to get my father to pose in the wrong way. Originally he argued with them, but now he argues no more. He does what they ask. They push him this way and that and worry about the expression on his face which is no longer what it was.

Then I know they will come to find me. I am next on the map. I am very popular for some reason. They come in search of me and my petrol pump as they have done for four years now. I do not await them eagerly because I know, before they reach me, that they will be disappointed.

"But this is not the boy."

"Yes," says Phonsey, "this is him alright." And he gets me to show them my certificate.

They examine the certificate suspiciously, feeling the paper as if it might be a clever forgery. "No," they declare. (Americans are so confident.) "No," they shake their heads, "this is not the real boy. The real boy is younger."

"He's older now. He used to be younger." Phonsey looks weary when he tells them. He can afford to look weary.

The Americans peer at my face closely. "It's a different boy."

But finally they get their cameras out. I stand sullenly and try to look amused as I did once. Gleason saw me looking amused but I can no longer remember how it felt. I was looking at Brian

Sparrow. But Brian is also tired. He finds it difficult to do his clownish antics and to the Americans his little act isn't funny. They prefer the model. I watch him sadly, sorry that he must perform for such an unsympathetic audience.

The Americans pay one dollar for the right to take our photographs. Having paid the money they are worried about being cheated. They spend their time being disappointed and I spend my time feeling guilty that I have somehow let them down by growing older and sadder.

Responding to the Selection

1. Now that you have read the story, what do you think the title aims to convey?

2. What do you think the narrator's father means by saying, "we have treated the town badly in our minds"?

3. Does this story have to be set in small-town Australia, or could it be located anywhere else in the world? Explain your answer.

4. What explains the villagers' joy upon first seeing the model of their village?

5. What possible interest does the model village hold for visiting American tourists?

A Consumer's Report

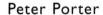

Peter Porter

AUSTRALIA

The name of the product I tested is *Life*,
I have completed the form you sent me
and understand that my answers are confidential.

I had it as a gift,
I didn't feel much while using it,
in fact I think I'd have liked to be more excited.
It seemed gentle on the hands
but left an embarrassing deposit behind.
It was not economical
and I have used much more than I thought
(I suppose I have about half left
but it's difficult to tell)—
although the instructions are fairly large
there are so many of them
I don't know which to follow, especially
as they seem to contradict each other.
I'm not sure such a thing
should be put in the way of children—
It's difficult to think of a purpose
for it. One of my friends says
it's just to keep its maker in a job.
Also the price is much too high.
Things are piling up so fast,
after all, the world got by
for a thousand million years
without this, do we need it now?
(Incidentally, please ask your man
to stop calling me "the respondent,"
I don't like the sound of it.)
There seems to be a lot of different labels,

sizes and colours should be uniform,
the shape is awkward, it's waterproof
but not heat resistant, it doesn't keep
yet it's very difficult to get rid of:
whenever they make it cheaper they seem
to put less in—if you say you don't
want it, then it's delivered anyway.
I'd agree it's a popular product,
it's got into the language; people
even say they're on the side of it.
Personally I think it's overdone,
a small thing people are ready
to behave badly about. I think
we should take it for granted. If its
experts are called philosophers or market
researchers or historians, we shouldn't
care. We are the consumers and the last
law makers. So finally, I'd buy it.
But the question of a "best buy"
I'd like to leave until I get
the competitive product you said you'd send.

Responding to the Selection

1. To whom is the speaker addressing this poem? Say whether or not you find this gimmick effective.

2. What do you think the product is, and why do you think the poet avoids describing it further than he does?

3. How does the poet use advertising language—the language of buying and selling—to good effect in this poem? Point to examples you especially like.

4. Name the three types of professionals that are supposed to be experts on this "product." Do you believe in their expertise?

5. What are some of the double meanings in this poem?

A Way of Talking

Patricia Grace

WORLD LENS

•••

NEW ZEALAND

Though first to inhabit the islands of New Zealand, the Maori people presently make up only 8 percent of the population. During the 19th-century colonial wars, they were unable to fight off the invading Europeans and Australians. In a country dominated by whites, the Maoris struggle to improve their civil and economic rights and preserve their culture. Patricia Grace, one of their foremost writers, uses Maori dialect in her fiction as a way to strengthen Maori identity.

Rose came back yesterday; we went down to the bus to meet her. She's just the same as ever Rose. Talks all the time flat out and makes us laugh with her way of talking. On the way home we kept saying, "E Rohe, you're just the same as ever." It's good having my sister back and knowing she hasn't changed. Rose is the hard-case one in the family, the kamakama[1] one, and the one with the brains.

Last night we stayed up talking till all hours, even Dad and Nanny who usually go to bed after tea. Rose made us laugh telling about the people she knows, and taking off professor this and professor that from varsity. Nanny, Mum, and I had tears running down from laughing; e ta Rose we laughed all night.

At last Nanny got out of her chair and said, "Time for sleeping. The mouths steal the time of the eyes." That's the lovely way she has of talking, Nanny, when she speaks in English. So we went to bed and Rose and I kept our mouths going for another hour or so before falling asleep.

This morning I said to Rose that we'd better go and get her measured for the dress up at Mrs. Frazer's. Rose wanted to wait a

---

1 **kamakama:** Maori for "eager" or "quick"

East Asia & the Pacific Rim

day or two but I reminded her the wedding was only two weeks away and that Mrs. Frazer had three frocks to finish.

"Who's Mrs. Frazer anyway," she asked. Then I remembered Rose hadn't met these neighbours though they'd been in the district a few years. Rose had been away at school.

"She's a dressmaker," I looked for words. "She's nice."

"What sort of nice?" asked Rose.

"Rose, don't you say anything funny when we go up there," I said. I know Rose, she's smart. "Don't you get smart." I'm older than Rose but she's the one that speaks out when something doesn't please her. Mum used to say, Rohe you've got the brains but you look to your sister for the sense. I started to feel funny about taking Rose up to Jane Frazer's because Jane often says the wrong thing without knowing.

We got our work done, had a bath and changed, and when Dad came back from the shed we took the station-wagon to drive over to Jane's. Before we left we called out to Mum, "Don't forget to make us a Maori bread for when we get back."

"What's wrong with your own hands," Mum said, but she was only joking. Always when one of us comes home one of the first things she does is make a big Maori bread.

Rose made a good impression with her kamakama ways, and Jane's two nuisance kids took a liking to her straight away. They kept jumping up and down on the sofa to get Rose's attention and I kept thinking what a waste of a good sofa it was, what a waste of a good house for those two nuisance things. I hope when I have kids they won't be so hoha.

I was pleased about Jane and Rose. Jane was asking Rose all sorts of questions about her life in Auckland. About varsity and did Rose join in the marches and demonstrations. Then they went on to talking about fashions and social life in the city, and Jane seemed deeply interested. Almost as though she was jealous of Rose and the way she lived, as though she felt Rose had something better than a lovely house and clothes and everything she needed to make life good for her. I was pleased to see that Jane liked my sister so much, and proud of my sister and her entertaining and friendly ways.

Jane made a cup of coffee when she'd finished measuring Rose for the frock, then packed the two kids outside with a piece of chocolate cake each. We were sitting having coffee when we heard a truck turn in at the bottom of Frazer's drive.

Jane said, "That's Alan. He's been down the road getting the Maoris for scrub cutting."

I felt my face get hot. I was angry. At the same time I was hoping Rose would let the remark pass. I tried hard to think of something to say to cover Jane's words though I'd hardly said a thing all morning. But my tongue seemed to thicken and all I could think of was Rohe don't.

Rose was calm. Not all red and flustered like me. She took a big pull on the cigarette she had lit, squinted her eyes up and blew the smoke out gently. I knew something was coming.

"Don't they have names?"

"What. Who?" Jane was surprised and her face was getting pink.

"The people from down the road whom your husband is employing to cut scrub." Rose the stink thing, she was talking all Pakehafied.[2]

"I don't know any of their names."

I was glaring at Rose because I wanted her to stop but she was avoiding my looks and pretending to concentrate on her cigarette.

"Do they know yours?"

"Mine?"

"Your name."

"Well . . . Yes."

"Yet you have never bothered to find out their names or to wonder whether or not they have any."

The silence seemed to bang around in my head for ages and ages. Then I think Jane muttered something about difficulty, but that touchy sister of mine stood up and said, "Come on Hera." And I with my red face and shut mouth followed her out to the station wagon without a goodbye or anything.

I was so wild with Rose. I was wild. I was determined to blow her up about what she had done, I was determined. But now that we were alone together I couldn't think what to say. Instead I felt an awful big sulk coming on. It has always been my trouble,

---

2 **Pakehafied:** like a white person; Pakeha is the Maori term for a white person

sulking. Whenever I don't feel sure about something I go into a big fat sulk. We had a teacher at school who used to say to some of us girls, "Speak, don't sulk." She'd say, "You only sulk because you haven't learned how and when to say your minds."

She was right that teacher, yet here I am a young woman about to be married and haven't learned yet how to get the words out. Dad used to say to me, "Look out girlie, you'll stand on your lip."

At last I said, "Rose, you're a stink thing." Tears were on the way. "Gee Rohe, you made me embarrassed." Then Rose said, "Don't worry Honey she's got a thick hide."

These words of Rose's took me by surprise and I realised something about Rose then. What she said made all my anger go away and I felt very sad because it's not our way of talking to each other. Usually we'd say, "Never mind Sis," if we wanted something to be forgotten. But when Rose said, "Don't worry Honey she's got a thick hide," it made her seem a lot older than me, and tougher, and as though she knew much more than me about the world. It made me realise too that underneath her jolly and forthright ways Rose is very hurt. I remembered back to when we were both little and Rose used to play up at school if she didn't like the teacher. She'd get smart and I used to be ashamed and tell Mum on her when we got home, because although she had the brains I was always the well behaved one.

Rose was speaking to me in a new way now. It made me feel sorry for her and for myself. All my life I had been sitting back and letting her do the objecting. Not only me, but Mum and Dad and the rest of the family too. All of us too scared to make known when we had been hurt or slighted. And how can the likes of Jane know when we go round pretending all is well. How can Jane know us?

But then I tried to put another thought into words. I said to Rose, "We do it too. We say, 'the Pakeha doctor,' or 'the Pakeha at the post office,' and sometimes we mean it in a bad way."

"Except that we talk like this to each other only. It's not so much what is said, but when and where and in whose presence. Besides, you and I don't speak in this way now, not since we were little. It's the older ones: Mum, Dad, Nanny who have this habit."

Then Rose said something else. "Jane Frazer will still want

to be your friend and mine in spite of my embarrassing her today; we're in the fashion."

"What do you mean?"

"It's fashionable for a Pakeha to have a Maori for a friend." Suddenly Rose grinned. Then I heard Jane's voice coming out of that Rohe's mouth and felt a grin of my own coming. "I have friends who are Maoris. They're lovely people. The eldest girl was married recently and I did the frocks. The other girl is at varsity. They're all so *friendly* and so *natural* and their house is absolutely *spotless*."

I stopped the wagon in the drive and when we'd got out Rose started strutting up the path. I saw Jane's way of walking and felt a giggle coming on. Rose walked up Mum's scrubbed steps, "Absolutely spotless." She left her shoes in the porch and bounced into the kitchen. "What did I tell you? Absolutely spotless. And a friendly natural woman taking new bread from the oven."

Mum looked at Rose then at me. "What have you two been up to? Rohe I hope you behaved yourself at that Pakeha place?" But Rose was setting the table. At the sight of Mum's bread she'd forgotten all about Jane and the events of the morning.

When Dad, Heke, and Matiu came in for lunch, Rose, Mum, Nanny and I were already into the bread and the big bowl of hot corn.

"E ta," Dad said. "Let your hardworking father and your two hardworking brothers starve. Eat up."

"The bread's terrible. You men better go down to the shop and get you a shop bread," said Rose.

"Be the day," said Heke.

"Come on my fat Rohe. Move over and make room for your Daddy. Come on my baby shift over."

Dad squeezed himself round behind the table next to Rose. He picked up the bread Rose had buttered for herself and started eating. "The bread's terrible all right," he said. Then Mat and Heke started going on about how awful the corn was and who cooked it and who grew it, who watered it all summer and who pulled out the weeds.

So I joined in the carryings on and forgot about Rose and Jane for the meantime. But I'm not leaving it at that. I'll find some way of letting Rose know I understand and I know it will be difficult for me because I'm not clever the way she is. I can't say things the same and I've never learnt to stick up for myself.

But my sister won't have to be alone again. I'll let her know that.

Responding to the Selection

1. What is it the young narrator must learn? Consider all the ways in which the author influences your opinion of this "way of talking."

2. Dialect is a regional variation of speech that includes differences in pronunciation, vocabulary, and grammar. Why do you think the author, Patricia Grace, sprinkles Maori dialect into her story?

3. Should the girls have handled the conversation with Jane Frazer differently? Explain your answer.

4. Are there other parts of the world where aboriginal (native) people have had to fight to gain their rights from colonizers? Give some examples from what you know as well as from other selections in this book.

5. Why does Rose say that it is "fashionable" for Pakehas (whites) to have Maoris for friends? Explain how she uses sarcasm as a strategy to teach her sister as well as to cope with the reality of being a "second-class" citizen in New Zealand.

East Asia & the Pacific Rim

Discussing

1. What do you think the last emperor of China would think of the poem "An Ancient Temple"? Consider the attitude both he and the speaker of the poem convey about the old days in China.

2. Look at the couples shown in the stories "The Tall Woman and Her Short Husband," "Tokyo," "Swaddling Clothes," and "Inem." What do you think contributes to the success or failure of their relationships? Look at clues in the characters' personalities and social backgrounds and discuss how those things may influence them.

3. War has had a profound effect on many of the characters in these selections. Compare the way war is used as a theme in "Cranes," "Thoughts of Hanoi," "Tokyo," and "The Shadow." Think about the attitude the writers seem to convey about this subject and the variety of ways in which they explore human beings reacting to war.

4. The award-winning writer Ha Jin writes in English although his first language is Chinese. He believes that the task of literature is to show "what is essential to the characters." Determine what is essential to the main characters in his story "Saboteur" or any other story here. What do they want, and what gets in their way?

5. Consider all of the selections from the Pacific Rim countries of Australia and New Zealand. Is there anything they share in common, either in theme, subject matter, or tone?

Writing

6. Imagine that your parents have arranged your marriage for you. Write a letter to your intended spouse and describe the kinds of things that you think he or she should know about you. Make sure the tone is "just right" because it is very important that you make a good impression.

7. In "A Consumer's Report," Peter Porter makes fun of advertising language. Find three or four examples of language from print advertisements and write an analysis of the word choices there. Do you see any claims the ad writer probably cannot support? Explain.

Speaking/Listening

8. Divide into two teams, affirmative and negative, and debate one of the following resolutions.

   Resolved: Royalty should be abolished along with all other systems of hereditary privilege.

   Resolved: Arranged marriages are a good way to find your lifelong partner.

Hands-on Project

Find some good reference works on Chinese calligraphy, especially any that take you through the drawing process step-by-step. Then, use paintbrushes, ink, and paper to practice these artful brush strokes. If there is someone in your community who can do a demonstration of this art, invite him or her to your class. You might even try decorating a kite with your Chinese characters as kites play an important part in many Asian cultures.

Personal Connections

After reading the selections in this unit, choose one of the following questions to write about in your journal.

1. Which characters or selections helped open your eyes to a new way of seeing the world?

2. What new understanding do you have about American culture, your family, or yourself?

3. Which differences among cultures do you think really matter? Explain.

RESEARCHING THE WORLD

General Research Subjects

The following general subjects are merely starting points for research. After choosing one that interests you, you will have to narrow your topic considerably.

Belief Systems	The Environment	Oppression and Exile
Celebrations and	Famous Figures	Popular Culture
Ceremonies	Food	Rural and Urban Life
Children and Family	Geography	Sports
Coming of Age	Globalism	Technology
Courtship and Marriage	Important Events	Travel
Crime and Justice	Language	Work and Leisure
The Economy	Literature and the Arts	
Education	The Media	

Specific Research Topics

Pick from the following topics or use them as starting points for your research. Some topics can be applied to more than one country in this region; others pertain to a single country or group of people. Note that in order to be a manageable size, many of these topics will require further narrowing.

Arts/Leisure

- Puppet dramas in Indonesian culture
- Japanese animé (cartoon artwork)
- Martial arts and ritual exercise (karate, tai chi)
- Scar literature (China)
- Chinese monuments (The Great Wall, Terra Cotta warriors)

Culture/Geography

- Social mores (Buddhism, Confucianism, Taoism)
- Buddhist tea ceremonies
- Coming of Age Day in Japan
- The Australian outback
- Maori and Aboriginal birth and death rites

History/Politics

- Genocide in the 20th century (Cambodia, East Timor)
- Atomic war (Hiroshima, Nagasaki)
- Dutch colonial rule in Indonesia
- Mao Tse-tung's reforms (the Great Leap Forward, the Cultural Revolution)
- The Chinese-Tibetan conflict

AUTHOR BIOGRAPHIES

Peter Carey (1943–) Born in Australia, Peter Carey now lives in New York with his wife and children. He has written several prizewinning novels, including *Oscar and Lucinda* (made into a 1997 movie starring Ralph Fiennes) and *The Unusual Life of Tristan Smith and Jack Maggs.* He often writes about life in his native Australia and his country's history, which he describes as "dismal." His most famous novel is probably *The True History of the Kelly Gang,* based on the life of the Australian outlaw Ned Kelly. One critic said that Carey's novel raised "a national legend to the level of an international myth."

Bei Dao (1949–) Bei Dao is the pen name of Zhao Zhenkai, who was born in Beijing, China. In 1969, he joined the Red Guard to take part in Chairman Mao Tse-tung's brutal Cultural Revolution. But he grew disillusioned with Maoism and became involved in China's democracy movement. He also helped create an intensely personal verse genre called "cloud/mist poetry." He was away from China in 1989 during the pro-democracy demonstration at Tiananmen Square, which ended in the massacre of hundreds of protesters. Nevertheless, the government accused him of helping to incite the protest, and he has remained in exile ever since. Despite his hardships, he warns poets not to underestimate their own importance, because poetry "came into the world when humans did. It's what makes human beings human." His works in English translation include *City of the Sun, The August Sleepwalker,* and *Forms of Distance.*

Patricia Grace (1937–) Born into the Maori culture, Patricia Grace often writes about relationships between New Zealand's indigenous Maoris and relative newcomers from Europe and Australia. In her stories, she uses Maori dialect to emphasize her own traditions. Grace's collection of short stories, *Waiariki,* was the first ever published by a Maori female writer. She has written several other collections of stories (including *The Dream Sleepers)* and novels (including *Potiki).* She also writes for children and has won awards for her novels, short stories, and children's books. Grace's advice to aspiring writers is, "Write, write, write—and read, read, read."

Fumiko Hayashi (1904–1951) Japanese writer Fumiko Hayashi lived much of her life in poverty. After completing high school, she held many different jobs in Tokyo. Sometimes she was homeless and hungry. Even then, Hayashi wrote realistic stories about poor working people—especially women. Her first novel, *Journal of a Vagabond*, appeared as a magazine series and was then published as a book. With her earnings from that novel, Hayashi traveled to Paris, where she continued writing. By the end of her life, Hayashi had published over 270 books, including novels, short stories, nonfiction, and poems. However, the early years of poverty had taken their toll. She died when her heart—strained from years of overwork—suddenly failed.

Feng Ji-cai (1942–) Chinese author Feng Ji-cai has many interests. He was a professional basketball player until an injury put an end to that career. Then he studied traditional Chinese painting and wrote in his spare time. After his first novel, *The Boxer*, was published, Feng turned to a career in writing, including novels, short stories, scripts, and nonfiction. He also studies Chinese history and culture. Feng said, "I don't want to only be a writer, which will limit my development. I preferred me as an intellectual." He explained that writing can be just reporting, but an intellectual considers wider matters—such as the culture, the past, and the future.

Ha Jin (1956–) Xuefei Jin, the fiction writer and poet known to Americans as Ha Jin, was born in China. As a youth, he served in the People's Liberation Army. He also struggled to get an education in the anti-intellectual climate of Chairman Mao Tse-tung's Cultural Revolution. In 1985, he came to the United States to study. The 1989 massacre of student protesters at Tiananmen Square in Beijing persuaded him not to return to China with his wife and son. Instead, he embarked on a writing career in the United States. His fiction and poetry have won many prizes, including the National Book Award for his novel *Waiting*. Perhaps Jin's greatest challenge was learning to write in English. "To me," he observed, "this meant much labor, some despair, and also, freedom."

Yukio Mishima (1925–1970) *Life* magazine called Yukio Mishima "the Japanese Hemingway"—and like Hemingway, he was troubled and controversial. Born Hiraoka Kimitake in an aristocratic Japanese family, he adopted the pseudonym Yukio Mishima to keep his father from learning that he was a writer. In his first novel, *Confessions of a Mask*, Mishima wrote autobiographically about what it was like to be homosexual in modern Japan. He went on to a successful career as a novelist, playwright, and essayist. His most famous novels include *The Sound of Waves* and *The Sailor Who Fell from Grace with the Sea*. In his life and writings, Mishima became fanatically devoted to Japan's authoritarian past. He protested the Westernization of Japan and created a tiny private army to promote Samurai values. The day he delivered his last novel to his publisher, Mishima publicly committed *seppuku*, ritual disembowelment.

Peter Porter (1929–) As a young journalist and aspiring poet and playwright, Peter Porter left his native Australia to see England. He made his home there, becoming an advertising copywriter. In England, he began to publish collections of his poetry: *Once Bitten, Twice Bitten; Poems, Ancient and Modern;* and *Words Without Music*. He gave up the advertising world to become a full-time poet, and is now known for his commentary on our consumer-oriented culture. Porter says that he has a poor sense of reality. "I need created reality around me." He has also translated the poetry of Michaelangelo and edited an African poetry anthology.

Aisin-Gioro P'u Yi (1906–1967) Aisin-Gioro P'u Yi became China's last emperor in 1908 at the age of three. A revolution brought the Chinese Nationalists to power in 1911, and P'u Yi was forced to abdicate in 1912, ending 2,000 years of imperial rule. During World War II, the Japanese made him the puppet emperor of a colony in Manchuria. When the war ended in 1945, the Soviets took him into custody. In 1950, he was sent back to China, which had come under Communist rule. He was imprisoned for war crimes but pardoned in 1959. He spent the rest of his life working in a botanical garden in Beijing. His autobiography, *From Emperor to Citizen*, was written under the strict supervision of the Communist government. A movie about his life, *The Last Emperor*, won the 1987 Oscar for best picture.

Toge Sankichi (1921–1953) Japanese poet Toge Sankichi began writing when he was a teenager. At age 24, he was a student in Hiroshima when the atomic bomb was dropped on that city. He survived the initial explosion but later suffered from leukemia—an effect of radiation from the bomb. Drawing on his personal experience,

Sankichi used poetry to describe the bomb blast and its after-effects, though he felt that he "couldn't strike the reality" of what it had been like. But he added that "somehow, this is the best present to those who are going to . . . consider the feelings we in Hiroshima have about the bomb." His *Atomic Bomb Anthology* includes his own poems. Sankichi died from leukemia when he was 36.

Hwang Sun-won (1915–) The author of short stories, novels, and poetry, Hwang Sun-won has lived through hard times in his native Korea. When the Japanese occupied the country, they banned writing in Korean. After World War II, the North was occupied by Soviet forces. Hwang and his family fled to the American-occupied South, but they were displaced again by the Korean War. Nevertheless, Hwang continued to write. His stories include a wide range of characters: outcasts from society, soldiers, country dwellers, and city people. His work appears in English in *The Book of Masks* and *Shadows of a Sound*.

Nguyen Thi Vinh (1924–) Nguyen Thi Vinh's life was disrupted by the brutal civil war in Vietnam that lasted from 1957 to 1975. As a result, much of her literature touches on the fragmentation of the Vietnamese people as political conflicts broke the bonds of family, friendship, and community. In the 1950s, Vinh relocated from her hometown in North Vietnam to Saigon, South Vietnam in order to escape Communist rule. She remained in the South even after the Communists gained control of the whole country in 1975. In the late eighties, Vinh finally left her homeland and traveled by boat to Norway, where she has resettled with her husband and children. She has published a book, *Norway and Me and Other Short Stories* (1994) and started her own publishing house, Anh Em, which produces work by her family and associates.

Pramoedya Ananta Toer (1925–) Born in Indonesia (then the Dutch West Indies), Toer was imprisoned in 1947 for opposing Dutch colonial rule. While in prison, he wrote *The Fugitive*, his first published novel. He was released after Indonesia achieved independence in 1949. But in 1965, he was arrested again for his Marxist sympathy and beaten so badly that he lost most of his hearing. He remained in prison until 1979, during which time he wrote a group of novels, The Buru Quartet. Even after his release, Toer wasn't allowed to leave the Indonesian capital of Jakarta until the fall of President Suharto's regime in 1998. The next year brought the publication of *The Mute's Soliloquy,* a collection of autobiographical writings. Indonesia's most respected prose writer, Toer once observed, "It is impossible to separate politics from literature or any other part of human life, because everyone is touched by political power."

Judith Wright (1915–2000) Australian poet, editor, anthologist, literary critic, short story writer, and children's writer Judith Wright was also a conservationist and an activist for the rights of aboriginal people. As a young woman, she studied the arts and held secretarial positions in Sydney, Australia. At the outbreak of World War I, Wright returned for to her family home in New South Wales. She said, "I knew then how closely connected I was to that landscape. I began to write again, and the poems came closer to what I'd hoped for." Her collections of poems include *The Moving Image* and *Woman to Man,* and she wrote short stories, biographies, and children's books, as well.

Research Handbook

Some investigations begin with questions that are literally a matter of life and death. *Who killed this murder victim? How can we cure this disease?* Others are born from an observation. *Why does this author write so much about orphaned children?* Some are sparked by your teacher's warning. *"Your research papers are due . . . ."*

Whatever your question, research skills can help you find information about any topic, from car stereos to the drum sounds in African poetry. But locating sources is just the beginning. To keep up with the new technical information produced in just one day, you'd have to read more than 20,000,000 words. Even reading 8 hours a day, you couldn't finish in less than a month. By that time, you'd be 5.5 months and billions of words behind (Murray, cited in Nelson, par. 10).

The vast amount of information available can make people feel confused or overwhelmed. But you can tame information overload. The handbook section on **Finding Information** will help you locate sources that are relevant to your topic. **Sharing Information** will help you select the best information and organize it so your audience finds it easy to understand.

FINDING INFORMATION

What is my research topic?

If "a journey of a thousand miles begins with a single step," a research project begins with a single topic. The topic may be assigned by your teacher, or you may be allowed to research any subject that interests you. In either case, you need to decide what you're trying to find out about before you begin your research. Otherwise, you'll be wandering through the information jungle without a compass.

Suppose you're assigned to write about magic realism in Latin American literature. "I don't even know what magic realism is," you might mutter. There's your first question: *What is magic realism?* "Aren't the ideas of *magic* and *realism* contradictory?" you grumble. There's a second question: *How are these contradictions handled by Latin American authors?* That brings up another question: *Which Latin American authors have I read?*

As you think about the different authors you've studied, you realize that you enjoyed one author more than all the others. Now you're starting to see how you might make this assigned topic fit your interests.

Suppose that you can choose any topic related to world literature. You may already have a question you want to research. Perhaps you're curious about diaries kept during the Holocaust, or you want to read more contemporary Arabic stories. On the other hand, you may find it hard to think of a topic. Looking over this book's Table of Contents or Researching the World feature might give you some ideas. You can also start with yourself instead of with the literature. For example, as you sit there trying to think of a topic, you might wish you were listening to your new CD instead. As you start to tap out the rhythm to one of the songs, you remember that Léopold Sédar Senghor wanted his poems to capture the complex rhythms of African music. As you start to wonder about the relationship between drums and Senghor's poetry, you realize that your interests have led you to a topic.

Finding a Topic

Assigned Topic	Self-Chosen Topic
• Analyze key words in the topic.	• Think about your questions or interests.
• Identify what you already know.	• Make a list of topics you'd like to know more about.
• Relate the topic to your interests.	• Choose a topic you want to explore.

What questions do I have about my topic?

A saying among researchers and writers is that asking the right question is 90 percent of the answer. Ninety percent? Isn't that exaggerating the importance of questions? You'll have a chance to see for yourself as you do your research.

Now is a good time to start keeping track of your questions about your topic. You can use a log or research journal to record your initial questions and those that arise as you learn more about a topic. Your question log might look something like the one on the next page.

Name   Class, Period

Question Log

Topic: *traditional African rhythms in Léopold Sédar Senghor's poems*

Date   The first questions that come to my mind about this topic are
           What are some traditional African rhythms?
           How does Senghor use traditional rhythms?
           Why does he include them in his poems?
           What instruments does he use besides drums?
           What poems could I use for examples?

At this point, the research questions are pretty broad. So, it is good to start with sources that provide general background about the topic, such as encyclopedia articles and *Twentieth Century Literary Criticism.* One critic mentions that Senghor was influenced by the *griots,* or storytellers, the poet heard as a child. This helps answer the question about traditional African rhythms. However, you might have new questions.

Jan 16   What are griots?
           What rhythms do griots use in their stories?
           How did the stories Senghor heard as a child shape his poetry?

At the beginning of your research, each answer you find is likely to suggest more questions. These questions will give you new directions to explore. At the same time, they keep you from getting lost and disoriented given the vast amount of information that exists. You will probably learn that Senghor was the first president of Senegal. This is a significant achievement, but it doesn't relate to any of your questions. So you look for more information on griots instead of focusing on Senghor's political career.

But what if the new questions are more interesting than the original ones? Many people find that new questions suggest a whole new topic. That's why your teacher may want to go over your questions with you. At the beginning of your research process, it's easy to change topics. You just need to be sure that your new subject will fulfill the assignment. The more time and effort you have invested in a topic, the more important it is to talk to your teacher before changing your focus.

Once you feel that you're familiar with the basic background information about your subject, review your questions. Which are the most interesting? Most important? Most likely to be questions your audience will have too? Choose ten or so questions to be the focus of your research. These questions will help you and your teacher track your progress as you dig more deeply.

Where do I find information?

The best place to start your research depends on two things: the topic and the assignment. To research a current topic, you might start with the Internet. But if you're looking for reference books or back issues of magazines, you'll find more resources at a library. The assignment might also specify that you use particular kinds of resources, such as a collection of references in the media center or personal interviews. The chart below shows some specialized resources for world literature and gives examples of different kinds of sources that your teacher might require. For example, say your teacher wants you to use at least two primary sources. *Primary sources* are firsthand information about a topic, such as eyewitness accounts, diaries, or historical documents. *Secondary sources* are materials based on firsthand sources, such as reference works and biographies. When you research literature, the works you study are considered primary sources. Critics' comments are secondary sources.

Type of Information	Best Place to Find
A quick overview of a subject	• General encyclopedias, such as *Encyclopaedia Britannica* • Specialized encyclopedias, such as *Cassell's Encyclopedia of World Literature*
Biographical information	• Reference works such as *Current Biography* or *Who's Who*, International edition • Biography of one author (see your library card catalog or a bookseller's Web site)

chart continued on next page

Type of Information	Best Place to Find
Critics' comments	• Reference series such as *Contemporary Authors* or *Poetry Criticism* • Reviews (Electric Library or *Book Review Index*) • The Internet Public Library (www.ipl.org/ref/litcrit)
Geographical information	• Atlases, such as *The Columbia Lippincott Gazetteer of the World* • The CIA's *World Factbook* (printed or http://www.odci.gov/cia/publications/factbook/index.html)
Literary terms and traditions	• Specialized reference works such as *A Handbook to Literature* and *Merriam-Webster's Encyclopedia of Literature*
Literary works	• *Granger's Index to Poetry* • *Play Index* • *Short Story Index*
News items or magazine articles	• *Reader's Guide to Periodical Literature* • Electronic databases such as Proquest or Electric Library
People to interview	• Acquaintances with firsthand experience of your subject • People who teach or write about your subject • Members of organizations related to your subject (see Gale's *Encyclopedia of Associations*) • Experts on the Internet (http://internet-101.com/bookmrks/bookmrk4c.htm)
Statistics	• Almanacs, such as *Information Please* • *International Index to Statistics*
Web sites	• Search engines, such as Google (www.google.com) • Meta-engines that combine several search engines, such as ProFusion (www.profusion.com) • Search engines specialized by subject (see your library's home page or Leiden University's 300+ links at http://www.leidenuniv.nl/ub/biv/specials.htm)

One important resource isn't on the chart: your public librarian or media center specialist. These expert guides can suggest sources and shortcuts you might not think of on your own. Also, they can help you request materials from other libraries through interlibrary loan.

You can also find great search tips by clicking the Help or Advanced Search links provided by Internet search engines.

What if I have trouble locating information?

Remember Juliet's question to Romeo: "What's in a name?" She and her beloved were from two rival families, but she didn't see why the names Capulet and Montague should keep them apart. When you're searching for information, Juliet's question is a good one to keep in mind. The names by which you retrieve information from library card catalogs are called *subject headings.* Digital information, whether in library catalogs or on the Internet, is retrieved by using *keywords* that describe your topic.

For example, you might decide to track down the quotation from George Herbert that begins "The Book of Sand." Point your browser to <www.google.com> and type *George Herbert* in the search box. That search returns about 810,000 hits, because Google searched for "George," "Herbert," and "George Herbert." Using quotation marks around "George Herbert" narrows the hits to about 42,800. So you add the keyword *rope.* That turns up a link to "The Collar," the poem from which the quotation is taken. You might also have tried other keywords, such as "rope of sands."

If you want, you can try another search engine. Using Google gives you a list of hits sorted according to the order in which you enter your keywords. Yahoo! is another good engine for general searches, because it is organized by categories. A Yahoo! search for "George Herbert" would take you to the Poets category, which has one site on George Herbert. Other search engines, like Alta Vista, Excite, and HotBot, allow advanced searches using AND, OR, or NOT. For example, you could eliminate all results containing "George Herbert Walker Bush" by searching for "George Herbert" NOT Bush.

Or, you might want to do your project on Japanese literature. You might start at the Internet Public Library <www.ipl.org>, but find no links to general sites about contemporary Japanese literature. So you search the catalog at the local library for the subject "Japanese literature" and find several anthologies, a history, and two critical works. You also find cross-references to several related subjects, including *folk literature, Japanese,* and *Japanese fiction.*

If at first you don't succeed, try these strategies.

1. Vary your keywords. If you don't find anything under *Jamaican literature,* try a word or phrase that has a similar meaning, such as *Caribbean literature.*

2. Double-check your search settings. An **author** search for *haiku* will return no results, but a **subject** or **keyword** search should be successful.

3. Look in more than one place. Use the Internet and the library, or try more than one search engine.

How do I sort through this information?

It is possible to have too much information. People who have to deal with too much unorganized information suffer from what some have called "information fatigue syndrome."

One way to reduce information fatigue is to use a general-to-specific search strategy. Start by reading sources that give a broad overview of your topic. Then look for sources that provide more in-depth answers to your research questions. If several sources overlap, read them together and take notes from the most complete source first. For example, perhaps one of your sources contains much more about griots than the others. Since you have taken notes from that one first, all you have to do for the rest is record any new details you find.

Another way to reduce information fatigue is to be selective. "Junk information" is as common as junk food. Of course, eating one candy bar is not going to totally destroy your health. But using even one biased or inaccurate source can ruin the credibility of your research project. You can use these criteria to screen your sources.

Criteria for Judging Sources

Timeliness	Is the information in this source outdated?
Completeness/Accuracy	Does this source cover the topic thoroughly? How does information in this source compare to other sources on this topic?
Bias	Is this source objective? • Does the source stand to profit from taking this position (as in a laboratory hired by a drug company to conduct pharmaceutical tests)? • Does this source include only evidence favorable to one side of a controversy? • Does this source reflect the views of a particular time in history, such as empire-builders' attitudes toward native peoples?
Credibility	What evidence do I have that this source is knowledgeable and believable? • academic or professional credentials • documentation, such as lists of references • recognition as an authority

How you apply these criteria will depend on your topic. For example, Japanese haiku were first written in the 16th century, so new information is unlikely to replace what we already know about their origins. However, novels have not been an important part of Africa's literary tradition until recently. As African novelists continue to experiment with the genre, sources about the novel in African literature will quickly become outdated.

Judging credibility is especially important when using resources from the World Wide Web. A search for Chinua Achebe's novel *Things Fall Apart* could turn up everything from a college student's book report to the works of W. B. Yeats (the poet who coined the title phrase) to author Chinua Achebe's home Web page. Sites associated with universities, libraries, and professional associations are generally more trustworthy than those created by individuals. Individuals' sites are more credible if they
- tell you who created the site and when it was last updated.
- are created by someone with expert knowledge.

- provide thorough coverage of the topic, with suggestions about finding additional information.
- are included in other sites' collections of recommended links.

How do I keep track of my sources?

The easiest way to keep track of your sources is to write information about each source on a 3″ x 5″ index card. Record the author's name and publication information before you take a single note. Then you won't have to retrace your steps when you're trying to credit the sources you used for your presentation or paper.

What information do you need? Examples of how to cite some commonly used sources are shown below. If your teacher wants to follow the Modern Language Association (MLA) style, you can find more detailed examples in guides like the *MLA Handbook for Writers of Research Papers*.

Source	Basic Format	Example
Book	Author's last name, first name. *Title of book or pamphlet: Including subtitle.* Ed. or trans. [if applicable] City of publication: Publisher, date of publication.	García Márquez, Gabriel. *One Hundred Years of Solitude.* Trans. Gregory Rabassa. New York: Harper, 1998.
Article	Author's last name, first name. "Article title." *Publication title* date: page numbers.	Simpson, Mona. "A Quiet Genius." *Atlantic Monthly* Dec. 2001: 126–136.
Article from electronic database	Author's last name, first name. "Article title." *Original publication title* date: pages [if known]. Name of database/service. Name of library through which you accessed service. Date of access.	Ross, Robert L. "Seeking and Maintaining Balance: Robinton Mistry's Fiction." *World Literature Today* 15 April 1999. Electric Library. Public Library of Des Moines. 29 Apr. 2002.

Online text	Author's last name, first name. Text title. [Ed. or trans.] Original place of publication. Publisher, date. Name of archive. Date of access <URL>.	Gao, Xingjian. "The Case for Literature." Stockholm, Sweden. The Nobel Foundation, 12 Oct. 2000. Nobel E-Museum. 29 Apr. 2000 <www.nobel.se/literature/laureates/2000/gao-lecture.e.html>.
Article in a familiar reference work	Author [if available]. "Article title." Reference title. [Edition.] Date.	White, Charles S. J. "Tagore, Sir Rabindranath." *World Book Encyclopedia*. 2000.
Web site	Author's last name, first name. Name of site. Date of your visit <URL>.	Allende, Isabel. "Isabel Allende." 29 Apr. 2002 <www.isabelallende.com>.

You can also add your own comments to source cards. For example, you might want to include information about where you found each source. If you discover that you forgot to write down a page number, you'll want to know whether to go back to the downtown library or its suburban branch.

How do I take notes?

Unless your teacher requires you to take notes a certain way, you can choose from several efficient ways to record and organize the information you need. For any of them, you need to record information in small chunks and include all the information you need to identify the source and any direct quotations. Breaking information into small chunks makes it easier to organize and write your final product. Identifying sources will help you give them proper credit within the paper and in the Works Cited page at the end of your paper.

The time-honored way to take notes is on 3″ x 5″ index cards, with a key word to identify the source and the page number (if available) at the top. Here is a note card with a summary of a speech by Chinese playwright Gao Xingjian.

Nobel site (pars. 14–16)

Accepting the Nobel Prize in 2000, Gao Xingjian said:
"Because of where I was born and the language I use, the cultural traditions of China naturally reside within me." While acknowledging that Chinese traditions shape his work, Gao Xingjian believes that literature transcends issues of national identity. "As the creator of linguistic art there is no need to stick on oneself a stock national label that can be easily recognised."

Some people prefer to take notes on the computer. Information from electronic databases and Web sites can be saved as word-processing files or cut-and-pasted into a document. If you save an entire article, indicate the material you expect to use by emphasizing it with highlighting or bold type, adding headings, or using the Comments feature in your word processor. You might even start a rough outline by copying the best parts into a new document and arranging them in the order you think you might use them. If you do, remember these two additional steps: include information to identify the source and paraphrase instead of plagiarizing.

How can I avoid plagiarizing?

Writers have a saying, "Easy writing is hard reading." When a writer just dumps words onto paper, the burden of sorting out what's important falls on the reader. That's not where it belongs, and your grade is likely to show it.

Ethical and legal issues are also involved. Since no one understands everything there is to know about a topic, you'll need to use sources. But the stand you take on the subject and the way you organize the material should be your own. Using other people's words and ideas without acknowledging them is called *plagiarism*. When best-selling authors like historian Doris Kearns Goodwin are accused of plagiarizing, they wind up in court, being sued by the authors whose work they have stolen. When students are caught, penalties depend on the school. They range from loss of credit for the assignment to failing the course to expulsion.

Copying from the Internet is so easy that some people assume it's all gain and no pain. However, teachers are always looking for new plagiarism busters. If your conscience doesn't stop you from cheating, you might find yourself caught by Turnitin or another plagiarism detection service.

The best way to avoid plagiarism is to use your own words or quotation marks. Using your own words for someone else's ideas is called *paraphrasing*. You still need to credit the source from which you took the paraphrase, but you do not need to use quotation marks. When you copy someone else's words, you must use quotation marks to acknowledge that you are using not just ideas, but exact words. Quote only ideas that are exceptionally well-stated or views that you want to make clear. For example, if you are trying to disprove a critic's opinion, quoting the opinion will help your audience follow your argument.

While there's no question about when you need to use quotation marks, the line between plagiarism and paraphrase isn't as clear. You may have no intention of stealing someone else's words. However, if your paraphrase is too close to the original, you may find yourself slipping into *unintentional plagiarism.* That means you've kept too much of the author's wording or organization. These examples illustrate acceptable and unacceptable uses of this passage from Ruth Behar's review of Isabel Allende's *Eva Luna* stories:

> "And of Clay Are We Created" was inspired by the 1985 avalanche in Colombia that buried a village in mud. Among those trapped was Omaira Sánchez, a thirteen-year-old girl who became the focus of attention of news-hungry photographers, journalists and television cameras that fixed their curious and helpless eyes on the girl who kept her faith in life as she bravely met her death. In that horrid audience of onlookers, there was one man, a reporter, who made the decision to stop observing Omaira from the lens of his camera and lay down in the mud to offer her what comfort he could as her heart and lungs collapsed. Allende, who was obsessed by "the torment of that poor child buried alive," wrote her story from the perspective of a woman—and she was that woman—"who watches the televised struggle of the man holding the girl" (15).

Unacceptable paraphrase • uses words from the source without quotation marks • is too close to source's organization	"And of Clay Are We Created" was inspired by a 1985 avalanche in Colombia. A thirteen-year-old girl trapped in the mud, Omaira Sánchez, became the focus of attention of news-hungry photographers. Allende, who was obsessed by "the torment of that poor child buried alive," wrote her story as if she were the woman watching the reporter who tried to help the girl (Behar, 15).
Unacceptable paraphrase • does use quotation marks but is too close to source's organization	"And of Clay Are We Created" is based on an actual event, a 1985 avalanche that buried a thirteen-year-old Colombian girl in mud. The girl "became the focus of attention of news-hungry photographers" and "a horrid audience of onlookers" (Behar, 15).
Acceptable paraphrase • quotes any exact words taken from source • does not depend on source's organization • shows why material is included	One reason that the relationship between Rolf Carlé and Azucena seems so real is that "And of Clay Are We Created" is based on an actual event, a 1985 Colombian avalanche that left thirteen-year-old Omaira Sánchez trapped in mud. As journalists provided live coverage of her ordeal, one reporter put down his camera to try to ease her death. Viewing "the torment of that poor child buried alive" moved Allende to write a story told by a woman "who watches the televised struggle of the man holding the girl" (Behar, 15).
Acceptable paraphrase • uses quotation marks • works quotation smoothly into the paper by identifying the source and showing why the quotation is used	Allende's inspiration for "And of Clay Are We Created" came from the ordeal of a thirteen-year-old Colombian girl trapped in the mud after an avalanche. Reviewer Ruth Behar describes how watching television coverage of the 1985 disaster affected the author. "Allende, who was obsessed by 'the torment of that poor child buried alive,' wrote her story from the perspective of a woman . . . 'who watches the televised struggle of the man holding the girl'" (15).

How can I avoid unintentional plagiarism?

These notetaking tips will help you avoid being too dependent on your sources.

- Take time to understand the material.
  - Look up difficult words.
  - Break long sentences down into shorter parts.
  - State the main point of what you have just read in your own words.
- Cover up the source as you take your notes. Then check to be sure that
  - your notes contain all the information you think you'll need.
  - your notes are accurate.
  - quotation marks set off any words you've taken directly from the source.
  - you've remembered to identify the source and location of the information (page numbers for printed material; paragraph numbers for Internet sources).

SHARING INFORMATION

You'll know it's time to stop searching when you've answered your research questions and are finding less and less new information. You now have the best answers available to your research questions.

How should I organize my ideas?

Sometimes your subject may practically organize itself. For example, you might want to do research on Sylvia Ashton-Warner, an innovative New Zealand educator who wrote three autobiographies about her writing career and her work with Maori children. Start by organizing your presentation chronologically, beginning with her earliest work.

If your topic doesn't suggest a logical organization, you can think about questions your audience might have and answer those questions in the order that will best help your audience understand the topic. For example, you might have researched South African writers in order to see how they responded to apartheid. Begin by defining *apartheid* and showing how this systematic separation of blacks and whites operated. This will prepare your audience to understand why South African writers wanted to expose the injustice of apartheid.

You can also start by writing a *thesis statement*—one sentence that sums up the point you're trying to prove. For example, after researching Chinua Achebe's *Things Fall Apart*, you might summarize your argument in this thesis statement: "Okonkwo's death represents not just the downfall of a village leader but the disintegration of an entire traditional culture." Then present the information you have gathered as proof of your thesis statement.

How should I credit sources in my paper or presentation?

Here's a general rule for citing sources: When in doubt, give credit! To avoid plagiarism, you must acknowledge any words, facts, or ideas taken from other people's works. The only exceptions: facts or ideas that are so widely known they are considered *common knowledge*. For example, the statement that Alice Munro is a Canadian writer appears in many sources and does not need to be credited. However, a critic's comment like this one from writer Mona Simpson needs to be attributed: "The highest compliment a critic can pay a short-story writer is to say that he or she is our Chekhov. More than one writer has made that claim for Alice Munro" (Simpson, par. 3). You should also give the source for any statistics you use.

Within your paper, acknowledge any source you use by giving the author's last name and page numbers inside parentheses following the quotation or idea you used in your paper. This is called *parenthetical documentation*. When you use the author's name to introduce the quotation, as in the quotation from Ruth Behar on page 599, you need only give the page number. If your source is from the World Wide Web or an electronic database, use the abbreviation *par.* or *pars.* and give paragraph numbers instead of page numbers, as in the sample notecard on page 598.

Every source mentioned in parenthetical documentation should be included in a Works Cited page at the end of your paper. Center the heading "Works Cited" and list your sources in alphabetical order. You can find sample Works Cited pages in guides like the *MLA Handbook for Writers of Research Papers* or Perfection Learning's *Write in Style*. See also page 603 in this handbook for an example.

If you give an oral presentation, you can introduce your sources just as you would introduce a long quotation in a paper. On slides or overhead transparencies, you can include parenthetical documentation with the text you display. Your teacher may also ask you to submit a summary of your presentation that includes a list of Works Cited.

Why shouldn't I write a presentation the same way I write a paper?

The biggest difference between a presentation and a paper is that your audience will read one and hear the other. To express your ideas effectively in a presentation, you need to

- Establish rapport with your audience.
  - Make eye contact at the beginning of your presentation.
  - Give your audience a reason to listen.
- Help your audience follow along.
  - Avoid long, involved sentences.
  - Use verbal cues, such as *"At the beginning of the novel . . ."* and *"The second theme I'm going to talk about . . ."*
- Use visual aids to reinforce your key points.
  - Use only a few words and make them large enough to be easily readable from the back of the room.
  - Use bold colors that compliment each other, especially in complex charts or graphs.
  - Use numbers or bullets to set off your most important points.
  - Avoid USING ALL CAPITAL LETTERS; it's hard to read.

Works Cited

Behar, Ruth. "Excerpt from In the House of the Spirits."
Short Stories for Students. Ed. Jennifer Smith. Vol. 11. Detroit: Gale, 2001.

Nelson, Mark R. "We Have the Information You Want, But Getting It Will Cost You: Being Held Hostage by Information Overload." ACM Crossroads Student Magazine. 29 Apr. 2002 <http://info.acm.org/crossroads/xrds1-1/mnelson.html>.

Simpson, Mona. "A Quiet Genius." Atlantic Monthly Dec. 2001: 126–136.

Index of Titles and Authors

Acknowledgements

Text Credits "Alone" by Tomas Tranströmer from *New and Collected Poems*, translated by Robin Fulton. Copyright © 1997 by Bloodaxe Books. Reprinted by permission of Bloodaxe Books.

"American Dreams" by Peter Carey from *The Fat Man in History*. Copyright © 1974, 1979 by Peter Carey. Reprinted by permission of International Creative Management on behalf of the author.

"An Ancient Temple" by Bei Dao, translated by Gordon T. Osing and De-An Wu Swihart from *Salt Hill*, Issue 5. Reprinted by permission of Gordon T. Osing, Professor at the University of Memphis, TN.

"And of Clay Are We Created" by Isabel Allende from *The Stories of Eva Luna*, translated by Margaret Sayers Peden. Copyright ©1989 by Isabel Allende. English translation, copyright © 1991 by Macmillan Publishing Company. Reprinted by permission of Scribner, a Division of Simon & Schuster, Inc.

"And Yet the Books" by Czeslaw Milosz from *Collected Poems: 1931–1987*. Copyright © 1988 by Cseslaw Milosz. Reprinted by permission of The Wylie Agency.

"An Arab Shepherd Is Searching for His Goat on Mount Zion" by Yehuda Amichai, translated/edited by Chana Bloch and Stephen Mitchell from *The Selected Poetry of Yehuda Amichai*. Copyright © 1996 by The Regents of the University of California. Reprinted by permission of The University of California Press.

"The Armenian Language Is the Home of the Armenian" by Moushegh Ishkhan. Reprinted by permission of Shaghzoyan Center, Beruit-Lebanon.

"At the Tourist Centre in Boston" by Margaret Atwood from *Selected Poems 1965–1975*. Copyright © 1976 by Margaret Atwood. Reprinted by permission of Houghton Mifflin Company and Oxford University Press, Canada. All rights reserved.

"The Balek Scales" by Heinrich Böll from *The Stories of Heinrich Böll*, translated by Leila Vennewitz. Copyright © by Heinrich Böll. Reprinted by permission of Verlag Kiepenheur & Wirsch via The Joan Daves Agency of New York, Leila Vennewitz and Northwestern University Press.

"Black Sheep" by Italo Calvino, translated by Timothy Parks from *Numbers in the Dark*. English translation copyright © 1995 by Timothy Parks. Used by permission of Pantheon Books, a division of Random House, Inc.

"The Book of Sand" by Jorge Luis Borges, translated by Andrew Hurley. Copyright © 1998 by Maria Kodama; translation copyright © 1998 by Penguin Putnam Inc. Used by permission of Viking Penguin, a division of Penguin Putnam Inc.

"Borders" by Thomas King from *One Good Story, That One*. Copyright © 1993 by Thomas King. Reprinted by permission of HarperCollins Publishers, Ltd. (Canada). All rights reserved.

"The Censors" by Luisa Valenzuela. Reprinted by permission of Rosario Santos.

from "'Clearances', In Memoriam M.K.H." by Seamus Heaney from *Opened Ground: Selected Poems 1966–1996*. Copyright © 1998 by Seamus Heaney. Reprinted by permission of Farrar, Straus and Giroux, LLC.

"A Consumer's Report" by Peter Porter from *Collected Poems*. Copyright © 1999 by Peter Porter. Reprinted by permission of the author.

"A Contribution to Statistics" by Wislawa Szymborska from *Poems, New and Collected: 1957–1997*, translated by Stanislaw Baranczak and Clare Cavanagh. Copyright © 1998 by Harcourt, Inc. Reprinted by permission of the publisher.

"Cranes" by Hwang Sun-won from *Flowers On Fire: Twentieth-Century Korean Stories*, translated by Peter H. Lee. Copyright © 1997 by Peter H. Lee. Reprinted by permission of Peter H. Lee.

"Crossroads: A Sad Vaudeville" by Carlos Solorzano from *Selected Latin American One-Act Plays*, Francesca Colecchia and Julia Matas, editors and translators. Copyright © 1973. Reprinted by permission of the University of Pittsburgh Press.

"Day of the Butterfly" by Alice Munro from *Dance of the Happy Shades*. Copyright © 1973 by Alice Munro. Reprinted by permission of the William Morris Agency on behalf of the author.

"The Destructors" by Graham Greene from *Collected Stories of Graham Greene*. Copyright © 1955, 1983 by Graham Greene. Used by permission of Viking Penguin, a division of Penguin Putnam, Inc. and David Higham Associates Limited.

"Do Not Go Gentle Into That Good Night" by Dylan Thomas from *The Poems of Dylan Thomas*. Copyright © 1952 by Dylan Thomas. Reprinted by permission of New Directions Publishing Corp. and David Higham Associates Limited.

"Eve to Her Daughters" by Judith Wright from *A Human Pattern: Selected Poems*. Copyright © 1996 by Judith Wright. Reprinted by permission of Tom Thompson.

"First Confession" by Frank O'Connor from *The Collected Stories of Frank O'Connor*. Copyright © 1981 by Harriet O'Donovan Sheehy, Executrix of the Estate of Frank O'Connor. Used by permission of Alfred A. Knopf, a division of Random House, Inc and Joan Daves Agency/Writers House, Inc.

"First Frost" by Andrei Voznesensky from *Antiworlds and the Fifth Ace: Poetry*, edited by Patricia Blake and Max Hayward. Copyright © 1963 by Encounter Ltd., renewed 1966, 1967 by Basic Books. Reprinted by permission of Basic Books, a member of Perseus Books, LLC.

"Five Hours to Simla" by Anita Desai from *Granta* Magazine, 57, Spring 1997. Copyright © 1997 by Anita Desai, reprinted by permission of the author.

from *From Emperor to Citizen: The Autobiography of Aisin-Gioro P'u Yi* by Aisin-Gioro P'u Yi. Copyright © 1964, 1965 by Foreign Languages Press. Reprinted by permission of Foreign Languages Press.

"Girls Can We Educate We Dads?" by James Berry from *When I Dance*. Copyright ©1991 by James Berry. Reprinted by permission of Harcourt, Inc.

"The Guitar" by Federico García Lorca, translated by Elizabeth du Gué Trapier. Reprinted by permission of The Hispanic Society of America.

"The Handsomest Drowned Man in the World" by Gabriel García Márquez from *Leaf Storm and Other Stories*. Copyright ©1971 by Gabriel García Márquez. Reprinted by permission of HarperCollins Publishers Inc.

"The Happy Man" by Naguib Mahfouz from *God's World*, edited by Akef Abudir and Roger Allen. Copyright ©1973, 1988 by Akef Abudir and Roger Allen. Reprinted by permission of Biblioteca Islamica, Inc.

"I Will Pronounce Your Name" by Léopold Sédar Senghor from *Black Orpheus*. Reprinted by permission of Editions du Seuil.

"In Trying Times" by Herberto Padilla from *Legacies*, translated by Alastair Reed and Andrew Hurley. Copyright © 1982 by the authors. Reprinted by permission of Alastair Reed on behalf of the authors.

"Inem" by Pramoedya Ananta Toer from *Pramoedya Ananta Toer: Six Indonesian Short Stories*, translated by Rufus S. Hendron. Copyright © 1968 by Rufus S. Hendron. Reprinted by permission of the author's agent, Anna Soler-Pont, Pontas Literary & Film Agency, Barcelona Spain.

"The Last Judgement" by Karel Capek, translated by Norma Comrado from *Tales From Two Pockets*. Copyright © 1994 by Catbird Press. Reprinted by permission of Catbird Press.

"Like the Sun" by R. K. Narayan from *Under the Banyan Tree*. Copyright © 1985 by R. K. Narayan. Used by permission of Viking Penguin, a division of Penguin Putnam Inc.

"Love after Love" by Derek Walcott from *Collected Poems: 1948–1984*. Copyright © 1986 by Derek Walcott. Reprinted by permission of Farrar, Straus & Giroux, LLC.

"Loyalties" by Adewale Maja-Pearce from *Loyalties*. Copyright © 1986 by Longman Group-Pearson Education. Reprinted by permission of Pearson Education.

"Marriage Is a Private Affair" by Chinua Achebe from *Girls At War and Other Stories*. Copyright © 1972, 1973 by Chinua Achebe. Used by permission of Doubleday, a division of Random House, Inc.

"The Moment Before the Gun Went Off" by Nadine Gordimer from *Jump and Other Stories*. Copyright © 1991 by Felix Licensing, B.V. Reprinted by permission of Farrar, Straus & Giroux, LLC.

"No Dogs Bark" by Juan Rulfo from *The Burning Plain and Other Stories*. Copyright © 1967, renewed 1996. Reprinted by permission of the University of Texas Press.

"No Witchcraft for Sale" by Doris Lessing from *African Stories*. Copyright © 1951, 1953, 1954, 1957, 1958, 1962, 1963, 1964, 1965, 1972, 1981 by Doris Lessing. Reprinted by permission of Simon & Schuster and Jonathan Clowes Ltd., London, on behalf of Doris Lessing.

"The Nobel Prize" by Boris Pasternak, translation by Henry Kamen. Copyright © 1962 by Henry Kamen. Reprinted by permission of PFD on behalf of Professor Henry Kamen.

"Not Waving But Drowning" by Stevie Smith from *Me Again: Uncollected Writings*. Copyright © 1981 by James MacGibbon. Reprinted by permission of Farrar, Straus & Giroux, LLC.

"Poor Fish" by Alberto Moravia. Copyright © 1954 by Alberto Moravia. Reprinted by permission of the publisher, Rizzoli Corriere della Sera, Milan, Italy.

"The Prisoner Who Wore Glasses" by Bessie Head from *Tales Of Tenderness & Power*. Copyright © 1977 by Bessie Head. Reprinted by permission of John Johnson (Authors' Agent) Ltd.

"Rhinoceros" by Eugene Ionesco from *The Colonel's Photograph*. Copyright © 1969 by Grove Press, Inc. Originally published as *La Photo Du Colonel*, Copyright © 1967 by Editions Gallimard. Reprinted by permission of Georges Borchardt, Inc. for the Editions Gallimard.

"Saboteur" by Ha Jin from *The Bridegroom*. Copyright © 2000 by Ha Jin. Used by permission of Pantheon Books, a division of Random House, Inc.

"Serenity" by Gabriela Mistral, translated by Doris Dana from *Selected Poems of Gabriela Mistral: A Bilingual Edition* (Baltimore: The Johns Hopkins University Press, 1971). Copyright © 1961, 1964, 1970, 1971 by Doris Dana. Reprinted by permission of Joan Daves Agency/Writer's House, Inc., New York, on behalf of the proprietors.

"The Shadow" by Toge Sankichi from *Hiroshima: Three Witnesses*, translated by Richard H. Minear. Copyright © 1990 by Princeton University Press. Reprinted by permission of Princeton University Press.

"Song of Becoming" by Fadwa Tuqan from *Anthology of Modern Palestinian Literature*, translated by Salma Khandra Jayyusi. Copyright © 1992 by Salma Khandra Jayyusi. Reprinted by permission of Salma Khandra Jayyusi.

"Swaddling Clothes" by Yukio Mishima from *Death In Midsummer*, translated by Ivan Morris. Copyright © 1966 by New Directions Publishing Corp. Reprinted by permission of New Directions Publishing Corp.

"Sweet Like a Crow" by Michael Ondaatje from *The Cinnamon Peeler*. Copyright © 1987, 1989 by Michael Ondaatje. Used by permission of Alfred A. Knopf, a division of Random House, Inc. and Ellen Levine Agency, Inc.

"The Swimming Contest" by Benjamin Tammuz © Copyright in the original Hebrew version the estate of Benjamin Tammuz, English translation by Joseph Shacter copyright © the Institute for the Translation of Hebrew Literature.

"The Tall Woman and Her Short Husband" by Feng Ji-Cai. Copyright © 1982 by Chinese Literature Press. English translation ©1998 by Gladys Yang. Reprinted by permission of the Foreign Languages Press.

"Telephone Conversation" by Wole Soyinka. Copyright © 1960 by Wole Soyinka. Reprinted by permission of the author.

Acknowledgements   607

"Ten Songs 1" by W. H. Auden from *Collected Poems by W. H. Auden*. Reprinted by permission of Faber and Faber Limited.

"The Third Bank of the River" by João Guimarães Rosa from *Primeiras Estórias*. Reprinted by permission of Ray-Güde Mertin.

"Thoughts of Hanoi" by Nguyen Thi Vinh from *A Thousand Years of Vietnamese Poetry*, translated by Nguyen Ngoc Bich. Copyright © 1974 by the Asia Society. Reprinted by permission of The Asia Society.

"Tokyo" by Fumiko Hayashi, translated by Ivan Morris. Copyright © 1956 by Grove Press, Inc. Reprinted by permission of Grove/Atlantic, Inc.

"Tonight I Can Write" by Pablo Neruda from *Selected Poems*, translated by W. S. Merwin, edited by Nathaniel Tarn and published by Jonathan Cape. Used by permission of The Random House Group, Limited.

"Two Bodies" by Octavio Paz from *Selected Poems*, translated by Muriel Rukeyser. Copyright © 1973 by Octavio Paz and Muriel Rukeyser. Reprinted by permission of New Directions Publishing Corp.

"A Way of Talking" by Patricia Grace from *Waiariki*. Copyright © 1975 by Pearson Education New Zealand. Reprinted by permission of Pearson Education, New Zealand.

"The Women's Baths" by Ulfat al-Idibi from *Modern Syrian Short Stories*, translated by Michel Azrak, revised by M. J. L. Young. Copyright © 1996 by Lynne Rienner Publishers, Inc. Used with permission of the publisher.

"The Youngest Doll" by Rosario Ferré from *Reclaiming Medusa, Short Stories by Contemporary Puerto American Women*. Copyright ©1986 by Rosario Ferré, copyright ©1988, 1997 by Diana Vélez. Reprinted by permission of Aunt Lute Books.

Every reasonable effort has been made to properly acknowledge ownership of all material used. Any omissions or mistakes are unintentional and, if brought to the publisher's attention, will be corrected in future editions.